Scott Foresman - Addison Wesley

Practice Masters

Grade 5

Scott Foresman - Addison Wesley

Editorial Offices: Menlo Park, California • Glenview, Illinois
Sales Offices: Reading, Massachusetts • Atlanta, Georgia • Glenview, Illinois
Carrollton, Texas • Menlo Park, California

http://www.sf.aw.com

Overview

Practice Masters provide additional practice on the concept or concepts taught in each core lesson.

For Learn and Explore lessons, the masters provide additional exercises that reflect those in the Connect section and/or the Skills and Reasoning section of the student edition Practice sets.

For Problem Solving lessons, the masters closely mirror the Problem Solving Practice sets in the student edition.

The *Practice Masters* also include Section Reviews that supplement the Section Review pages in the student edition. These Section Review masters also provide Mixed Review problems (from previous sections of the student edition). Cumulative Review masters are included at the end of each chapter to provide a comprehensive review of skills covered up through that chapter.

ISBN 0-201-31237-9

Printed in the United States of America

1 2 3 4 5 6 7 8 9 10 – BW – 02 01 00 99 98 97

Contents

Name ___________________________

Practice 1-1

Reading Graphs

Use the bar graph to answer **1–5**.

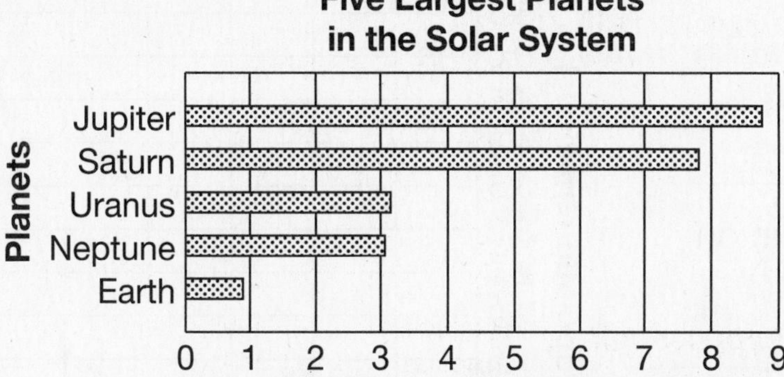

1. Which is the largest planet in the solar system? ___________

2. Which planet has a diameter of about 80,000 miles? ___________

3. About how many miles is Neptune's diameter? ___________

4. Which planet is second largest? ___________

5. About how much larger is Jupiter's diameter than Saturn's?

____

Use the line plot to answer **6–11**.

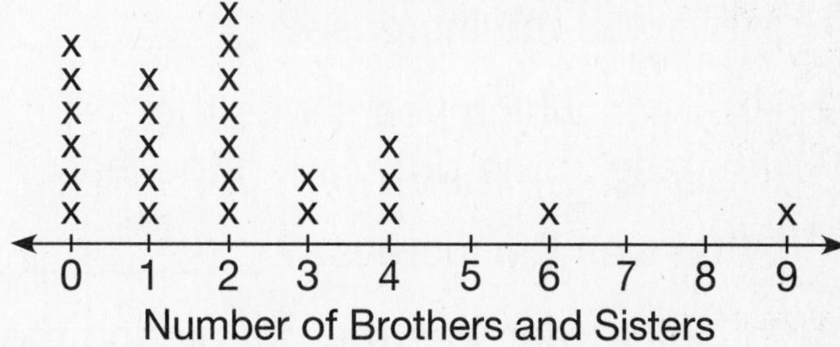

6. How many students have no brothers or sisters?

____

7. How many students have 1 brother or sister?

____

8. What is the most common number of brothers and sisters that students have? ___________

9. How many classmates have more than 3 brothers and sisters? ___________

10. How many students have less than 3 brothers and sisters? ___________

11. How many students were questioned for this line plot? ___________

Name ______________________

Practice 1-2

Reading Line Graphs

Use the line graph to answer **1–11**.

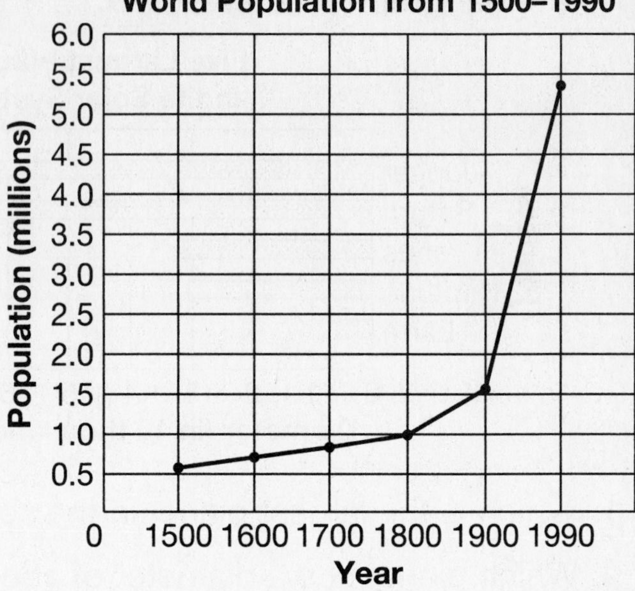

1. What was the population of the world in 1500?

____

2. What was the population of the world in 1990?

____

3. Write the coordinates that represent the world population in 1600.

____

4. About how many more people were there in 1700 than in 1500? ______________________

5. What has happened to the world population since 1500? ______________________

6. Between which years was the increase in population the greatest? ______________________

What was the increase? ______________________

7. Between which years was the increase in the population the least? ______________________

What was the increase? ______________________

8. In which year was the population the least? ____________

9. In which year was the population the greatest? ____________

10. Write the coordinates that represent the number of people in 1800.

____

11. What is the scale on the horizontal axis?

____

Name ______________________________

Practice 1-3

Reading Stem-and-Leaf Plots

Every year, the best soccer teams in the state play in a state tournament. This plot shows the number of times the top ten teams have played in this tournament.

Use the plot to answer **1–4**.

Stem	Leaf
2	6 4 1
1	4 0
0	8 6 6 5

1. In what order are the stems arranged from top to bottom?

____

2. How many teams have played 20 times or more? __________

3. Middletown has played in the state tournament the second greatest number of times. How many times have they played?

____

4. River City and Yorktown have each played in the state tournament the same number of times. How many times have they played in the tournament? ________

Mr. Morgan's class took part in a read-a-thon. This plot shows how many books his students read.

Stem	Leaf
2	4 3 1 2 0
1	9 4 3 7 4 0 0
0	8 9 3 9 9 8 5

Use the plot to answer **5-9**.

5. Emma read the most books. How many did she read? __________

6. How many students participated in the read-a-thon? __________

7. Did most students read more than 15 books? Explain.

____

8. How many students read more than 20 books? __________

9. What was the least number of books read? __________

Name ______________________________

Practice
1-4

Range, Mode, and Median

This line plot shows the number of hours spent doing homework for a week.

Use the line and plot to answer **1** and **2**.

Hours Spent Doing Homework

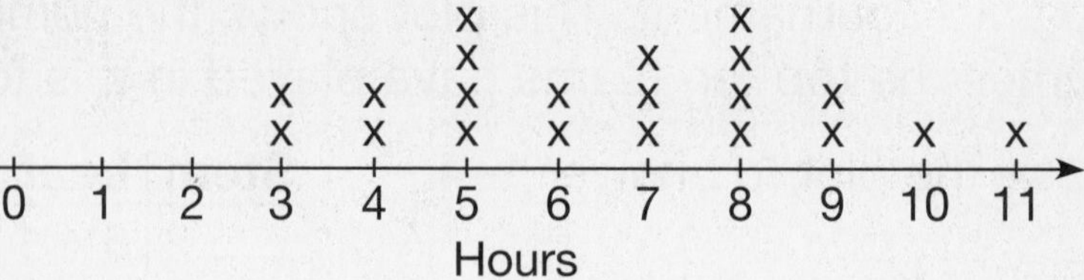

1. For the above data, give the

a. range ____________ **b.** mode ____________

c. median ____________

2. Did about half the students do homework for less than 6 hours?

Explain. ______________________________

____

Use the stem-and-leaf plot to answer **3–4**.

3. Give the: **a.** range ____________

b. mode ____________

c. median ____________

4. Did the Dallas Cowboys score more than 26 points in about half of the games they played in 1995? Explain.

____

Points Scored by the Dallas Cowboys
(1995)

Stem	Leaf
3	5 1 4 4 4 4 7
2	3 3 3 8 0 4 1
1	7 7

Use the line plot to answer **5–6**.

Price of Inline Skates

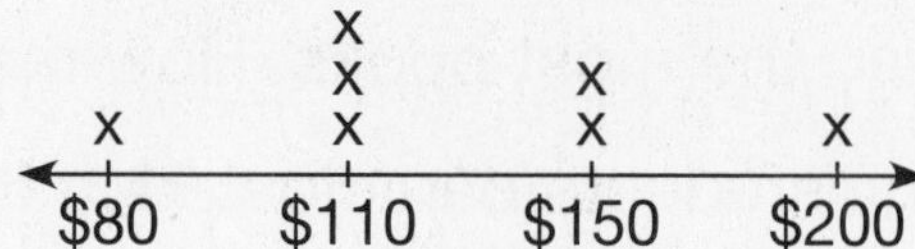

5. Give the:

a. range ________ **b.** mode ________ **c.** median ________

6. Is it true that most of the inline skates cost less than $100? Explain.

____

Name ______________________________

Practice
1-5

Introduction to the Problem Solving Guide

How many BMX and mountain bikes were sold?

You can use the bar graph to learn how many BMX and mountain bikes were sold.

Use the graph to answer **1–5**.

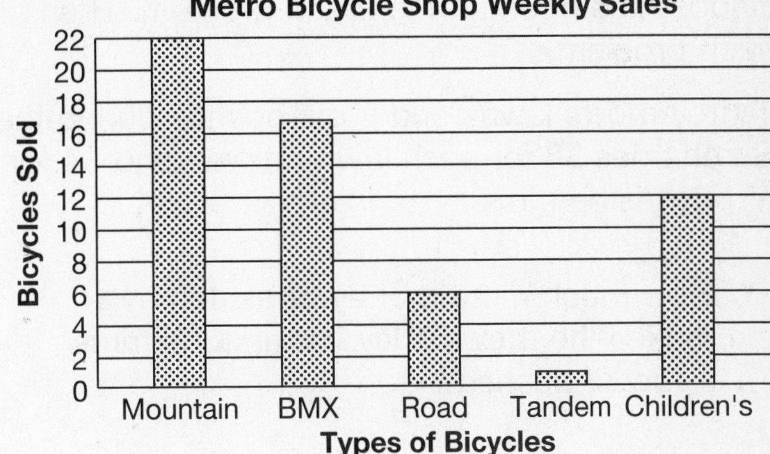

1. What information do you need to answer the question?

____

2. What operation would you use to solve the problem? __________

3. Give the answer. ______________________

Choose the number sentence you would use to solve the problem.

4. How many more mountain bikes were sold than road bikes? ______

A. 22 + 6 = 28 **B.** 22 − 6 = 16

5. What is the total number of road and tandem bikes sold? ______

A. 6 + 1 = 7 **B.** 6 − 1 = 5

Use any strategy to solve each problem.

6. Roger bought a mountain bike for $130. He used $85 of his own money, and his father paid the rest. How much did his father pay? ______________

7. One family bought 3 children's bicycles. Each cost the same amount. If their total bill was $225, what was the cost of each bicycle? ______________

8. For 4 days, the bicycle shop sold the same number of bicycles each day. They sold a total of 52 bicycles in all. How many did they sell on the first day? ______________

Name ______________________________

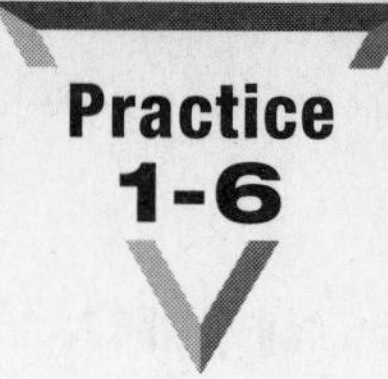

Analyze Word Problems: Choose an Operation

Choose the operation for each problem. Then solve each problem.

Jeffrey mows lawns and trims bushes during the spring. He charges $8 for each lawn mowed and $4 for each row of bushes he trims.

1. How much more money does Jeffrey make if he mows 1 lawn than if he trims 1 row of bushes? ______________

2. a. Jeffrey earned $20 for the bushes he trimmed. How many rows of bushes did he trim? ______________

   b. How much money did he make mowing 5 lawns? ______________

   c. How much did he earn in all? ______________

Write the operation needed for each problem. Then solve each problem.

3. Martina delivers newspapers to 60 houses on her route. She had so many customers, she decided to give 12 customers to her brother. To how many houses does Martina deliver now? ______________

4. Louisa charges each customer the same amount to rake leaves. In one week, 3 of her customers paid her $18.75. How much did each customer pay? ______________

5. Steven drinks 3 glasses of water a day. How many glasses of water does he drink in a week? ______________

Name ____________________

Practice 1-7

Exploring Algebra: What's the Rule?

Find the rule for each table. Give the rule using words and a variable.

1.

A	B
3	1
9	3
12	4
18	6
21	7

____

____

2.

A	B
0	0
14	2
28	4
35	5
49	7

____

____

3.

A	B
1	6
7	12
11	16
15	20
21	26

____

____

Complete each table. Give its rule using words and a variable.

4.

A	B
☐	18
9	27
12	☐
15	45
18	54

____

____

5.

A	B
8	1
48	☐
56	7
☐	8
72	9

____

____

6.

A	B
△	△△△
☐	△△△△△
△△△△△	△△△△△△△
△△△△△△△	☐
△△△△△△△△△	△△△△△△△△△△△

____

____

Write each rule using a variable.

7. Divide a number by 8

____

8. 2.1 more than a number

____

Write each rule using words.

9. $n \times 12$

____

10. $n \div 6$

____

Name ______________________________

Review and Practice

(Lesson 1) Use the line plot to answer **1** and **2**.

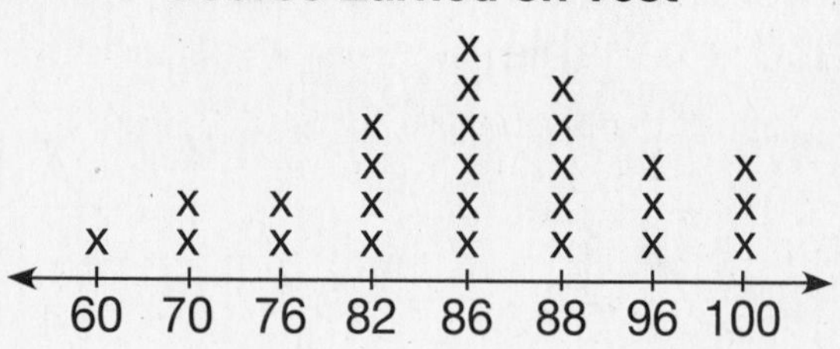

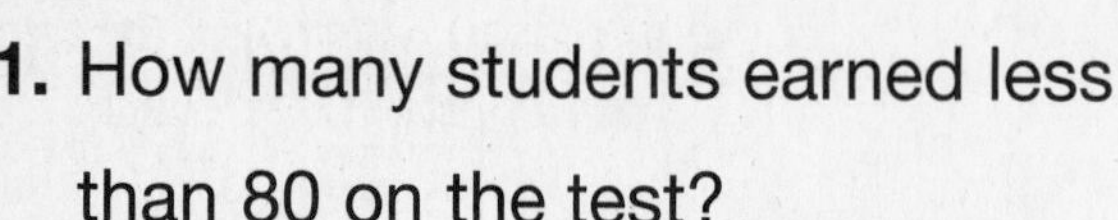

1. How many students earned less than 80 on the test? ______

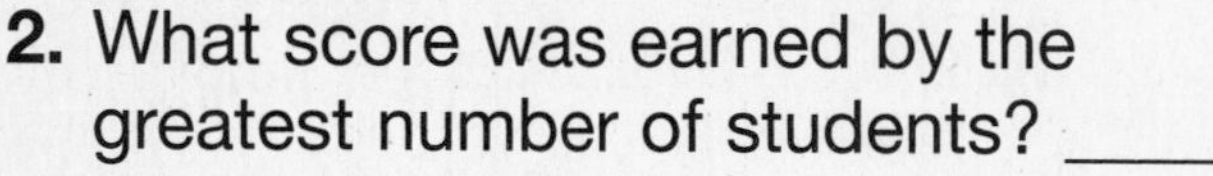

2. What score was earned by the greatest number of students? ______

(Lesson 2) Use the line graph to answer **3–5**.

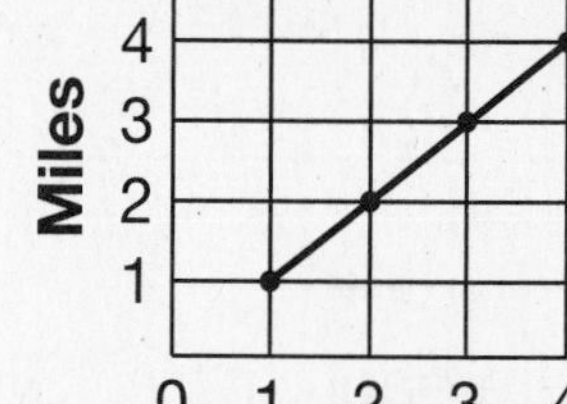

3. What does this line graph show? ______

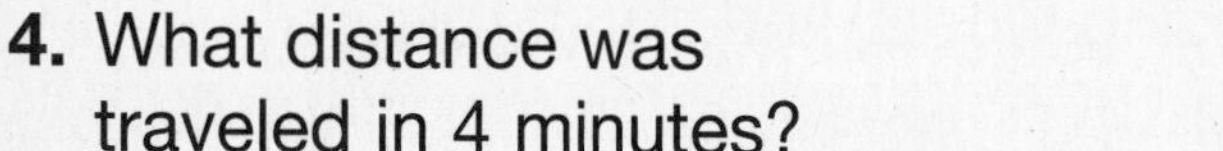

____

____

4. What distance was traveled in 4 minutes? ______

5. What does the ordered pair (3,3) stand for?

____

(Lessons 3 and 4) Use this stem-and-leaf plot to answer **6–8**.

Stem	Leaf
0	7 8 9 9 9
1	3 3 4 6
2	1 1 2 3 4
3	0 1

6. What is the mode for the number of pages read? ______

7. What is the range of the number of pages read? ______

8. What is the median number of pages read? ______

(Lessons 5 and 6) Solve.

9. The average number of books Jill reads per month is 4. About how many books will she read in 6 months? ______

(Lesson 7) Complete the table. Write its rule using a variable.

10.

A	1	3	5	7	9
B	5	15	____	____	____

Rule: ______

(Mixed Review) Find each sum or difference.

11. 16 + 9 = ______

12. 24 − 8 = ______

13. 17 − 9 = ______

14. 6 + 36 = ______

Name ______________________________

Scales and Bar Graphs

Use the graphs to answer **1–5**.

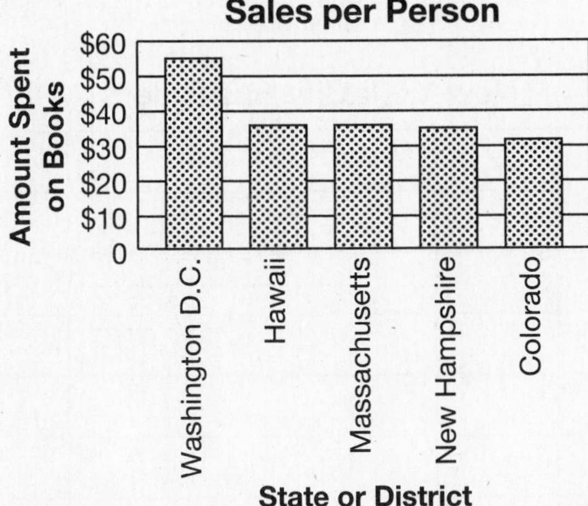

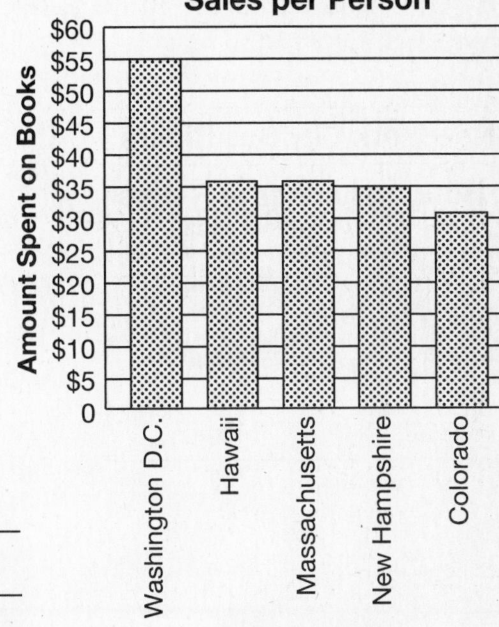

1. What is the scale of Graph A? ________

2. What is the scale of Graph B? ________

3. Do both graphs show the same amount of money spent on books in each state? ________

4. Which graph implies the least difference in the amount of money spent on books in each state? ___________

5. Which graph is easier to read? Explain. ____________________________

____

6. Choose a scale and make a bar graph of the data in the table.

Patton Middle School Students' Favorite Colors	
Color	**Number of Students**
blue	14
red	29
hot pink	25
green	12
yellow	36

7. What scale did you choose? Why?

____

____

Name ______________________________

Practice
1-9

Exploring Making Line Graphs

1. Line graphs are used to show changes or __________ in data.

2. Use this table to make a line graph.

New York City Bus Riders	
Hour	**Number of Riders** (thousands)
12 P.M.	125
2 P.M.	115
4 P.M.	140
6 P.M.	185
8 P.M.	145

New York City Bus Riders

Number of Riders (thousands): 200, 190, 180, 170, 160, 150, 140, 130, 120, 110, 100, 0

Hours: 12 P.M., 2 P.M., 4 P.M., 6 P.M., 8 P.M.

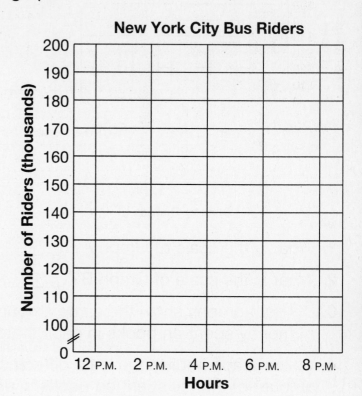

3. Use the graph to determine about how many riders there would be at 3 P.M. ______________________________

____

4. a. Between which times shown on the graph did the number of riders decrease? ______________________________

____

b. Why do you think fewer people traveled at these times?

____

____

Name ________________________________

Practice 1-10

Exploring Making Stem-and-Leaf Plots

1. Make a stem-and-leaf plot for the temperature data.

Daily Highs for the Month of July in degrees Farenheit											
88	74	78	86	90	91	94	92	85	87	83	79
81	90	87	84	83	79	84	85	90	83	78	83

Stem	Leaf

2. Most of the temperatures fell between ______ and ______ degrees.

Use the table to answer **3–8**.

National Ice Hockey Final 1995–1996 Standings			
Atlantic Division	**Wins**	**Pacific Division**	**Wins**
Washington	39	Colorado	47
New Jersey	37	Vancouver	32
Philadelphia	45	Anaheim	35
New York	22	Calgary	34
Tampa Bay	38	Los Angeles	24
Florida	41	Edmonton	30
New York	41	San Jose	20

3. Make a stem-and-leaf plot for the Atlantic Division wins.

Stem	Leaf

4. Make a stem-and-leaf plot for the Pacific Division wins.

Stem	Leaf

5. Which division had more teams win 40–49 games?

____

6. Which division had only one team win less than 30 games?

____

7. The median number of games won by the:

Atlantic Division: ______ Pacific Division: ______.

8. Describe the shapes of stem–and-leaf plots for the divisions.

____

____

Name ____________________

Practice 1-11

Analyze Strategies: Use Logical Reasoning

Use logical reasoning to solve each problem.

1. A family of four—mother, father, son, and daughter—sits down to have dinner together. Father and son sit across from one another, while the daughter sits to her father's right. Where does each person sit?

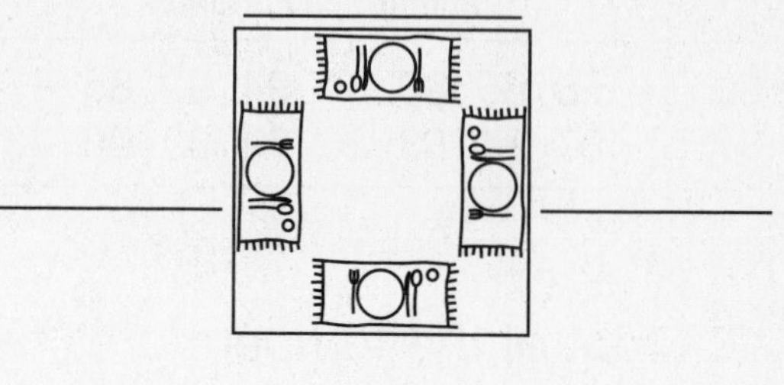

2. At a fast food restaurant, Peter and Patricia can choose from burgers, hot dogs, chicken, and fish. Peter and Patricia both eat two entrees, but neither eats the same one. Patricia is allergic to fish. Neither Peter nor Patricia will eat a burger and chicken together. What entrees did each choose?

____

____

____

Use any strategy to solve each problem.

3. Here is some information about campers' favorite card games. No one liked to play *Old Maid*. *Go Fish* was liked slightly better than *Snap*, but not as well liked as *500 Rummy. War* got one more vote than *Old Maid*. *Concentration* was more favored than *Go Fish*, but just a little less liked than *500 Rummy.* List the order of the campers' favorite games.

____

4. A road cleanup crew needs 2 volunteers for every 15 miles of road.If there are 60 miles of roads to be cleaned, how many volunteers are needed? ____________________

5. A cook wants to use $150 to buy hams and turkeys. The hams cost $45 and turkeys cost $35. How many hams and turkeys can the cook buy?

____

Name ____________________

Practice
Chapter 1
Section B

Review and Practice

(Lesson 8) Choose a scale and make a bar graph of the data in the table.

1.

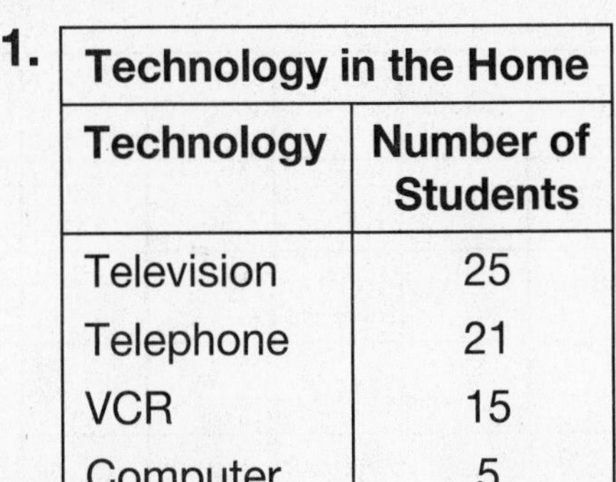

Technology in the Home	
Technology	**Number of Students**
Television	25
Telephone	21
VCR	15
Computer	5

Technology

Number of Students

(Lesson 9) Make a line graph. Use the data in the table.

2.

Enrollment at East Elementary	
Year	**Number of Students**
1996	370
1997	375
1998	382

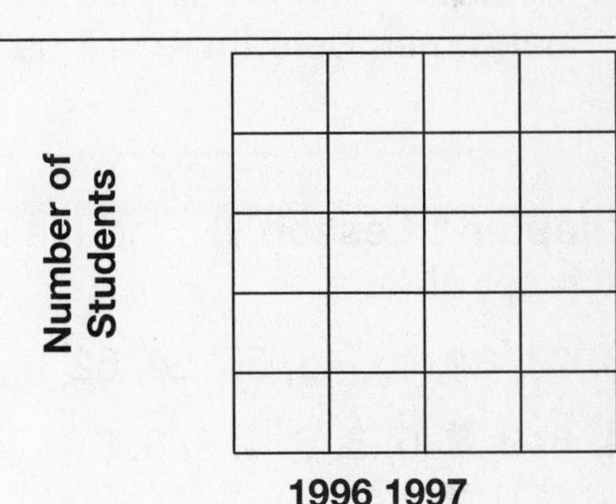

(Lesson 10) Make a stem-and-leaf plot for the data given.

3.

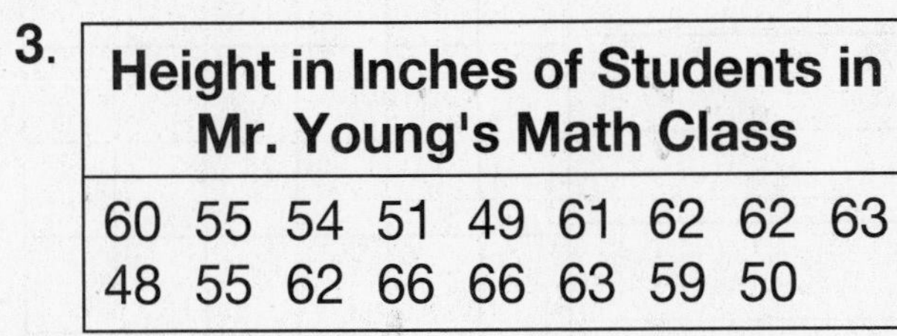

Height in Inches of Students in Mr. Young's Math Class								
60	55	54	51	49	61	62	62	63
48	55	62	66	66	63	59	50	

(Mixed Review) Find each product or quotient.

4. $5 \times 7 =$ ________ **5.** $56 \div 8 =$ ________ **6.** $7 \times 9 =$ ________

7. $32 \div 4 =$ ________ **8.** $25 \div 5 =$ ________ **9.** $6 \times 7 =$ ________

10. $18 \div 3 =$ ________ **11.** $4 \times 7 =$ ________ **12.** $81 \div 9 =$ ________

Name ______________________________

Practice
Chapter 1

Cumulative Review

(Chapter 1 Lessons 2 and 9) Use the data to complete the line graph and answer the question.

1.

Number of Band Members per Year	
Year	**Number**
1995	40
1996	50
1997	55
1998	58

____

Number

0

Year

2. What can you predict about the number of band members there will be in the future?

____

(Chapter 1 Lesson 4) Find the range, mode, and median for each set of data.

3. 23, 34, 45, 43, 56, 24, 62 ________, ________, ________

4. 8, 9, 8, 6, 8, 6, 4, 9, 3, 6 ________, ________, ________

(Chapter 1 Lesson 8) Use the data to complete the bar graph.

5.

Number of Instruments in the Band	
Instrument	**Number**
Clarinet	12
Flute	8
Trombone	4
Saxophone	3
Trumpet	10

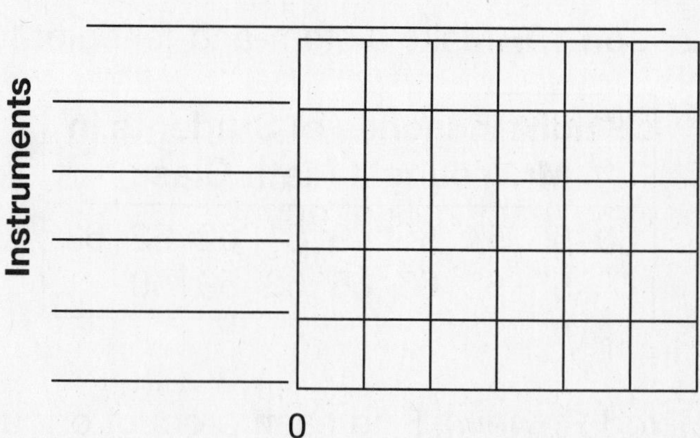

(Facts Review) Add, subtract, multiply or divide.

6. $2 \times 6 =$ ________ **7.** $45 \div 9 =$ ________ **8.** $3 \times 12 =$ ________

9. $4 + 7 =$ ________ **10.** $17 - 9 =$ ________ **11.** $15 + 8 =$ ________

Name ____________________

Practice
2-1

Exploring a Million

Use a calculator to answer **1–2.**

1 hour = 60 minutes | 1 day = 24 hours | 1 week = 7 days

1. If your heart beats 70 times every minute, how many times does it beat:

a. in one hour? ________ **b.** in 3 hours? ________

c. in one day? ________ **d.** in one week? ________

2. How long would it take for your heart to beat 1,000,000 times? ____________

Use patterns to solve **3–7**.

3. Suppose you have sheets of grid paper that are 5 × 5. Would you need more or less of these sheets than the 10 × 10 sheets to show one million squares? Explain.

____

____

4. A roll of pennies holds 100 pennies. How many pennies are in:

a. 3 rolls? ____________

b. 10 rolls? ____________

c. 100 rolls? ____________

d. 1,000 rolls? ____________

5. How many rolls of pennies makes one million pennies? ____________

6. 500 pennies are worth $5. How much are each of these groups of pennies worth in dollars?

a. 800 pennies = $ ________ **b.** 1,000 pennies = $ ________

c. 5,000 pennies = $ ________ **d.** 25,000 pennies = $ ________

7. How much is one million pennies worth in dollars? ________

Name ______________________

Practice
2-2

Place Value Through Millions

Write each number in word form.

1. 2,430,156 ______________________

____

2. 83,705,019 ______________________

____

3. 614,720,308 ______________________

____

Write each number in standard form.

4. fifty-three million, two hundred sixteen thousand, eight hundred four ______________________

5. four hundred sixty-four million, five hundred two thousand, forty-three ______________________

6. seven million, seventy-six thousand, two hundred eighty-nine ______________________

7. 80,000,000 + 9,000,000 + 400,000 + 7,000 + 200 + 60 + 5 ______________________

8. 100,000,000 + 10,000,000 + 7,000,000 + 300,000 + 50,000 + 600 + 50 ______________________

9. Look at these numbers.

3,500 30,500 3,000,500

a. How are the three numbers alike? ______________________

____

____

b. How are the three numbers different? ______________________

____

____

Name ______________________________

Practice 2-3

Exploring Place-Value Relationships

Complete the following pattern.

1. 100 = 10 × ________ = $10^{\square}$

2. 1,000 = ________ × ________ × ________ = $10^{\square}$

3. 10,000 = ________________________ = $10^{\square}$

4. 100,000 = ________________________ = ________

5. 1,000,000 = ________________________ = ________

6. How many 10s make 100? __________

7. How many 100s make 100,000? __________

8. How many 1,000s make 100,000? __________

9. How many 10,000s make 1 million? __________

10. How many 100s make 1 million? __________

Write each number using exponents.

11. 10,000 ________

12. 10 ________

13. 1,000 ________

14. 1,000,000 ________

15. 100,000 ________

16. 100 ________

Complete.

17. $10^{\square}$ = 10,000,000

18. $10^{\square}$ = 100,000,000

19. $\square^2$ = 100

20. $10^{\square}$ = 10,000

21. How does the number on the right of the equals sign help you to find the exponents in **17–20**?

____

Name ______________________________

Practice 2-4

Place Value Through Billions

Write each number in standard form.

1. three billion, six hundred million, thirty thousand ____________
2. seventy-eight billion, forty-two million, nine thousand, eleven ____________
3. four hundred billion, ninety million ____________
4. thirty billion, three hundred million, thirty thousand, three hundred three ____________

Complete.

5. 130,009,400,660 = one hundred thirty __________, __________ million, four ____________ thousand, six hundred sixty
6. 42,100,080,005 = ____________ billion, one __________________, eighty ______________, five
7. 900,090,700,007 = nine __________________, __________ million, seven ______________________, seven
8. How many 1,000,000s in 1,000,000,000? __________
9. How many 1,000s in 1,000,000,000? ______________
10. How many 100,000,000s in fifty billion? __________

Write the place-value position for each digit in 240,786,305,900.

11. 6 ____________
12. 4 ________________
13. 2 ____________________
14. 8 ________________
15. 7 ____________________
16. 3 ________________________

17. In the number 7,472,352,101 give the value of each 7.

____

Name ______________________________

Practice
2-5

Comparing and Ordering

Write >, <, or = to complete.

1. 94,276 ◯ 89,376

2. 14,050 ◯ 9,876

3. 472,343 ◯ 473,668

4. 2,202,020 ◯ 2,202,020

5. five hundred thirty-six thousand ◯ 537,719

6. 16,740,280 ◯ sixteen million, four hundred seventy thousand, two hundred, eighty

7. 30 billion, 20 thousand ◯ 89 million, 60 thousand

8. seven million, six hundred thousand, fifty ◯ 7,603,050

9. 419,786,372 ◯ four hundred nineteen billion, six

Order these numbers from least to greatest.

10. 421,089   376,005   377,500   420,980

____

11. 78,400,000   78,004,000,000   78,000,004

____

12. 54,798   54,978   54,897   53,999

____

13. 911,345   910,435   901,435   911,453

____

14. 28,079,043   28,709,043   28,719,043

____

15. What digit could be in the ten millions place of a number that is greater than 25,000,000 but less than 73,000,000? Explain.

____

____

Name ______________________

Practice
2-6

Rounding Greater Numbers

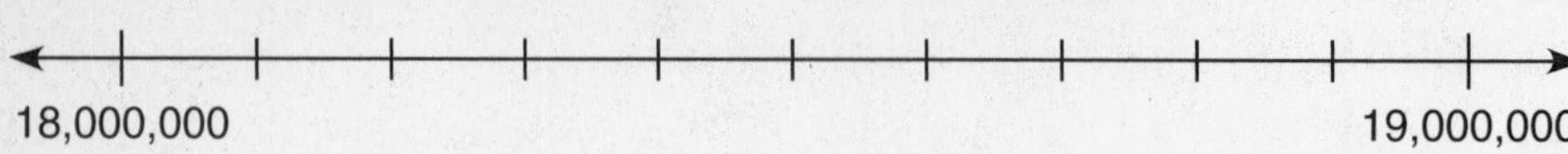

1. Use the number line to help you round 18,521,425 to the nearest million. __________

Round to the nearest hundred thousand.

2. 872,768 __________

3. 8,243,956 __________

4. 2,035,467 __________

5. 43,974,012 __________

Round to the nearest million.

6. 8,643,231 __________

7. 75,499,999 __________

8. 987,645,312 __________

9. 489,753,274 __________

Round to the nearest ten million.

10. 78,634,021 __________

11. 7,630,998,432 __________

12. 646,000,000 __________

13. 801,009,999 __________

14. If 789,364,768 rounds to 789,400,000, to which place did you round?

____

15. What is the greatest number that rounds to 65,000,000 when rounded to the million place? __________

Use the table to answer **16** and **17**.

16. Which city has a population closest to 1,000,000 people?

____

17. Which two cities would have the same population if rounded to the nearest 10,000?

City	Population in 1990
Austin, Texas	846,227
Louisville, Kentucky	948,829
Memphis, Tennessee	1,007,306
Las Vegas, Nevada	852,737

____

Name ________________________________

Practice
Chapter 2
Section A

Review and Practice

Vocabulary Write whether each is true or false.

1. A period is one of the symbols: 0, 1, 2, 3, 4, 5, 6, 7, 8, 9. __________
2. A number line shows numbers in order. __________
3. A digit is a group of three numbers. __________

(Lesson 1) What is the value in dollars of the money in each stack?

4. one hundred $10 bills __________ 5. ten $100 bills __________

(Lesson 3) Complete.

6. 10 × __________ = 50,000 7. __________ × 800 = 80,000

8. $10^{\square}$ = 100,000

(Lessons 2 and 4) In the number 79,402,356,108 write the value of:

9. 4 ________________ 10. 7 ________________

11. 9 ________________ 12. 2 ________________

13. Write one hundred fifty million, two hundred fifty-seven thousand, nine hundred forty-five in standard form. ________________

(Lesson 5) Write >, <, or = to complete.

14. 235,641 ◯ 93,584 15. 90,006 ◯ ninety thousand six

16. 899,002 ◯ six hundred million 17. 89,903 ◯ 89,099

(Lesson 6) Use the table to answer **18** and **19**.

18. Write the letter for the breed that has registered about:
    a. 70,000 dogs __________
    b. 100,000 dogs __________

19. To the nearest thousand, how many Labrador retrievers are registered? ______________

Top 5 American Kennel Club Registrations

Breed	Registrations
A. Labrador Retrievers	124,899
B. Rottweilers	104,160
C. German Shepherds	79,936
D. Cocker Spaniels	75,882
E. Golden Retrievers	68,125

(Mixed Review) Find each product or quotient.

20. 36 ÷ 9 = _______ 21. 7 × 7 = _______ 22. 48 ÷ 6 = _______

Name ______________________________

Practice 2-7

Tenths and Hundredths

Write each decimal shown.

1. ______________

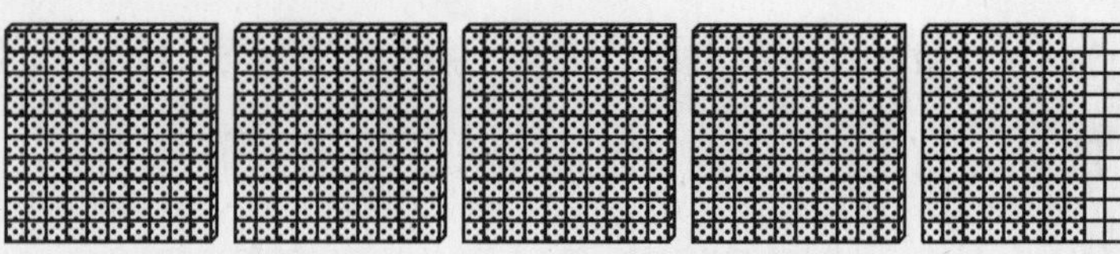

2. ______________

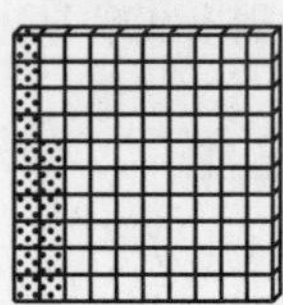

Draw place-value blocks to show each decimal.

3. 0.56 **4.** 4.30

Write each number in decimal form.

5. 40 hundredths **6.** 6 tenths **7.** 4

__________ __________ __________

8. three and seventy-four hundredths ___________

9. seven and three hundredths ___________

10. Can you show 0.02 using only tenths place-value blocks? Explain.

____

____

11. Which is greater, 5.34 or 5.43? Do you have to look at the hundredths place to decide? Explain.

____

Name ___________________________________

Practice 2-8

Exploring Equivalent Decimals

Complete. Write =, >, or < for each answer.

1. 0.04 ◯ 0.40 **2.** 0.50 ◯ 0.5

3. 1.40 ◯ 14.0 **4.** 2.3 ◯ 2.30

Write two decimals that name each shaded part.

5. ____________

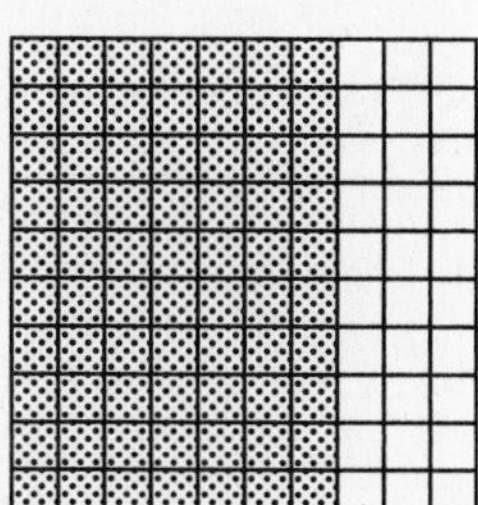

6. ____________

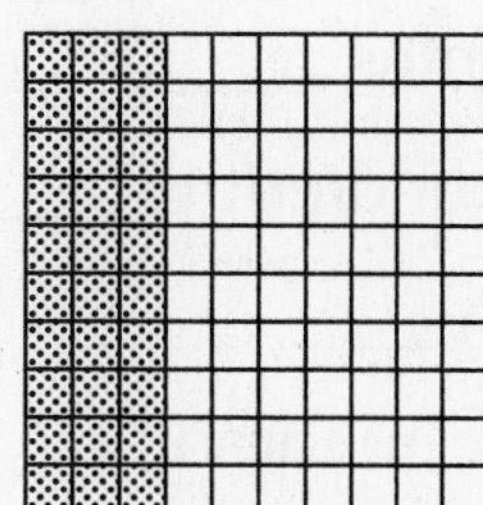

Write each as an equivalent decimal using tenths.

7. 0.20 ________ **8.** 0.60 ________ **9.** 0.80 ________ **10.** 0.40 ________

Write each as an equivalent decimal using hundredths.

11. 0.1 ________ **12.** 0.6 ________ **13.** 0.7 ________ **14.** 0.3 ________

In each group, write which decimals are equivalent.

15. 0.2 0.20 0.02 ____________ **16.** 0.40 0.04 0.4 ____________ **17.** 0.5 0.05 0.50 ____________

18. On a hot summer's day, you read the temperature on two different thermometers. The first thermometer reads 90.9°F. The second thermometer reads 90.90°F. Did you get the same reading on both thermometers? Explain. ________________

Name ___________________________

Thousandths

Write each number in decimal form.

1. 8 tenths __________
2. 8 hundredths __________
3. 800 thousandths __________
4. 8 thousandths __________
5. 8 __________
6. four and three tenths __________
7. eight and three hundredths __________
8. six and one tenth __________
9. four and sixty-six hundredths __________
10. three and eight thousandths __________
11. nine and six hundred eighty-eight thousandths __________
12. one and one hundred eleven thousandths __________
13. nine and twenty-one thousandths __________
14. two and one hundred nine thousandths __________
15. Which is greatest and which is least? 9.9, 9.09, 9.990? Explain.

____

____

____

16. Using the digits 0, 4, 7, and 9, write the greatest decimal possible, in thousandths.

 ___ . ___ ___ ___

17. Using the digits 0, 3, 5, and 9, write the least decimal possible, in thousandths.

 ___ . ___ ___ ___

Name ___________________________

Practice
2-10

Decimals on the Number Line

Complete the number line.

1.

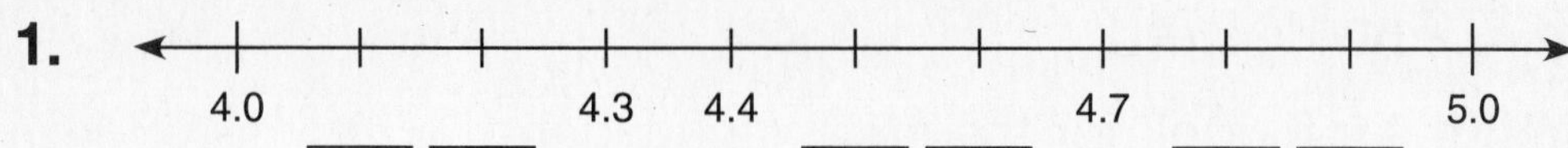

Name the number shown by each letter.

2.

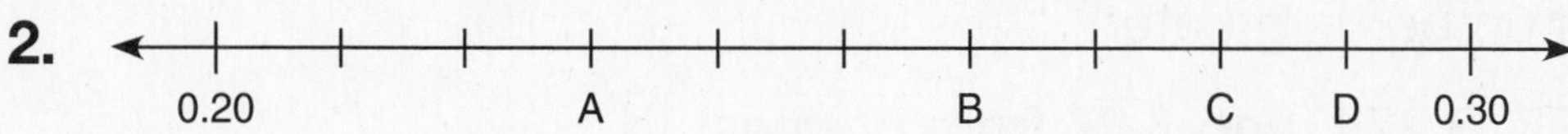

A ________ B ________ C ________ D ________

Use the number line shown to answer **3** and **4**. Name two numbers:

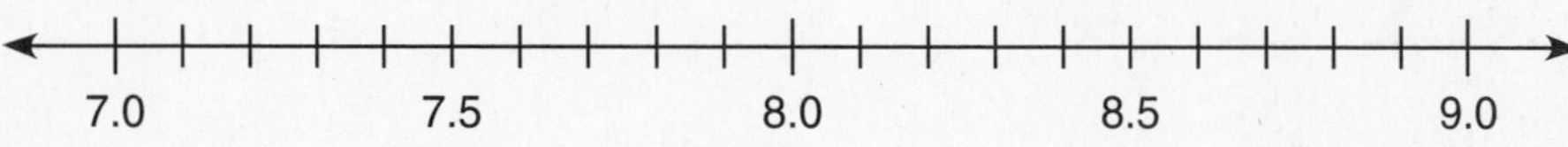

3. Between 7.5 and 8.0 ___________________________

4. Between 8.0 and 8.5 ___________________________

Use the number line shown to answer **5–7**.

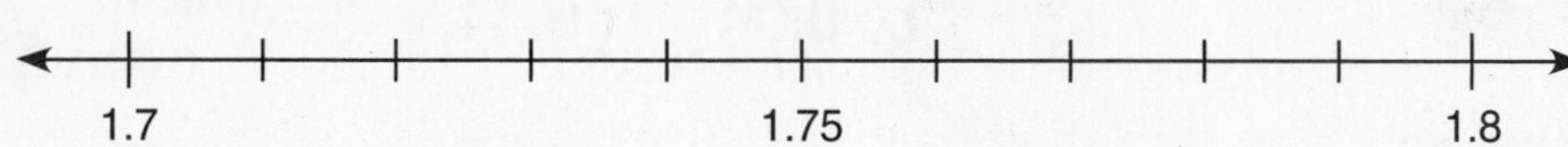

5. Name three numbers between 1.7 and 1.8. ______________

____

6. Is 1.799 between 1.7 and 1.8? Explain your thinking. __________

____

7. Is 1.07 the half-way point between 1.7 and 1.8? Tell how you know.

____

Name ______________________________

Practice 2-11

Exploring Comparing and Ordering Decimals

1. Compare 3.277 and 3.274.

a. Starting at the left, look for the first place where the digits are different. What place is it?

____

b. Which number is greater? _______________

2. Order 3.277, 3.274, and 3.27 from greatest to least by comparing numbers two at a time. Use > or < to compare.

a. 3.277 ◯ 3.274

b. 3.274 ◯ 3.27

c. The order from greatest to least is ____________________

3. Order 0.4, 0.04, 4.00, and 0.44 from least to greatest by comparing numbers two at a time. Use < or > to compare.

a. 0.04 ◯ 0.4

b. 0.04 ◯ 0.44

c. 0.44 ◯ 4.00

d. The order from least to greatest is ____________________

Write >, <, or = to complete.

4. 0.2 ◯ 0.03

5. 0.4 ◯ 0.54

6. 0.89 ◯ 2.1

7. 0.7 ◯ 79

8. 0.4 ◯ 0.44

9. 0.2 ◯ 0.20

10. 2.6 ◯ 2.36

11. 3.9 ◯ 3.09

12. 0.1 ◯ 0.16

13. 0.3 ◯ 0.34

14. 4.1 ◯ 4.19

15. 2.1 ◯ 2.10

16. 0.3 ◯ 0.03

17. 0.5 ◯ 0.56

18. 8.7 ◯ 8.07

19. 7.3 ◯ 7.33

20. 3.39 ◯ 33.9

21. 5.1 ◯ 5.09

Name ______________________________

Practice 2-12

Rounding Decimals

Round each number to the place of the underlined digit.

1. 73.49	**2.** 2.009	**3.** 36.415	**4.** 4.708
5. 0.82	**6.** 0.887	**7.** 9.77	**8.** 2.207
9. 7.757	**10.** 46.960	**11.** 42.59	**12.** 9.65
13. 0.68	**14.** 34.225	**15.** 4.05	**16.** 4.56
17. 19.01	**18.** 0.087	**19.** 4.050	**20.** 6.957
21. 0.3	**22.** 0.824	**23.** 3.989	**24.** 6.064
25. 48.05	**26.** 3.25	**27.** 0.857	**28.** 0.055
29. 7.019	**30.** 11.297	**31.** 3.54	**32.** 0.9

33. Name two decimals with digits in the hundredths place that could be rounded to the tenths place as 0.4.

34. Name two decimals with digits in the tenths place that could be rounded to the ones place as 1.

Name ______________________________

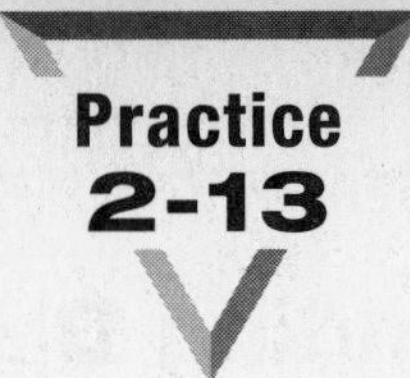

Analyze Strategies: Draw a Picture

Draw a picture to solve.

1. Jessica, Sarah, Annie, Tiffany, and Megan decide to go to an early movie that will cost them each $4. Jessica and Tiffany want to split a container of popcorn that costs $2. Megan and Annie want to share nachos that cost $4. Sarah wants to buy the souvenir movie poster for $3. Everyone brings $6.

   a. Will everyone have enough money for the movie and the items they want to buy?

   ____

   b. Who will spend the most money? __________

   c. How much money will Jessica have left? ________

2. Sam is 12 years old. Garrett is younger than Sam but older than David and Mark. David is 9 and Mark is 10.

   What is Garrett's age? ________

3. The school is having a skating party. The students decide to do a line dance. They form three lines. The longest line is 60 students. One of the other lines has half as many students but is twice as long as the third line. How many students are in each of the other two lines?

   ____

4. Danny, Philip, Jennifer, and Emily are having a bike race. Jennifer only finishes ahead of Philip, who comes in last. Emily finishes behind Danny. What was the order of the finish from first to last?

   ____

5. Jean is younger than Dan but older than Rob. Sue is the oldest of the four. Who is the youngest?

   ____

Name ____________________

Review and Practice

(Lessons 7 and 9) Write each number in decimal form.

1. 29 hundredths ________

2. 7 hundredths ________

3. 16 thousandths ________

4. 7 tenths ________

5. eight and forty hundredths ________

6. nine and two hundred three thousandths ________

(Lesson 8) In each group circle equivalent decimals.

7. 0.4 0.04 0.40

8. 0.02 0.20 0.2

(Lesson 10) Name the number shown by each letter.

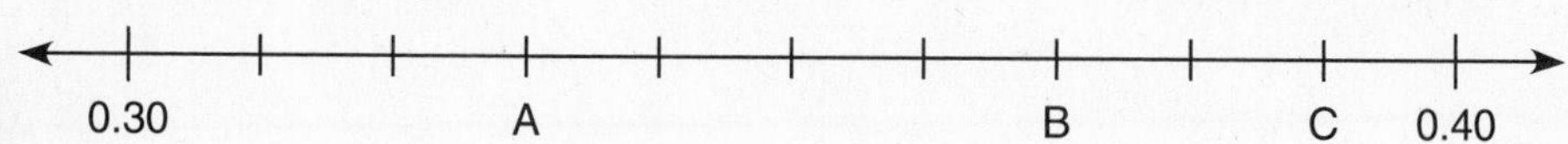

9. A ________ **10.** B ________ **11.** C ________

(Lesson 11) Write >, <, or = to complete.

12. 0.71 ◯ 0.231 **13.** 0.6 ◯ 0.600 **14.** 2.38 ◯ 1.8

15. 6.07 ◯ 6.070 **16.** 0.29 ◯ 0.3 **17.** 5.8 ◯ 6.7

(Lesson 12) Round each number to the place of the underlined digit.

18. $0.\underline{6}51$ ________ **19.** $\underline{5}.63$ ________

20. Carolyn owes Michael 72¢. She only has dimes.
What is the nearest amount she can give him? ________

(Mixed Review) Write >, <, or =.

21. 6 + 9 + 3 ◯ 9 + 4 + 6 **22.** 18 − 5 ◯ 17 − 4

23. 9 × 3 ◯ 15 + 13 **24.** 5 + 0 ◯ 0 × 8

Name ______________________________

Practice 2-14

Estimating Sums and Differences

Estimate each sum or difference.

1. 232
− 75

2. $9.67
+ 3.44

3. 718
+ 457

4. $6.98
− 4.87

5. 728
96
+ 293

6. 382
249
+ 777

7. $11.93
+ 2.55

8. 599
+ 607

9. 431
− 65

10. $5.68
+ 7.55

11. 737
+ 216

12. $4.76
− 2.99

13. 525
37
+ 168

14. 345
268
+ 188

15. $9.99
− 4.89

16. 699
+ 103

17. 906
− 367

18. $6.59
− 3.80

19. 608
− 398

20. $6.78
− 2.80

Estimate. Write >, <, or = to complete.

21. 67 + 49 ◯ 130

22. $16.75 − $7.00 ◯ $23.00

23. 48 + 34 + 95 ◯ 170

24. 444 + 856 ◯ $1,300

25. If you decrease both addends when rounding to add, what can you say about your estimated sum?

____

Name ____________________

Practice
2-15

Adding and Subtracting Whole Numbers

Find each sum or difference. Then estimate to check your answer.

1. $\begin{array}{r} 686 \\ +208 \\ \hline \end{array}$

2. $\begin{array}{r} 506 \\ -331 \\ \hline \end{array}$

3. $\begin{array}{r} 748 \\ +992 \\ \hline \end{array}$

4. $\begin{array}{r} 252 \\ +3{,}889 \\ \hline \end{array}$

5. $\begin{array}{r} 376 \\ +\quad 49 \\ \hline \end{array}$

6. $\begin{array}{r} 776 \\ -634 \\ \hline \end{array}$

7. $\begin{array}{r} 600 \\ -277 \\ \hline \end{array}$

8. $\begin{array}{r} 308 \\ -\quad 87 \\ \hline \end{array}$

9. $\begin{array}{r} 47 \\ 599 \\ 23 \\ +\quad 55 \\ \hline \end{array}$

10. $\begin{array}{r} 548 \\ 329 \\ 101 \\ +\quad 88 \\ \hline \end{array}$

11. 372 + 65 + 133 + 435 = ____________

12. 446 + 9,675 + 11,007 + 329 + 32 = ____________

13. Subtract 8,435 from 9,074. ____________

14. Find the sum of 4,882, 12,443, 3,229, and 356. ____________

15. Find 7,999 + 4,999 mentally. Explain why it is easier to do this sum mentally than by writing it out.

____

____

16. Find 3,000 − 1,002 mentally. Explain your reasoning.

____

____

17. Find 399 + 598 + 701 mentally. ____________

Name ______________________________

Practice 2-16

Exploring Adding and Subtracting Decimals

Use place-value blocks to add or subtract.

1. 0.34 + 0.59 = ____

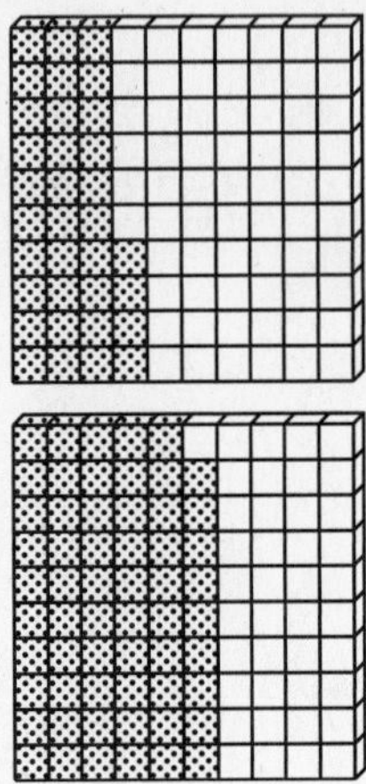

2. 0.67 − 0.59 = ____

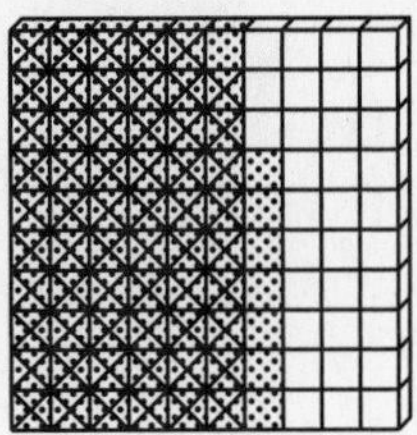

Use place-value blocks or drawings to find each sum or difference.

3. 4.32 + 5.87 = ____

4. 5.41 − 1.74 = ____

5. 5.29 + 8.47 = ____

6. 4.1 − 3.7 = ____

7. 3.8 + 5.6 = ____

8. 6.8 + 2.6 = ____

9. 9.53 − 4.79 = ____

10. 15.7 + 0.6 = ____

11. 6.2 + 9.5 = ____

12. 8.35 − 0.79 = ____

13. 4.23 + 5.74 + 6.8 = ________

14. 5.9 − 2.8 = ________

Complete. Use place-value blocks or drawings to help you.

15. 4.87 − ________ = 1.23

16. 2.35 + ________ = 8.40

17. Explain how you can show 4.37 using dollars, dimes, and pennies.

____

____

 Use with pages 90–91.

Name ______________________________

Practice 2-17

Adding Decimals

Find each sum.

1. 6.23 + 8.94

2. 4.03 + 5.67

3. 4.05 + 0.96

4. 5.20 + 0.36

5. 6.31 + 7.41

6. 4.24 + 0.56 + 3.65

7. \$3.49 + 0.87 + 2.26

8. 0.84 + 2.76 + 0.12

9. 4.59 + 2.77 + 6.0

10. 3.9 + 1.1 + 8.0

11. \$5.29 + 0.44

12. 6.5 + 0.47

13. 0.67 + 3.2 + 1.25

14. 2.0 + 3.69 + 2.77

15. 43.0 + 2.60

16. 3.5 + 4.5 + 3 = ________

17. 0.86 + 0.5 = ________

18. 4.6 + 6.7 + 2 = ________

19. 0.73 + 0.48 = ________

20. Find the sum of 4.99 and 3.45. ________

21. Find the sum of 3.9 + 3.09 + 30.9. ________

22. Explain why you cannot write 9.2 as 9.02.

____

____

Name ______________________

Practice 2-18

Subtracting Decimals

Find each difference.

1. \$7.99 − 4.99	**2.** 13.0 − 2.47	**3.** 35.50 − 0.87	**4.** 8.9 − 0.54	**5.** 3.33 − 2.67
6. 14.89 − 6.55	**7.** \$4.00 − 3.49	**8.** 8.9 − 7.0	**9.** 5.0 − 0.6	**10.** 2.08 − 0.99
11. \$4.44 − 2.99	**12.** 4.0 − 0.67	**13.** 8.45 − 4.96	**14.** 3.98 − 0.79	**15.** 14.2 − 13.27
16. 6.5 − 0.76	**17.** 4.7 − 4.07	**18.** \$9.99 − 3.68	**19.** 9.09 − 5.99	**20.** \$1.00 − 0.79

21. 8 − 4.65 = ________ **22.** 14.6 − 8.76 = ________

23. Find the difference of 7 and 3.64. ________

24. If you have zeros in the tenths and hundredths place in the first number and fives in the tenths and hundredths place of the second number, how do you subtract?

____

____

Complete.

25. 4.7 − ________ = 0.6 **26.** ________ − 1.75 = 2.68

Name ______________________________

Practice
2-19

Analyze Word Problems: Choose an Operation

Write the letter of the number sentence you would use.

1. The deluxe soccer gear set costs \$55. The regular soccer set costs \$27. What is the difference in costs between the two sets?

A. \$27 + \$55 = \$82

B. \$55 − \$27 = \$28

C. \$27 + \$82 + \$55 = \$164

____

Write the number sentence or sentences you would use.
Then solve each problem.

2. The special chess set is \$14 less than the deluxe chess set, which costs \$68. How much is the special chess set?

____

3. Brandon planned on using \$80 to buy the deluxe chess set. He wanted to use his leftover money to buy a book on chess strategy which costs \$10.99. How much money will Brandon have left?

____

____

4. Brianna had \$34 in babysitting money plus \$12 allowance. She would also like to buy the deluxe chess set. How much more money will she need?

____

5. Steven and his sister Jenna want to buy a gift for their parents that costs \$54. Steven has \$15 and Jenna has \$24. Do they have enough money to buy the gift? If not, how much more money do they need?

____

____

Name ______________________________

Practice
Chapter 2
Section C

Review and Practice

(Lessons 14 and 15) Find each sum or difference. Estimate to check.

1. 544 − 397

2. 878 + 663

3. 502 − 47

4. $12.16 + 5.08

5. $62.90 − 23.17

6. $34.07 + 25.27

7. 5,002 − 357

8. 16,892 + 5,308

9. 24,000 − 13,571

(Lessons 16 and 17) Find each sum.

10. 42.26 + 5.08

11. $62.90 + 16.88 + 35.02

12. 9.7 + 3.72 + 1.08

13. 5.2 + 0.3 + 28.17

(Lessons 16 and 18) Find each difference.

14. 7.03 − 3.47

15. $16.75 − 13.57

16. 3.81 − 0.5

17. 9 − 1.61

(Lesson 19) Choose any strategy to solve the problem.

18. Amy had $15 to buy a CD for $12.95. The tax on the purchase was $0.65. How much money did Amy have left?

____

(Mixed Review) Multiply.

19. 400 × 2 __________

20. 3 × 300 __________

21. 200 × 9 __________

22. 4 × 600 __________

Name ______________________________

Practice
Chapters 1–2

Cumulative Review

(Chapter 1 Lesson 2) Use the data from the graph to answer each question.

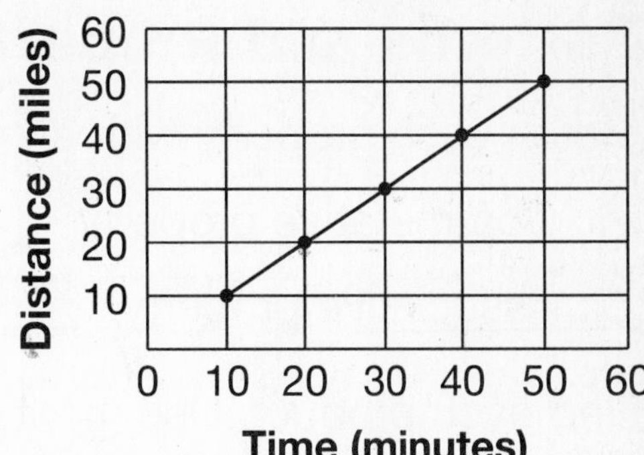

1. How many miles were traveled in 20 minutes?

____

2. How many miles would you expect to travel in 60 minutes? __________

(Chapter 1 Lesson 4) Find the range, median, and mode for each set of numbers.

3. 10, 12, 12, 9, 3 __________, __________, __________

4. 29, 25, 20, 20, 15, 22 __________, __________, __________

(Chapter 1 Lesson 6) Write a number sentence and use it to solve the problem.

5. Seth estimates he will need 45 minutes to do his homework. He needs 15 minutes to do spelling. The rest of the time he will do his math homework. How many minutes will Seth spend doing math homework?

____

(Chapter 2 Lesson 4) Write each number in standard form.

6. three billion, four hundred thirty-six million __________

7. ten billion, five million, six hundred twenty-one thousand, two hundred thirteen __________

(Chapter 2 Lesson 12) Round each number to the place of the underlined digit.

8. $45.\underline{5}1$ ______ **9.** $0.0\underline{0}9$ ______ **10.** $\underline{3}.93$ ______

(Chapter 2 Lesson 15) Add or subtract.

11. $\begin{array}{r} 369 \\ -\ 197 \\ \hline \end{array}$ **12.** $\begin{array}{r} 371 \\ +\ 263 \\ \hline \end{array}$ **13.** $\begin{array}{r} 901 \\ -\ 38 \\ \hline \end{array}$ **14.** $\begin{array}{r} 66{,}092 \\ +\ 13{,}505 \\ \hline \end{array}$

Name ______________________________

Practice 3-1

Exploring Multiplication Patterns and Properties

Match each property with an example.

1. Commutative property _____ **a.** $6 \times (3 \times 5) = 6 \times (5 \times 3)$

2. Associative property _____ **b.** $4 \times (8 \times 10) = (4 \times 8) \times 10$

Find each product. Use mental math.

3. $20 \times 80 =$ ________ **4.** $6 \times 80 =$ ________

5. $40 \times 40 =$ ________ **6.** $17 \times 20 =$ ________

7. $12 \times (5 \times 10) =$ ________ **8.** $(80 \times 3) \times 20 =$ ________

9. $100 \times (3 \times 90) =$ ________ **10.** $6 \times (60 \times 3) =$ ________

Complete.

11. $40 \times$ ________ $= 1{,}600$ **12.** $30 \times$ ________ $= 900$

13. $50 \times$ ________ $= 30{,}000$ **14.** ________ $\times 80 = 3{,}200$

15. $60 \times$ ________ $= 42{,}000$ **16.** ________ $\times 70 = 700{,}000$

Complete. For each product the factors are the same.

17. ______ $\times$ ______ $= 4{,}900$ **18.** ______ $\times$ ______ $= 250{,}000$

19. ______ $\times$ ______ $= 1{,}600$ **20.** ______ $\times$ ______ $= 90{,}000$

Find each product. Use mental math and multiplication properties.

21. $(22 \times 25) \times 4 =$ ________ **22.** $2 \times (47 \times 5) =$ ________

23. $(2 \times 36) \times 5 =$ ________ **24.** $(60 \times 900) \times 100 =$ ________

25. How many \$10 bills are equal to three \$20 bills? ________

26. How many zeros are in the product of $4 \times 25 \times 200$? Explain.

____

27. Which is greater, the product of $50 \times 200 \times 3$ or $5 \times 20 \times 300$? Explain.

____

____

Name ______________________________

Practice 3-2

Estimating Products

Estimate each product.

1. 9×34 __________
2. 53×6 __________
3. 8×47 __________
4. 66×4 __________
5. 11×48 __________
6. 37×29 __________
7. 72×31 __________
8. 58×32 __________
9. 19×41 __________
10. 27×433 __________
11. 742×68 __________
12. 77×518 __________

13. 98×21
14. 71×63
15. 649×42
16. 262×68

17. 309×47
18. 487×31
19. 49×49
20. 135×77

21. Estimate the product of 416 and 72. __________
22. The product of what two numbers is about 400?

    ____
23. The product of 42 and what number is about 1,200?

    ____
24. The product of what two numbers is about 42,000?

    ____
25. The product of 345 and what number is 21,000?

    ____

Name ______________________

Practice 3-3

Multiplying Whole Numbers

Estimate Find each product. Estimate to check.

1. 66×29 **2.** 95×56 **3.** 73×45 **4.** 83×77 **5.** 115×39

6. $324 \times 8 =$ ________ **7.** $289 \times 5 =$ ________

8. 294×9 **9.** 326×6 **10.** 565×24 **11.** 683×37 **12.** 333×99

13. $24 \times 309 =$ ________ **14.** $41 \times 37 =$ ________

15. 375×9 **16.** 544×6 **17.** 663×24 **18.** 792×36 **19.** 436×87

20. Find the product of 84 and 93. ________

21. Multiply 409 and 37. ________

22. What is the greatest number of times you would regroup when multiplying a 3-digit factor by a 2-digit factor? Give an example.

____

____

____

23. Which is greater, 456×65 or 465×56?

____

Name ______________________

Distributive Property

Find each product.

1. $32 \times 9 =$ ________

2. $304 \times 8 =$ ________

3. $5 \times 801 =$ ________

4. $698 \times 3 =$ ________

5. $6 \times 703 =$ ________

6. $2 \times 599 =$ ________

7. $801 \times 9 =$ ________

8. $597 \times 7 =$ ________

9. $29 \times 4 =$ ________

10. $42 \times 8 =$ ________

11. $697 \times 3 =$ ________

12. $40 \times 89 =$ ________

13. $79 \times 12 =$ ________

14. $298 \times 11 =$ ________

15. Multiply 347 and 28. ________

16. Find the product of 80 and 14. ________

17. Would you use the distributive property to find 810×9? Explain.

____

18. Use the distributive property and multiplication patterns to find $62 \times 5 \times 10$.

____

____

Name ______________________________

Practice
3-5

Choosing a Calculation Method

Choose a method. Find each product.

1. $\begin{array}{r} 63 \\ \times 99 \\ \hline \end{array}$

2. $\begin{array}{r} 800 \\ \times \ 20 \\ \hline \end{array}$

3. $\begin{array}{r} 242 \\ \times \ 87 \\ \hline \end{array}$

4. $\begin{array}{r} 110 \\ \times \ 9 \\ \hline \end{array}$

5. $\begin{array}{r} 199 \\ \times \ 33 \\ \hline \end{array}$

6. $\begin{array}{r} 47 \\ \times 42 \\ \hline \end{array}$

7. $\begin{array}{r} 490 \\ \times 400 \\ \hline \end{array}$

8. $\begin{array}{r} 76 \\ \times 67 \\ \hline \end{array}$

9. 346 × 56 = ________

10. 290 × 200 = ________

11. 705 × 120 = ________

12. 83 × 15 = ________

13. Find the product of 483 and 264. __________

14. Multiply 204 and 8. ________

15. Jan and her friend each solve 483 multiplied by 276. Jan's answer is 85,988. Her friend's answer is 133,308. Which answer is reasonable? Explain.

____

16. Estimate the product of 52 and 328. Is it closer to 15,000 or 20,000? Explain.

____

Name ______________________________

Practice
3-6

Exploring Patterns with Multiples

This chart shows some multiples of 4 and 5.

4	4	8	12	20	24	28	32	36	40	44
5	5	10	15	20	25	30	35	40	45	50

1. Shade the common multiples of 4 and 5. Which is the least common multiple? ______

Find the LCM for each pair or set of numbers.

2. 3 and 4 ______ **3.** 5 and 9 ______ **4.** 2 and 8 ______

5. 6 and 8 ______ **6.** 2 and 3 ______ **7.** 7 and 10 ______

8. 10 and 20 ______ **9.** 3 and 9 ______ **10.** 9 and 10 ______

11. 5 and 6 ______ **12.** 4 and 8 ______ **13.** 2 and 7 ______

14. 2, 4, and 6 ______ **15.** 3, 5, and 7 ______

16. 2, 4, and 8 ______ **17.** 2, 5, and 10 ______

18. 3, 6, and 9 ______ **19.** 2, 3, and 7 ______

20. 3, 4, and 7 ______ **21.** 2, 3, and 9 ______

22. Use your calculator to find the LCM for 35 and 25. Enter ON/AC + 25 = = and so on. List the multiples. Do the same for 35. What is the first multiple that is a multiple for both 25 and 35?

______

23. Make a list of the multiples of 30. Do you need to make a list of multiples of 7 to find the LCM of 30 and 7? Explain.

____

____

24. What if you want to find the greatest common multiple of 7, 9, and 0? Could you do this? Explain.

____

____

Name ________________________________

Practice 3-7

Decision Making

A local movie theater sells tickets for $6.00 each and a box of popcorn for $2.00. But if you pay $36.00 for a movie pass, you can see 8 movies in 8 weeks, and get 1 free box of popcorn with each movie. Would you choose to buy the movie pass or not?

What are you asked to do? Decide whether to get a movie pass or not.

How much would you have to pay for a ticket and a box of popcorn at the regular price? $6.00 + $2.00 = $8.00

How much would each movie and a box of popcorn cost if you got the movie pass? $36.00 ÷ 8 = $4.50

About how often would you have to see a movie to go 8 times in 8 weeks? Once a week

---

1. Would it make sense to get the pass if you only go to the movies once or twice in 8 weeks? Explain.

____

2. Would it make sense to get the pass if you to go the movies 8 times in 8 weeks? Explain.

____

____

Suppose the same movie theater offered a $12.00 movie pass that allowed you to see 3 movies in the next year.

3. How much would each movie cost? __________

4. How much money would you save if you bought the pass and saw 3 movies that year? __________

5. How much money would you lose if you only saw 1 movie that year? __________

6. Would you buy this movie pass? Explain.

____

Name ______________________________

Review and Practice

Vocabulary Fill in each blank with a word from the word bank.

commutative	distributive	least common multiple	multiple

1. $5 \times (3 + 4) = (5 \times 3) + (5 \times 4)$ is an example of the ________________ property.

2. $5 \times 3 = 3 \times 5$ is an example of the ________________ property.

3. 16 is a ________________________ of 2.

4. 48 is the ________________________ of 16 and 24.

(Lesson 1) Find each product. Use mental math and multiplication properties.

5. $50 \times 3 =$ __________

6. $40 \times 70 =$ __________

7. $60 \times (3 \times 30) =$ __________

8. $80 \times 25 \times 4 =$ __________

(Lesson 2) Estimate each product.

9. 65×27 ______________

10. 38×72 ______________

11. 81×19 ______________

12. 52×94 ______________

(Lessons 3–5) Find each product.

13. 584×7

14. 98×13

15. 92×45

16. 705×4

17. 600×80

18. 362×42

19. 375×43

20. 481×93

(Lesson 6) Find the LCM for each set of numbers.

21. 6 and 32 __________

22. 3, 6, and 7 __________

(Mixed Review) Solve.

23. $8 \div 4 \times 6 - 10 =$ __________

24. $4 \times 4 \div 8 + 3 =$ __________

Name ______________________________

Practice
3-8

Exploring Decimal Patterns

Draw arrows to show the number of places to move the decimal. Then write the product.

1. 2.38 × 10 ________ **2.** 2.38 × 100 ________ **3.** 2.38 × 1,000 ________

4. 0.356 × 10 ________ **5.** 0.356 × 100 ________ **6.** 0.356 × 1,000 ________

Find each product.

7. 4.7 × 10 = ________
4.7 × 100 = ________
4.7 × 1,000 = ________

8. 0.96 × 10 = ________
0.96 × 100 = ________
0.96 × 1,000 = ________

9. 0.06 × 10 = ________
0.06 × 100 = ________
0.06 × 1,000 = ________

10. 8.437 × 10 = ________
8.437 × 100 = ________
8.437 × 1,000 = ________

Place the decimal point in the product. Write extra zeros if necessary.

11. 1.63 × 10 = 1 6 3

12. 3.72 × 100 = 3 7 2

13. 0.035 × 1,000 = 3 5

14. 0.0068 × 1,000 = 6 8

15. 1.063 × 100 = 1 0 6 3

16. 7.04 × 1,000 = 7 0 4

Find each product. Use mental math.

17. 100 × 2.93 = ________

18. 1,000 × 3.049 = ________

19. 5.47 × 10 = ________

20. 8.05 × 1,000 = ________

21. 100 × 0.635 = ________

22. 10 × 0.514 = ________

23. Money 10 members of the science club each paid $2.50 for a field trip. How much did they pay all together? ________

Name ______________________________

Practice 3-9

Estimating Decimal Products

Estimate each product. Explain what you did.

1. 5.2×6 ______________ **2.** 7.8×5 ______________

3. 9.1×3 ______________ **4.** 1.7×8 ______________

5. 39.7×9 ______________ **6.** 25.1×4 ______________

7. 4.19×8 ______________ **8.** 88.9×2 ______________

9. 72.3×49 ____________________

10. 728.1×28 ____________________

11. 6.6×97 ____________________

12. 32×511.9 ____________________

Is each product greater than 250? Write yes or no. Explain.

13. 25.3×8 ____________________

14. 9×29.97 ____________________

15. 10×22.19 ____________________

16. 52.37×5 ____________________

17. 47.3×6 ____________________

18. 11×22.3 ____________________

Is each product greater than 2,500? Write yes or no. Explain.

19. 927.4×2 ____________________

20. 24.1×99 ____________________

21. 111×27.43 ____________________

22. 19.86×198 ____________________

23. 24.4×100 ____________________

24. 51.2×51.2 ____________________

25. Estimate the product of 51.07 and 9.87. ____________

26. Estimate the product of 98.57 and 303. ____________

27. Estimate the product of 68.9 and 74.2. ____________

Name ______________________________

Practice
3-10

Multiplying Whole Numbers and Decimals

Find each product.

1. 3.14 × 7 = __________

2. 6.05 × 8 = __________

3. 15.45 × 6 = __________

4. 4.51 × 13 = __________

5. 29.4 × 76 = __________

6. 89.03 × 39 = __________

7. $15.75 × 6 = __________

8. $33.99 × 4 = __________

9. $12.45 × 13 = __________

10. $21.95 × 11 = __________

11. $3.95 × 24 = __________

12. $74.63 × 8 = __________

13. 18 × 347.6 = __________

14. 93 × 72.6 = __________

15. 9 × $26.37 = __________

16. 6 × $147.50 = __________

Choose the number that is closest to the actual product.

17. $3.25 ×11 ________ **A.** $300 **B.** $50 **C.** $30

18. $6.80 × 39 ________ **A.** $28 **B.** $280 **C.** $180

19. $4.75 × 22 ________ **A.** $1,000 **B.** $100 **C.** $80

20. 2.008 × 100 ________ **A.** 20 **B.** 2,000 **C.** 200

21. What is the product of 7.09 and 16? __________

22. What is the product of $1.85 and 34? __________

23. Bill says the product of 6 and 3.79 is 227.4. Is he correct? Explain.

____

____

24. Circle each multiplication sentence whose product is a whole number.

3 × 45.7 12.2 × 5 6 × 8.5 7.6 × 4

23.5 × 45 6.15 × 4 5 × 32.8 4 × 7.25

Name ____________________________________

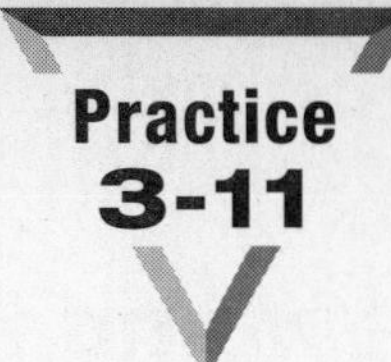

Analyzing Word Problems: Multiple-Step Problems

Solve each problem.

1. Sandwiches at the diner are $3.75, a salad costs $1.19, and a glass of juice costs $0.99. A family went to the diner and ordered 3 sandwiches, 2 salads, and 3 glasses of juice.

   a. How much will the family pay for the 3 sandwiches? __________

   b. How much will the family pay for the 2 salads? __________

   c. How much will the family pay for the 3 glasses of juice? __________

   d. How much is the total bill? __________

Solve each problem. Chose any strategy.

2. The hobby shop sells many different varieties of kites. Box kites are $6.69, diamonds are $5.95, and dragon kites are $11.98.

   a. Mr. Sanders bought 2 box kites and 2 diamond kites for his 4 children. How much did he spend? __________

   b. Ms. Byars bought 3 box kites and 2 dragon kites for her 5 children. How much did she spend? __________

3. A video store charges $2.50 for new movies and $1.50 for children's movies. If a family rents 2 new movies and 3 children's movies, how much will they pay? __________

4. At a state fair, the Lanier family had 120 jars of their homemade jelly to sell. Large jars were $4.50 each and small jars were $2.50 each.

   a. How much would you pay if you bought 3 large jars and 4 small ones? ____________

   b. By the end of the day, the Laniers sold 40 large jars of jelly. They made $330 in all. How much did they make selling small jars of jelly? ____________

   c. How many small jars of jelly did they sell? ____________

   d. How many jars did the Laniers have leftover? ____________

Name ____________________

Review and Practice

Vocabulary Underline the word that correctly to completes the sentence.

1. 4 and 25 are (compatible, decimal) numbers for multiplication.

2. The product of 0.23 and 10 is a (compatible, decimal) number.

(Lesson 8) Find each product.

3. $6.04 \times 10 =$ ________ **4.** $1.85 \times 100 =$ ________

5. $0.92 \times 100 =$ ________ **6.** $0.0065 \times 1{,}000 =$ ________

7. $1.98 \times 10 =$ ________ **8.** $0.0236 \times 1{,}000 =$ ________

(Lesson 9) Estimate each product.

9. 16×8.46 ____________ **10.** 6.12×82 ____________

11. 307×9.5 ____________ **12.** 4.78×30 ____________

13. 25×0.12 ____________ **14.** 1.11×73 ____________

(Lesson 10) Use estimation to place the decimal point in each product.

15. $6.15 \times 98 = 6\ 0\ 2\ 7$ **16.** $9.82 \times 35 = 3\ 4\ 3\ 7$

17. $52.7 \times 23 = 1\ 2\ 1\ 2\ 1$ **18.** $11.1 \times 49 = 5\ 4\ 3\ 9$

19. $\$1.23 \times 9 = \$1\ 1\ 0\ 7$ **20.** $\$6.88 \times 707 = \$4\ 8\ 6\ 4\ 1\ 6$

(Lesson 11) Solve each problem.

21. A granola bar sells for $0.55. An eight-pack of the same bars costs $4.00. How much could you save on a purchase of an eight-pack? ________

22. A candle maker can make 3 candles from 6 pounds of wax. How many pounds of wax would be needed to make 15 of the same candles? ____________

(Mixed Review) Multiply or divide.

23. $3 \times 8 =$ ________ **24.** $45 \div 9 =$ ________

25. $42 \div 7 =$ ________ **26.** $5 \times 7 =$ ________

27. $8 \times 9 =$ ________ **28.** $36 \div 6 =$ ________

Name ________________________________

Practice 3-12

Exploring Decimal Multiplication

1. Use the 10 × 10 grid to show 0.7 of 0.9.

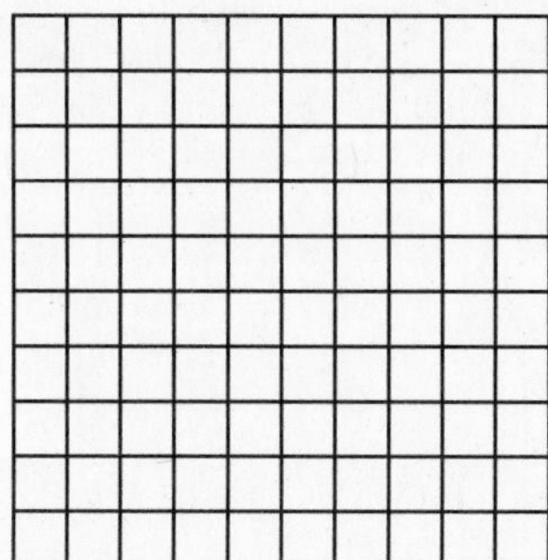

a. Use yellow to shade 0.7 on the grid as 7 rows.

b. Use blue to shade 0.9 on the grid as 9 columns.

c. Count the green squares. 0.7 of 0.9 is ________.

Find each product. You can use 10 × 10 grids to help.

2. 0.4 of 0.5 ________

3. 0.3 of 0.7 ________

4. 0.4 of 0.7 ________

5. 0.9 of 0.2 ________

6. 0.8 of 0.5 ________

7. 0.8 of 0.9 ________

8. 0.8 of 0.6 ________

9. 0.3 of 0.6 ________

10. 0.6 of 0.6 ________

11. 0.4 of 0.6 ________

12. 0.6 of 0.3 ________

13. 0.8 of 0.7 ________

14. 0.5 of 0.6 ________

15. 0.3 of 0.9 ________

16. 0.4 of 0.1 ________

17. 0.9 of 0.9 ________

18. Find the product of 0.7 and 0.7. ________

19. The product is 0.64. One of the factors is 0.8. What is the other factor? ________

20. Write two numbers whose product is 0.35. ________

21. Write two numbers whose product is 0.49. ________

22. A can of dog food weighs 0.6 lb. Arthur's dog gets 0.5 can of food for dinner. How much does the dog's dinner weigh?

____

Name ______________________________

Practice
3-13

Multiplying Decimals by Decimals

Find each product. Round to the nearest cent when necessary.

1. 3.45×0.4

2. $\$7.10 \times 42$

3. 1.45×4.5

4. $\$43.38 \times 1.65$

5. 3.81×4.121

6. 6.09×5.4

7. 0.091×74.4

8. 4.799×5

9. 231×0.301

10. $\$17.32 \times 0.04$

11. 3.5×3.5

12. $\$12.30 \times 4$

13. Find the product of 49.3 and 0.22. __________

14. Find the product of $8.43 and 24.5. Round to the nearest cent.

____

15. The product of 4,005 × 6,004 is 24,046,020. What is the product of 4.005 and 6.004?

____

16. Without doing the multiplication, tell how many decimal places are in the product of 4.97 and 3.456.

____

17. Without doing the multiplication, tell how many decimal places are in the product of 72.35 and 14.12.

____

Name ______________________

Practice 3-14

Finding High and Low Estimates

Between which two numbers will each product be found?

1. 8.6 × 8.762 ______

   A. 8 and 9 B. 16 and 48 C. 64 and 81

2. 7.9 × 5.23 ______

   A. 7 and 5 B. 57 and 75 C. 35 and 48

3. 9.6 × 0.74 ______

   A. 9 and 16 B. 0 and 10 C. 9 and 63

Estimate low and high. Then find each product.

4. 5.4 × 6 = ______

   Estimate:

   ______

5. 41.3 × 7 = ______

   Estimate:

   ______

6. 9.3 × 4 = ______

   Estimate:

   ______

7. 7.8 × 3 = ______

   Estimate

   ______

8. $\begin{array}{r} 14.4 \\ \times\ 6.2 \\ \hline \end{array}$

   Estimate:

   ______

9. $\begin{array}{r} 4.9 \\ \times 8.1 \\ \hline \end{array}$

   Estimate:

   ______

10. $\begin{array}{r} 6.9 \\ \times 3.2 \\ \hline \end{array}$

    Estimate:

    ______

11. $\begin{array}{r} 7.9 \\ \times 8.3 \\ \hline \end{array}$

    Estimate

    ______

12. Estimate low and high. Then find the product of 89.4 and 4.8.

    ____

13. What 2 decimal factors when multiplied result in a product between 15 and 24? ______________

14. How can you use estimation to know that the product of 4.5 and 6.89 is more than 24?

    ____

Name ______________________

Practice 3-15

Decimals and Zeros

Find each product. Write zeros where needed.

1. $0.2 \times 0.3 =$ ________

2. $7.2 \times 0.0007 =$ ________

3. $1.25 \times 0.05 =$ ________

4. $0.004 \times 0.08 =$ ________

5. $3.4 \times 0.0006 =$ ________

6. $0.04 \times 0.04 =$ ________

7. $5.05 \times 4.02 =$ ________

8. $0.08 \times 10.05 =$ ________

9. 0.008×0.004

10. 0.07×0.006

11. 8.9×0.003

12. 2.1×0.08

13. 12×0.005

14. 0.045×0.004

15. 7.005×0.06

16. 5.05×5.04

17. 12.4×0.004

18. 18.4×0.0002

19. 9.3×0.0044

20. 76×0.0003

21. Find the product of 0.25 and 3.9. ________

22. Find the product of 6.2 and 0.4. ________

23. Is the product of 0.006 and 1.5 greater or less than 1.5? Explain.

____

____

Name ______________________________

Practice 3-16

Analyzing Strategies: Guess and Check

Use the Guess and Check strategy to solve each problem.

Two owners compared the weights of their dogs. Together, the two dogs weigh 36 lb. The spaniel weighs 6 lb more than the poodle.

1. What is a reasonable first guess for the weight of the poodle?

____

2. The two dogs together weigh 36 lb. Is it possible for the spaniel to weigh 24 lb? Explain.

____

3. How much did each dog weigh?

____

Use Guess and Check or any strategy to help solve each problem.

4. Together, Fred and Frank have been working 25 years. Frank has worked 7 years longer than Fred. How many years has each been working?

____

5. The cross country team is planning a 30 km relay. Each team member will run either 4 or 6 km. The same number of team members will run each distance. How many team members will run each distance?

____

6. At the hardware store, doorbells cost $12, while doorknobs cost $8. Greg's Refinishing Company spent $120 on 12 items. How many of each item did they buy?

____

7. Lawrence has $10. He gets a $6 a week allowance for doing household chores. How many weeks will it take him to save for a video game that costs $52?

____

Name ______________________

Practice
Chapter 3
Section C

Review and Practice

(Lesson 12) Place a decimal in each product.

1. 0.4 × 0.7 = 0 2 8

2. 0.08 × 5 = 0 4 0

3. 0.2 × 0.9 = 0 1 8

3. 0.15 × 9 = 0 1 3 5

(Lesson 13) Find each product. Round to the nearest cent when necessary.

5. 14.4 × 6.2

6. 4.9 × 8.1

7. $6.90 × 3.2

8. 7.9 × 8.3

(Lesson 14) Between which two numbers will each product be found?

9. 3.91 × 0.95 ______ **A.** 1 and 3 **B.** 3 and 4 **C.** 4 and 5

10. 6.6 × 9.2 ______ **A.** 54 and 70 **B.** 40 and 54 **C.** 6 and 9

11. 9.43 × 7.99 ______ **A.** 7 and 9 **B.** 56 and 63 **C.** 63 and 80

(Lesson 15) Find each product. Insert zeros where necessary.

12. 3.009 × 0.0028

13. 8.59 × 1.01

14. 0.00038 × 0.05

(Lesson 16) Solve.

15. Sandro's skateboard cost $8 more than Kim's. Together their skateboards cost $80. How much did each pay for their skateboards?

____

(Mixed Review) Add or subtract.

16. 73.5 + 3.5

17. 36.81 + 3.5

18. 122.89 − 32.98

19. $23.00 − 5.99

Name ______________________

Practice
Chapters 1–3

Cumulative Review

(Chapter 1 Lesson 10) Use the data to answer 1 and 2.

Number of Sit-ups in Gym Class									
23 13	24 19	15 20	16 30	23 32	30 30	30 20	14 10	22 22	33 23

1. Make a stem-and-leaf plot for the number of sit-ups in gym class.
2. What is the median, range, and mode of the number of sit-ups?

____

(Chapter 2 Lesson 9) Write each number in decimal form.

3. 8 thousandths ________ 4. 40 hundredths ________

5. three hundred one thousandths ________

(Chapter 2 Lesson 18) Subtract.

6. $\begin{array}{r} \$3.69 \\ -\ 1.97 \\ \hline \end{array}$ 7 $\begin{array}{r} 9.71 \\ -2.03 \\ \hline \end{array}$ 8. $\begin{array}{r} 6.01 \\ -3 \\ \hline \end{array}$ 9. $\begin{array}{r} 8 \\ -1.35 \\ \hline \end{array}$

(Chapter 3 Lesson 3) Find each product.

10. $\begin{array}{r} 267 \\ \times\ \ 5 \\ \hline \end{array}$ 11. $\begin{array}{r} 612 \\ \times\ \ 6 \\ \hline \end{array}$ 12. $\begin{array}{r} 501 \\ \times\ \ 3 \\ \hline \end{array}$ 13. $\begin{array}{r} 736 \\ \times\ \ 8 \\ \hline \end{array}$

(Chapter 3 Lesson 6) Find the LCM for each set of numbers.

14. 3 and 7 ________ 15. 5, 6, and 10 ________

(Chapter 3 Lesson 15) Find each product. Insert zeros where necessary.

16. $\begin{array}{r} 2.019 \\ \times 0.005 \\ \hline \end{array}$ 17. $\begin{array}{r} 1.567 \\ \times 0.016 \\ \hline \end{array}$ 18. $\begin{array}{r} 0.000043 \\ \times\ \ \ \ \ \ 0.03 \\ \hline \end{array}$

Name ______________________________

Practice 4-1

Reviewing the Meaning of Division

Find each quotient.

1. $56 \div 7 =$ ______ **2.** $42 \div 6 =$ ______ **3.** $24 \div 4 =$ ______

4. $32 \div 8 =$ ______ **5.** $30 \div 5 =$ ______ **6.** $54 \div 6 =$ ______

7. $36 \div 6 =$ ______ **8.** $21 \div 3 =$ ______ **9.** $35 \div 7 =$ ______

10. $72 \div 9 =$ ______ **11.** $36 \div 4 =$ ______ **12.** $15 \div 5 =$ ______

13. $12 \div 3 =$ ______ **14.** $64 \div 8 =$ ______ **15.** $49 \div 7 =$ ______

16. Identify each number in the equations $7 \times 4 = 28$ and $28 \div 7 = 4$ as a factor, a product, a divisor, a dividend, or a quotient.

7	×	4	=	28
↓		↓		↓
__________		__________		__________

28	÷	7	=	4
↓		↓		↓
__________		__________		__________

17. If you know that $6 \times 3 = 18$, you also know that $3 \times 6 = 18$. Solve for n

a. $18 \div 6 = n$ __________

b. $18 \div 3 = n$ __________

18. Laura's uncle would not tell his age. Instead he gave some clues: "When you divide my age by 5, the quotient is less than 10. I am younger than 55 but older than 35." What is his age?

____

Name ______________________________

Practice 4-2

Exploring Patterns to Divide

Complete the patterns.

1. $36 \div 4 =$ ________

$360 \div 4 =$ ________

$3{,}600 \div 4 =$ ________

$36{,}000 \div 4 =$ ________

2. $42 \div 7 =$ ________

$420 \div 7 =$ ________

$4{,}200 \div 7 =$ ________

$42{,}000 \div 7 =$ ________

3. $64 \div 8 =$ ________

$640 \div 8 =$ ________

$6{,}400 \div 8 =$ ________

$64{,}000 \div 8 =$ ________

4. $20 \div 5 =$ ________

$200 \div 5 =$ ________

$2{,}000 \div 5 =$ ________

$20{,}000 \div 5 =$ ________

Use patterns and basic facts to divide mentally.

5. $27 \div 9 =$ ________

6. $270 \div 9 =$ ________

7. $3{,}600 \div 6 =$ ________

8. $12{,}000 \div 2 =$ ________

9. $350 \div 5 =$ ________

10. $1{,}500 \div 3 =$ ________

11. $49{,}000 \div 7 =$ ________

12. $7{,}200 \div 8 =$ ________

Complete.

13. $1{,}800 \div \square = 600$

14. $\square \div 6 = 80$

15. $21{,}000 \div \square = 3{,}000$

16. $400 \div \square = 80$

17. $\square \div 4 = 400$

18. $24{,}000 \div \square = 8{,}000$

Name ______________________________

Practice
4-3

Estimating Quotients

Estimate each quotient.

1. 635 ÷ 9 ________

2. 233 ÷ 6 ________

3. 371 ÷ 6 ________

4. 517 ÷ 7 ________

5. 386 ÷ 5 ________

6. 145 ÷ 8 ________

7. 163 ÷ 3 ________

8. 801 ÷ 9 ________

9. 117 ÷ 2 ________

10. 468 ÷ 9 ________

11. 554 ÷ 7 ________

12. 354 ÷ 4 ________

13. Estimate the quotient of 203 ÷ 6. ________

14. Estimate the quotient of 391 ÷ 8. ________

15. Estimate the quotient of 264 ÷ 3. ________

16. You know that 481 ÷ 7 is about 70. Is the exact quotient greater than or less than the estimate? Find estimates for 4,810 ÷ 7, 48,100 ÷ 7, and 48 ÷ 7.

____

17. You know that 332 ÷ 4 is about 80. Find estimates for 33 ÷ 4 and 33,200 ÷ 4.

____

18. You know that 351 ÷ 6 is about 60. Find estimates for 3,510 ÷ 6 and 35,100 ÷ 6.

____

Name ______________________________

Practice
Chapter 4
Section A

Review and Practice

Vocabulary Use the example to answer each question.

$$3\overline{)28}\ \ 9\text{ R1}$$

1. Which number is the quotient? ________
2. Which number is the dividend? ________
3. Which number is the divisor? ________
4. Which number is the remainder? ________

(Lesson 1) Find each quotient. Use mental math.

5. 24 ÷ 3 = ________
6. 25 ÷ 5 = ________
7. 36 ÷ 9 = ________
8. 56 ÷ 8 = ________
9. Whitney poured 36 ounces of juice in 6 glasses. How many ounces of juice are in each glass? ____________

(Lesson 2) Find each quotient. Use mental math.

10. 4,500 ÷ 9 = ________
11. 40,000 ÷ 5 = ________
12. 1,200 ÷ 2 = ________
13. 540 ÷ 6 = ________

Complete.

14. 14,000 ÷ ________ = 7,000
15. ________ ÷ 8 = 30

(Lesson 3) Estimate each quotient by substituting compatible numbers.

16. 163 ÷ 2 ________
17. 459 ÷ 9 ________
18. 761 ÷ 8 ________
19. 358 ÷ 4 ________

(Mixed Review) Add or subtract.

20. $\begin{array}{r} 6{,}512 \\ +\ \ 739 \\ \hline \end{array}$
21. $\begin{array}{r} 3{,}003 \\ -\ 1{,}439 \\ \hline \end{array}$
22. $\begin{array}{r} 117 \\ -\ \ 99 \\ \hline \end{array}$
23. $\begin{array}{r} 997 \\ +\ \ 53 \\ \hline \end{array}$

Name ______________________________

Practice
4-4

Exploring Dividing

Complete. You may use play money to help.

1. $7\overline{)\$9.28}$ = $\$\square.3\square$ R $\square$

$$
\begin{array}{r}
\$\square.3\square \text{ R } \square \\
7\overline{)\$9.28} \\
-7 \\
\hline
\square 2 \\
-\square\square \\
\hline
1\square \\
-14 \\
\hline
\square
\end{array}
$$

2. $3\overline{)\$8.93}$ = $\$\square.9\square$ R $\square$

$$
\begin{array}{r}
\$\square.9\square \text{ R } \square \\
3\overline{)\$8.93} \\
-\square \\
\hline
2\,9 \\
-\square\square \\
\hline
\square 3 \\
-21 \\
\hline
\square
\end{array}
$$

3. $4\overline{)\$9.53}$

4. $6\overline{)\$8.75}$

5. $2\overline{)\$3.72}$

6. $7\overline{)\$7.94}$

7. $3\overline{)\$4.36}$

8. $3\overline{)\$9.34}$

9. $5\overline{)\$8.97}$

10. $4\overline{)\$6.41}$

Name ______________________________

Practice
4-5

Dividing by 1-Digit Divisors

Divide.

1. 96 ÷ 4 __________

2. 622 ÷ 5 __________

3. 473 ÷ 2 __________

4. 547 ÷ 3 __________

5. $2\overline{)483}$

6. $7\overline{)247}$

7. $3\overline{)881}$

8. $8\overline{)964}$

9. $2\overline{)726}$

10. $4\overline{)973}$

11. $5\overline{)362}$

12. $4\overline{)739}$

13. Estimate the quotient for 735 ÷ 3. What number is in the hundreds place in the quotient?

____

14. When dividing a 3-digit number by a 1-digit number, for what divisors can you get a remainder of 8? Explain.

____

Name ______________________

Analyze Word Problems: Interpret Remainders

Solve. Use the picture to answer **1–3**.

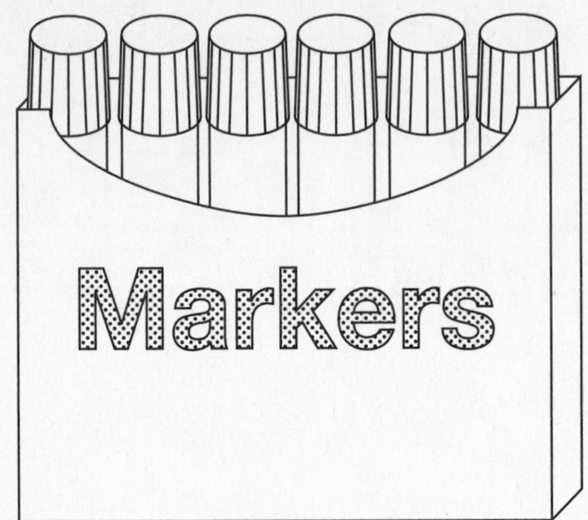

1. If you need markers for a class of 28 students, how many full boxes will you use? ______

2. How many more markers will you need after using the full boxes? ______

3. If you opened enough boxes to supply the entire class with markers, how many boxes would you open? ______

4. In the store room, folders are stored in packages of 8. What is the least number of packages needed for a class of 35 students? ______

5. The cafeteria workers keep small milk cartons in the refrigerator in stacks of 6. If each worker carries no more than one stack, what is the least number of cafeteria workers needed to carry small milk cartons for a class of 32?

______

6. In the cafeteria's refrigerator, cups of yogurt are kept in stacks of 9. If each worker carries no more than one stack, what is the least number of workers needed to carry cups of yogurt for a class of 42?

______

7. In the teachers' lunchroom, teachers sit at tables for 6. There are 22 teachers eating lunch. How many tables must be set up?

______

Name ___________________________

Practice 4-7

Deciding Where to Place the First Digit

Divide. Check your answer.

1. $7\overline{)381}$ **2.** $5\overline{)208}$ **3.** $6\overline{)682}$

4. $8\overline{)329}$ **5.** $4\overline{)173}$ **6.** $8\overline{)484}$

7. $5\overline{)571}$ **8.** $4\overline{)925}$ **9.** $6\overline{)674}$

10. 317 ÷ 4 = __________ **11.** 815 ÷ 7 = __________

12. 997 ÷ 3 = __________ **13.** 411 ÷ 9 = __________

14. 859 ÷ 4 = __________ **15.** 371 ÷ 7 = __________

16. Divide 723 by 5. __________

17. Find 673 divided by 4. __________

18. The divisor is 6 and the dividend is 752. Divide. __________

19. The divisor is 9 and the dividend is 255. Divide. __________

Name ____________________

Practice
4-8

Zeros in the Quotient

Divide. Multiply to check.

1. $6\overline{)242}$ **2.** $3\overline{)90}$ **3.** $7\overline{)213}$

4. $9\overline{)918}$ **5.** $5\overline{)2{,}004}$ **6.** $3\overline{)627}$

7. $4\overline{)8{,}012}$ **8.** $6\overline{)2{,}460}$ **9.** $5\overline{)3{,}015}$

10. $7\overline{)709}$ **11.** $8\overline{)2{,}408}$ **12.** $6\overline{)1{,}892}$

13. $5\overline{)2{,}205}$ **14.** $3\overline{)1{,}229}$ **15.** $9\overline{)6{,}311}$

Use mental math to find each quotient.

16. 360 ÷ 6 = ________ **17.** 5,600 ÷ 8 = ________

18. 42,000 ÷ 7 = ________ **19.** 180 ÷ 3 = ________

20. 48,000 ÷ 8 = ________ **21.** 15,000 ÷ 5 = ________

22. Divide 965 by 9. ________

23. Are there any zeros in the quotient of 495 ÷ 4? How can you tell without finding the quotient?

____

Name ______________________________

Practice
4-9

Exploring Mean

Complete each sentence using a word from the word bank.

56 64 72 72 81 83 97

mean
median
mode

1. The __________ is 72 because it is the number that appears most.
2. To find the __________, add all the numbers and divide by 7.
3. The __________ is 72 because it is the middle number.

Find the mean, median, and mode for each set of data.

4. 115, 124, 130, 122, 124

   __________, __________, __________

5. $5.26, $5.50, $4.87, $4.04, $6.21, $5.26,

   __________, __________, __________

6. $7.08, $7.78, $8.07, $8.70, $8.87

   __________, __________, __________

7. Find the mean, median, and mode for the set of data in the bar graph.

   ____

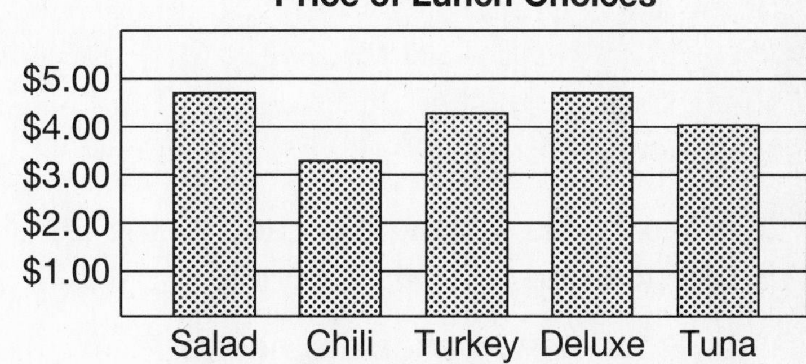

8. Can the median of a set of numbers ever be the greatest number in the set of data? Explain.

   ____

   ____

9. Suppose you wanted to find the mean, median, and mode of 55, 56, 57, 58, 59. How could you find them mentally?

   ____

   ____

Name ______________________________

Practice
Chapter 4
Section B

Review and Practice

Vocabulary Fill in each blank with a word from the word bank.

mean	median	mode

1. The __________ is the middle number of an ordered set of numbers.

2. The __________ is the average of a set of numbers.

3. The __________ is the most common value in a set of data.

(Lessons 4, 5, 7, and 8) Divide. Multiply to check your answer.

4. $15.50 ÷ 5 = ________ **5.** $9.68 ÷ 8 = ________

6. $6\overline{)2,406}$ **7.** $7\overline{)287}$ **8.** $3\overline{)762}$

9. $4\overline{)4,191}$ **10.** $8\overline{)417}$ **11.** $9\overline{)3,687}$

12. A box holds 7 candles. Each of the 29 students in science class needs 1 candle.

a. How many boxes are needed? ____________

b. How many candles will be left over? ____________

(Lesson 9) Find the mean, median, and mode for each set of data.

13. 15, 17, 15, 11, 12 ________, ________, ________

14. 5, 8, 8, 10, 11, 6 ________, ________, ________

15. $27, $36, $51, $42, $36, $48 ________, ________, ________

(Mixed Review) Add.

16. 7 + 5 + 2 + 8 = ________ **17.** 1+ 8 + 2 + 9 = ________

Name ____________________

Practice 4-10

Exploring Products and Quotients

Match each number sentence with the property it shows.

________	**1.** $6 \times 9 = 9 \times 6$	**a.** Zero property
________	**2.** $729 \times 1 = 729$	**b.** One property
________	**3.** $(8 \times 3) \times 4 = 8 \times (3 \times 4)$	**c.** Commutative property
________	**4.** $0 \times 1,267 = 0$	**d.** Associative property

Complete. Write >, <, or =.

5. $23 \times 6 = n$	**a.** n ◯ 23	**b.** n ◯ 6
6. $36 \div 3 = n$	**a.** n ◯ 36	**b.** n ◯ 3
7. $17,549 \times 1 = n$	**a.** n ◯ 17,549	**b.** n ◯ 1
8. $n \div 8 = 0$	**a.** n ◯ 8	**b.** n ◯ 0
9. $4,195 \div 1 = n$	**a.** n ◯ 4,195	**b.** n ◯ 1
10. $157 \div 5 = 31$ R n	**a.** n ◯ 157	**b.** n ◯ 5

Write whether each equation is true or false. Explain how you know.

11. $45 \div 9 = 9 \div 45$ ____________________

12. $0 \times 14,275 = 0$ ____________________

13. $587 \div 587 = 1$ ____________________

14. $0 \div 4,113 = 4,113$ ____________________

15. $81 \div 9 = 9 \div 81$ ____________________

16. $24 \times 3 = 3 \times 24$ ____________________

17. Peter said he divided 7 into a number and got zero. What is the number? Explain how you know.

____

Name ______________________________

Practice
4-11

Dividing Money

Find each quotient. Multiply to check.

1. $7\overline{)\$42.00}$

2. $4\overline{)\$4.04}$

3. $3\overline{)\$13.32}$

4. $5\overline{)\$25.15}$

5. $6\overline{)\$34.32}$

6. $7\overline{)\$71.89}$

7. $3\overline{)\$182.10}$

8. $5\overline{)\$325.35}$

9. $8\overline{)\$469.44}$

Use a calculator to divide. Write each answer to the nearest cent.

10. $5.11 ÷ 4 = ________

11. $12.77 ÷ 5 = ________

12. $7\overline{)\$898.13}$

13. $8\overline{)\$73.45}$

14. $6\overline{)\$2{,}014.10}$

15. $3\overline{)\$745.31}$

16. For $42.01 ÷ 2, $297.66 ÷ 6, and $8.43 ÷ 8, are any of the quotients less than a dollar? How can you tell?

____

____

Name ______________________________

Practice 4-12

Dividing Decimals

Find each quotient.

1. $4\overline{)25.424}$

2. $6\overline{)16.032}$

3. $5\overline{)33.195}$

4. $9\overline{)59.283}$

5. $8\overline{)18.512}$

6. $3\overline{)31.701}$

7. $7\overline{)8.169}$

8. $2\overline{)14.948}$

9. $5\overline{)22.325}$

Find the length of the side of each square.

10.

Perimeter = 12.744 cm

____

11.

Perimeter = 26.108 m

____

12. Is 66.781 ÷ 7 = 22.903 a reasonable answer? Explain why or why not.

____

____

Name ______________________________

Practice
4-13

Factors and Divisibility

Find the factors for each number.

1. 25 ______________________

2. 12 ______________________

3. 21 ______________________

4. 40 ______________________

5. 36 ______________________

6. 45 ______________________

7. 49 ______________________

8. 33 ______________________

9. 30 ______________________

10. 56 ______________________

11. What are the factors of 65? ______________________

12. What are the factors of 28? ______________________

13. What are the factors of 32? ______________________

14. What are the factors of 27? ______________________

15. Is 3 a factor of 261? Explain how you know.

____

16. Is 10 a factor of 325? Explain how you know.

____

17. Is 6 a factor of 492? Explain how you know.

____

____

____

____

Name ________________________________

Practice 4-14

Exploring Prime and Composite Numbers

Complete each sentence using a word from the word bank.

composite number
factors
factor tree
prime number
products

1. A ____________________ has exactly two different factors.

2. 21 is an example of a ____________________.

3. You can use a ____________________ to show the factors of a composite number.

4. A composite number has more than two ____________________.

Write whether each number is prime or composite.

5. 38 __________ **6.** 19 __________ **7.** 83 __________

Use factor trees to find the prime factors of each number.

8. 12 **9.** 32 **10.** 30

Write the missing factors.

11. 1, ☐, ☐, 4, ☐ 12 **12.** 1, ☐, 49

13. Can a whole number ending in 8 be prime? Explain. ____________

____

Name ___________________________________

Practice 4-15

Analyze Strategies: Work Backward

Work backward to solve each problem.

1. On Sundays, Bernie's Bagel shop gets very busy. Two hours after they opened, Bernie's sold one third of their bagels. During the next hour, they sold another 50 bagels. During the rest of the day, half of the remaining bagels were bought. At closing, there were only 25 bagels left.

   a. How many bagels were left at closing? ______________

   b. What operation undoes dividing the number of bagels in half?

   ____

   c. What operation undoes subtracting 50? ______________

   d. How many bagels were in the store when it opened on Sunday?

   ____

Use any strategy to solve each problem.

2. Arlene keeps track of her weekly expenses. At the end of a week, she had $2.35 left. She had bought 2 bottles of juice for $0.80 each and one package of markers for $4.55. How much did Arlene have at the beginning of the week?

   ____

3. The tag on the shirt shows that the price has been lowered twice. What was the original price of the shirt?

   ____

4. Louis had homework in 2 subjects. He finished his homework at 6:00 P.M. He spent 30 minutes doing his science homework. He spent twice that amount of time doing his reading homework. At what time did Louis start his homework?

   ____

Name ________________________________

Practice
Chapter 4
Section C

Review and Practice

Vocabulary Write true or false for each statement.

1. A whole number greater than 1 that has more than two different factors is a composite number. ____________

2. Any number that divides another number with a remainder of 2 is called a factor. ____________

(Lesson 10) Complete.

3. __________ ÷ 678 = 0 **4.** 389 × __________ = 389

(Lesson 11) Find each quotient. Round to the nearest cent.

5. $3\overline{)\$16.00}$ **6.** $7\overline{)\$125.10}$ **7.** $4\overline{)\$8.31}$

(Lesson 12) Find each quotient.

8. $2\overline{)13.162}$ **9.** $6\overline{)37.662}$ **10.** $7\overline{)8.491}$

(Lesson 13) Find all the factors for each number.

11. 8 ____________ **12.** 18 ____________

13. 36 ____________

(Lesson 14) Use factor trees to find the prime factors of each number.

14. 20 **15.** 31 **16.** 50

(Mixed Review) Find each sum or difference.

17. 426 + 238 = __________ **18.** 204 − 97 = __________

Name ______________________________

Practice
Chapters 1–4

Cumulative Review

(Chapter 2 Lesson 18) Subtract.

1. $\begin{array}{r} \$23.12 \\ -\ \ \ 8.97 \\ \hline \end{array}$ **2.** $\begin{array}{r} 0.71 \\ -0.46 \\ \hline \end{array}$ **3.** $\begin{array}{r} \$5.00 \\ -\ \ 3.99 \\ \hline \end{array}$ **4.** $\begin{array}{r} 3 \\ -1.35 \\ \hline \end{array}$

(Chapter 3 Lesson 13) Find each product.

5. $\begin{array}{r} 2.67 \\ \times\ \ 0.5 \\ \hline \end{array}$ **6.** $\begin{array}{r} \$6.12 \\ \times\ \ \ 26 \\ \hline \end{array}$ **7.** $\begin{array}{r} 4.81 \\ \times\ \ 7.3 \\ \hline \end{array}$ **8.** $\begin{array}{r} 8.36 \\ \times 0.58 \\ \hline \end{array}$

(Chapter 3 Lesson 15) Find each product. Insert zeros where necessary.

9. $\begin{array}{r} 1.075 \\ \times 0.003 \\ \hline \end{array}$ **10.** $\begin{array}{r} 1.092 \\ \times 0.006 \\ \hline \end{array}$ **11.** $\begin{array}{r} 2.3 \\ \times 0.00008 \\ \hline \end{array}$

(Chapter 4 Lessons 7, 8, and 12) Find each quotient.

12. $5\overline{)69}$ **13.** $9\overline{)369}$ **14.** $7\overline{)1{,}456}$

15. $4\overline{)820}$ **16.** $8\overline{)4{,}809}$ **17.** $3\overline{)9{,}245}$

18. $6\overline{)19.404}$ **19.** $2\overline{)6.238}$ **20.** $9\overline{)37.926}$

 Use with page 217.

Name ______________________________

Practice
5-1

Exploring Division Patterns

You can use number sense and basic facts to divide with multiples of 10.

1. a. What basic fact would you use to find 810 ÷ 90? __________

b. 810 ÷ 90 = __________

2. a. What basic fact would you use to find 42,000 ÷ 70? __________

b. 42,000 ÷ 70 = __________

Find each quotient. Use mental math.

3. 2,400 ÷ 60 = __________

4. 2,700 ÷ 90 = __________

5. 350 ÷ 50 = __________

6. 1,800 ÷ 300 = __________

7. 32,000 ÷ 80 = __________

8. 60,000 ÷ 200 = __________

9. 4,000 ÷ 500 = __________

10. 63,000 ÷ 70 = __________

11. 1,600 ÷ 40 = __________

12. 720 ÷ 90 = __________

Complete.

13. 1,200 ÷ __________ = 40

14. 24,000 ÷ __________ = 80

15. __________ ÷ 500 = 50

16. __________ ÷ 80 = 800

For each pair, write whether the quotient is the same or different. Explain.

17. 500 ÷ 50 and 5,000 ÷ 500

____

18. 240 ÷ 3 and 24,000 ÷ 30

____

19. How would you find 49,000 ÷ 7?

____

____

Name ________________________________

Practice
5-2

Estimating Quotients: High and Low

Estimate each quotient. Give a high and low estimate.

1. 16,786 ÷ 50 ____________

2. $26,521 ÷ 30 ____________

3. 4,033 ÷ 60 ____________

4. 6,945 ÷ 80 ____________

5. 22,487 ÷ 40 ____________

6. $33,132 ÷ 70 ____________

7. 5,399 ÷ 80 ____________

8. 13,452 ÷ 30 ____________

9. 3,000 ÷ 90 ____________

10. 4,465 ÷ 60 ____________

11. 57,029 ÷ 70 ____________

12. 1,553 ÷ 20 ____________

13. $3,909 ÷ 50 ____________

14. 2,517 ÷ 40 ____________

15. 14,129 ÷ 30 ____________

16. 57,221 ÷ 60 ____________

17. 4,417 ÷ 50 ____________

18. 26,951 ÷ 80 ____________

19. How is estimating the quotient of 4,740 and 60 similar to estimating the quotient of 474,000 and 600?

____

____

20. How is estimating the quotient of 6,840 and 90 similar to estimating the quotient of 684,000 and 9,000?

____

____

Name ______________________

Practice
5-3

Estimating with 2-Digit Divisors

Estimate each quotient using compatible numbers.

1. 821 ÷ 18 ______
2. 592 ÷ 33 ______
3. 3,465 ÷ 49 ______
4. 809 ÷ 92 ______
5. 7,468 ÷ 82 ______
6. $24,424 ÷ 59 ______
7. 585 ÷ 58 ______
8. 21,000 ÷ 74 ______
9. $557 ÷ 83 ______
10. 362 ÷ 51 ______
11. 4,106 ÷ 55 ______
12. $8,123 ÷ 20 ______
13. 32,128 ÷ 36 ______
14. $1,107 ÷ 21 ______
15. 3,727 ÷ 45 ______

16. Estimate the quotient of 989 ÷ 48. Is the exact quotient greater than or less than your estimate?

____

17. Estimate the quotient of 607 ÷ 22. Is the exact quotient greater than or less than your estimate?

____

18. Which quotient is greater: 4,322 ÷ 18 or 4,322 ÷ 19? ______

19. Which quotient is greater: 1,868 ÷ 32 or 1,868 ÷ 27? ______

Name ______________________________

Practice
Chapter 5
Section A

Review and Practice

Vocabulary Write true or false for each statement.

1. Six is the quotient. __________

2. 17 is the dividend. __________

$$6\overline{)17}\ \text{ quotient } 2\text{ R}5$$

(Lesson 1) Find each quotient. Use mental math.

3. 1,800 ÷ 30 = __________

4. 24,000 ÷ 80 = __________

5. 450 ÷ 90 = __________

6. 5,600 ÷ 700 = __________

7. Are the quotients for 560 ÷ 8 and 56,000 ÷ 80 the same or different? __________

(Lesson 2) Estimate each quotient. Give a high and low estimate.

8. 16,993 ÷ 20

____

9. 49,695 ÷ 90

____

10. 7,613 ÷ 80

____

11. 35,800 ÷ 60

____

(Lesson 3) Estimate each quotient by using compatible numbers.

12. 4,499 ÷ 93 ______________

13. 33,617 ÷ 59 ______________

14. $1,178 ÷ 33 ______________

15. 712,540 ÷ 86 ______________

16. Which quotient is greater: 54,689 ÷ 63 or 54,689 ÷ 59?

____

(Mixed Review) Find each product.

17. 517×39

18. 803×439

19. 347×99

20. 997×62

Name ______________________________

Practice 5-4

Dividing by 2-Digit Divisors

Complete.

1. $16\overline{)74}$ = 4 R_____

2. $29\overline{)205}$ = 7 R_____

3. $42\overline{)396}$ = 9 R_____

4. $33\overline{)166}$ = 5 R_____

5. $78\overline{)686}$ = 8 R_____

6. $61\overline{)377}$ = 6 R_____

Divide.

7. $54\overline{)175}$

8. $96\overline{)488}$

9. $13\overline{)117}$

10. $25\overline{)167}$

11. $82\overline{)351}$

12. $47\overline{)401}$

13. $77\overline{)309}$

14. $50\overline{)400}$

15. $69\overline{)503}$

16. $70\overline{)150}$

17. $36\overline{)323}$

18. $28\overline{)175}$

19. 174 ÷ 8 = __________

20. 424 ÷ 61 = __________

21. 527 ÷ 98 = __________

22. 215 ÷ 35 = __________

23. What is 189 divided by 44? __________

24. Divide 166 by 20. __________

25. Can a divisor be less than a remainder? Explain.

____

____

____

Name ________________________________

Practice 5-5

Dividing Greater Numbers

Divide. Check your answer.

1. $17\overline{)85}$ 2. $36\overline{)288}$ 3. $52\overline{)1,300}$

4. $68\overline{)1,090}$ 5. $75\overline{)4,575}$ 6. $43\overline{)516}$

7. $29\overline{)2,233}$ 8. $84\overline{)924}$ 9. $37\overline{)851}$

10. 98 ÷ 14 = __________ **11.** 704 ÷ 44 = __________

12. 1,801 ÷ 56 = __________ **13.** 2,059 ÷ 71 = __________

14. 621 ÷ 27 __________ **15.** 376 ÷ 34 = __________

Estimate. Use your number sense to choose the best answer for **16–18.**

16. 512 ÷ 30 is ______

A. less than 17 **B.** more than 17 **C.** exactly 17

17. 1,180 ÷ 60 is ______

A. less than 2 **B.** less than 20 **C.** more than 20

18. 8,999 ÷ 50 is ______

A. less than 150 **B.** more than 200 **C.** between 150 and 200

19. Divide 686 by 26. __________

20. 735 divided by 49 is what number? __________

21. If your divisor is 63, what is the greatest possible remainder you could have? __________

Name ____________________

Practice 5-6

Dividing: Choosing a Calculation Method

Divide and check. Tell what calculation method you used and why.

1. $30\overline{)90}$ **2.** $14\overline{)210}$ **3.** $40\overline{)165}$

4. $10\overline{)1{,}000}$ **5.** $17\overline{)51{,}000}$ **6.** $70\overline{)490}$

7. $62\overline{)7{,}626}$ **8.** $37\overline{)238}$ **9.** $60\overline{)360}$

10. $35\overline{)2{,}474}$ **11.** $60\overline{)256}$ **12.** $50\overline{)350}$

13. $70\overline{)49{,}000}$ **14.** $18\overline{)288}$ **15.** $20\overline{)180}$

16. $27\overline{)765}$ **17.** $16\overline{)256}$ **18.** $50\overline{)250}$

19. $36\overline{)843}$ **20.** $26\overline{)832}$ **21.** $24\overline{)888}$

22. $80\overline{)640}$ **23.** $38\overline{)342}$ **24.** $71\overline{)614}$

25. $4\overline{)320}$ **26.** $15\overline{)264}$ **27.** $21\overline{)861}$

28. 720 ÷ 90 = __________ **29.** 8,889 ÷ 29 = __________

30. 32,000 ÷ 80 = __________ **31.** 36,045 ÷ 60 = __________

Name ___________________________

Practice
5-7

Zeros in the Quotient

Divide and check.

1. $18\overline{)735}$ **2.** $48\overline{)30,256}$ **3.** $15\overline{)1,063}$

4. $36\overline{)28,980}$ **5.** $22\overline{)4,565}$ **6.** $82\overline{)62,324}$

7. $25\overline{)7,642}$ **8.** $63\overline{)30,902}$ **9.** $46\overline{)9,649}$

10. $92\overline{)10,120}$ **11.** $75\overline{)17,313}$ **12.** $44\overline{)26,547}$

13. 41,883 ÷ 82 = __________ **14.** 11,780 ÷ 29 = __________

15. 16,585 ÷ 54 = __________ **16.** 9,377 ÷ 18 = __________

17. 15,417 ÷ 28 = __________ **18.** 16,192 ÷ 23 = __________

Use number sense to decide whether each answer is reasonable.

19. $\begin{array}{r} 702 \\ 56\overline{)39,312} \end{array}$ **20.** $\begin{array}{r} 42 \\ 35\overline{)17,675} \end{array}$ **21.** $\begin{array}{r} 410 \\ 34\overline{)14,280} \end{array}$

__________ __________ __________

Name ______________________________

Practice
5-8

Exploring Algebra: Using Expressions

Decide what operation is needed; then replace the variable with a number and do the computation.

1. There are 12 space meals in a box. How many space meals are in n boxes?

Evaluate $12 \times n$.

a. For $n = 5$.

$12 \times n = 12 \times$ _____

$=$ _____ space meals

b. For $n = 12$.

$12 \times n = 12 \times$ _____

$=$ _____ space meals

Evaluate each expression for $n = 6$ and $n = 15$.

2. $n + 15$ _____ _____

3. $5 \times n$ _____ _____

4. $n \div 3$ _____ _____

5. $n - 5$ _____ _____

6. $207 + n$ _____ _____

7. $10 \times n$ _____ _____

8. $36 - n$ _____ _____

9. $30 \div n$ _____ _____

Complete.

10.

n	$n + 9$
6	
15	
23	

11.

n	$n \div 4$
8	
16	
20	

12.

n	$n - 15$
30	
25	
48	

13.

n	$n \times 9$
3	
7	
9	

14. If $n = 8$, what is $7 \times n$? _______

15. If $n = 64$, what is $n \div 8$? _______

16. A baker uses 3 cups of wheat flour and n cups of rye flour in the bread. Write an expression for the total number of cups used.

____

Name ______________________________

Practice
5-9

Analyzing Strategies: Use Objects/Act It Out

Use objects to solve each problem.

1. You want to design a small hotel in the shape of a cube. Each side of the hotel will be four rooms long. Use cubes to make a model.

   a. How many rooms will be on the first floor? __________

   b. How many floors high will the hotel be? __________

   c. How many rooms will be in the hotel in all? __________

   d. If you use the design, how many rooms will have no windows? __________

Use any strategy to solve each problem.

2. In the hotel you designed in the shape of a cube, each outside wall in each room has one window. How many rooms have a total of

   a. only one window? __________

   b. two windows? __________

3. You want to design a hotel with 24 rooms so that each room has a window on each of two walls.

   a. How many rooms will be on each floor? __________

   b. How many floors will the hotel have? __________

   c. How many windows are needed for the hotel? __________

4. You want to build a fence in the shape of a square around the hotel. Each side of the square has 12 posts. There are posts on each corner of the square. How many posts will be needed in all? __________

5. Mr. Munez used 4.5 gallons of paint to paint each room in the hotel. The hotel has 8 floors and each floor has 9 rooms. How many gallons of paint did Mr. Munez use to paint all of the rooms in the hotel?

   ____

6. A hotel has 36 one-bed rooms, 42 two-bed rooms, and 12 suites. How many rooms are there in the hotel? ____________

Name ___________________________

Practice
Chapter 5
Section B

Review and Practice

(Lessons 4 and 5) Divide.

1. 32)155 **2.** 92)472 **3.** 47)787

4. 64)13,322 **5.** 38)15,599 **6.** 99)3,970

(Lesson 6) Divide and check. Tell which method you used.

7. 30)90,600 **8.** 15)3,847

method: ___________ method: ___________

(Lesson 7) Divide and check.

9. 3,621 ÷ 34 = ___________ **10.** 45,127 ÷ 43 = ___________

(Lesson 9) Solve.

11. 26 fifth graders collected 500 canned goods. If some students collected one more can than the rest, how many collected 19 and how many collected 20?

____

(Mixed Review) Find each quotient.

12. 4,800 ÷ 60 = ___________ **13.** 6,300 ÷ 700 = ___________

Name ______________________________

Practice 5-10

Dividing Money

Divide and check.

1. $25\overline{)\$12.50}$ **2.** $18\overline{)\$7.92}$ **3.** $13\overline{)\$8.97}$

4. $15\overline{)\$24.00}$ **5.** $23\overline{)\$32.43}$ **6.** $40\overline{)\$246.00}$

7. $537.60 ÷ 35 = __________ **8.** $35.25 ÷ 75 = __________

Use your number sense to select the best answer.

9. $2.20 ÷ 40 is __________

a. less than $0.05 **b.** more than $0.05

10. $325 ÷ 50 is __________

a. more than $7.00 **b.** between $6.00 and $7.00

Estimate to decide whether each quotient in **11–13** is more or less than $1.00.

11. $32\overline{)\$45.00}$ **12.** $32\overline{)\$31.00}$ **13.** $7\overline{)\$8.08}$

__________ __________ __________

14. Find the quotient of $412.80 ÷ 40 = __________

15. If you had $325.50 to share with 25 people, how much should each person get? __________

Name ____________________

Practice 5-11

Decision Making

Rock & Roll Hall of Fame and Museum Cleveland, Ohio
Admission: $12.95 Adults, $9.50 Children
Hours: 10:00 A.M. to 5:30 P.M.

Features
Ground Level Artists' Careers Interactive Videos Mystery Train Cinema
Level 2 Memphis Recording Studio
Level 3 Museum Café
Level 4 Rock & Roll Cinema
Level 5 Radio Studio Past Hall of Fame Inductees
Level 6 Hall of Fame

1. You want to plan a day for you and your family at the Rock & Roll Hall of Fame. You buy 2 adult and 2 children admissions.

   How much do you spend? __________

2. Your family will drive 2 hours to the museum. You want to arrive at 10:00 A.M.

   What time should you leave? __________

3. You plan to spend 3 hours at the museum.

   At what time will you leave? __________

4. On which level will you eat lunch? __________

5. Name 3 levels you want to visit. ____________________

   ____

6. Plan a schedule. Include rest periods, gift shop, and lunch in your schedule.

Time	Activity	Time	Activity
______	Leave home	______	______
______	Arrive museum	______	______
______	______	______	______
______	______	______	______
______	______	______	______
______	______	______	______
______	______	______	Leave museum
______	______	______	Arrive home

Name ______________________________

Practice
5-12

Exploring Decimal Patterns in Division

Complete the table.

	÷	10	100	1,000
1.	1,346.5			
2.	596.3			
3.	876.42			
4.	66.75			
5.	2,002.2			

Find each quotient. Use mental math.

6. 302.6 ÷ 10 = __________ **7.** 78.61 ÷ 100 = __________

8. 362 ÷ 1,000 = __________ **9.** 13.4 ÷ 100 = __________

10. 378 ÷ 1,000 = __________ **11.** 6.25 ÷ 100 = __________

12. $925 ÷ 10 = __________ **13.** 8.49 ÷ 100 = __________

14. 4.3 ÷ 1,000 = __________ **15.** 32.25 ÷ 10 = __________

16. 823 ÷ 1,000 = __________ **17.** 73 ÷ 1,000 = __________

Use 10, 100, or 1,000 to complete each.

18. 32.7 ÷ __________ = 3.27 **19.** 632.7 ÷ __________ = 6.327

20. 435 ÷ __________ = 4.35 **21.** $85 ÷ __________ = $0.85

22. 78 ÷ __________ = 0.078 **23.** 0.26 ÷ __________ = 0.00026

Choose the word or number to complete **24–25.**

24. If you divide 3.67 by 1,000, 0 is in the __________ and hundredths places in the quotient.

25. Dividing 81.7 by 10 gives the same quotient as dividing __________ by 1,000.

26. If you were to divide 58.3 by 1,000, how many places would you move the decimal point? Explain.

____

Name ______________________

Review and Practice

(Lesson 10) Find each quotient.

1. $30\overline{)\$316.20}$ **2.** $17\overline{)\$15.98}$ **3.** $54\overline{)\$68.58}$

4. $22\overline{)\$73.26}$ **5.** $86\overline{)\$7.74}$ **6.** $40\overline{)\$88.40}$

(Lesson 11) Use any strategy to solve each problem.

7. Would it be cheaper per ounce to buy a 20-ounce bottle of soda for $1.35 or a 64-ounce bottle for $5.00?

____

8. The bus for your field trip is arriving at 8:00 A.M. It is a half-hour trip to the glass factory. There are three tours available for the class. Tour A lasts 2 hours; tour B lasts 1 hour 45 minutes; and tour C lasts 75 minutes. If you must be back at school by noon which tours could your class take?

____

(Lesson 12) Find each quotient. Use mental math.

9. $54.16 \div 10 =$ ________ **10.** $1{,}245 \div 100 =$ ________

11. $4.1 \div 10 =$ ________ **12.** $3{,}745.9 \div 1{,}000 =$ ________

13. $0.37 \div 100 =$ ________ **14.** $0.2 \div 1{,}000 =$ ________

(Mixed Review) Subtract.

15. $\begin{array}{r} 45.67 \\ -\ \ 2.45 \\ \hline \end{array}$ **16.** $\begin{array}{r} 39.00 \\ -16.8 \\ \hline \end{array}$ **17.** $\begin{array}{r} 55 \\ -\ \ 2.89 \\ \hline \end{array}$ **18.** $\begin{array}{r} 7.1 \\ -5.8 \\ \hline \end{array}$

Name ______________________________

Practice
Chapters 1–5

Cumulative Review

(Chapter 2 Lesson 19) Choose an operation then solve.

1. Rob is 60 inches tall. He has grown 7 inches in the last 5 years. How tall was he 5 years ago? ____________

(Chapter 3 Lesson 16) Solve.

2. At the scout shop a compass costs $5 and a flashlight costs $8. The scouts spent a total of $90 on 15 items. How many compasses and how many flashlights did they buy?

____

(Chapter 4 Lesson 15) Solve.

3. If you add 3 to Sandro's age and divide by 3 you get 6. How old is Sandro? ________

(Chapter 4 Lesson 12) Find each quotient.

4. $3\overline{)29.202}$

5. $5\overline{)8.275}$

6. $6\overline{)67.224}$

(Chapter 5 Lessons 4 and 10) Divide.

7. $23\overline{)221}$

8. $16\overline{)133}$

9. $48\overline{)153}$

10. $21\overline{)\$99.96}$

11. $13\overline{)\$8.97}$

12. $40\overline{)\$675.20}$

Name ___________________________________

Practice 6-1

Lines and Angles

Write the name for each.

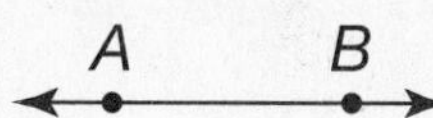

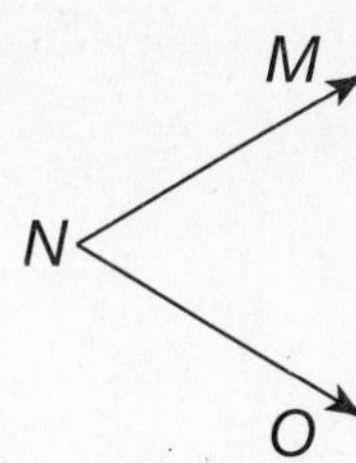

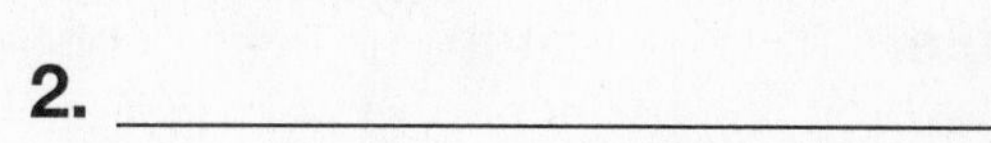

1. ______________________ **2.** ______________________

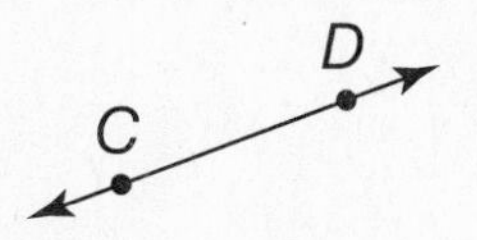

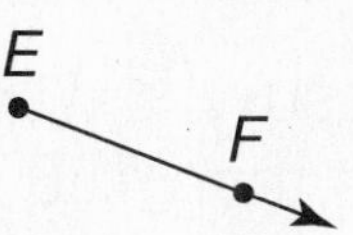

3. ______________________ **4.** ______________________

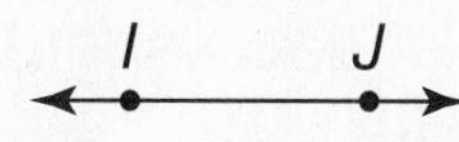

5. ______________________ **6.** ______________________

Name each in the figure at the right.

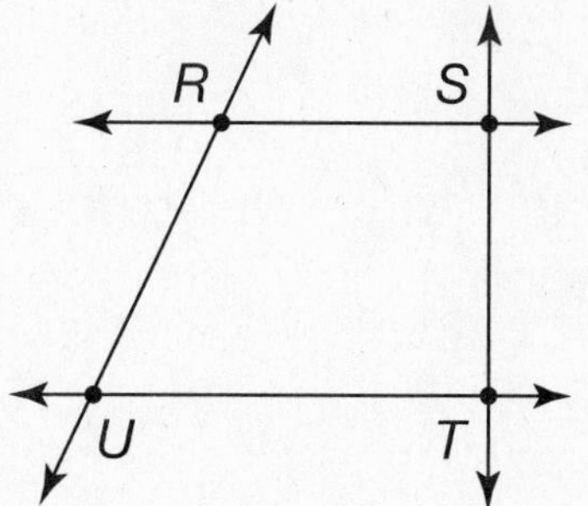

7. the rays that form $\angle T$

____

8. the angle that has *R* as its vertex

____

9. perpendicular lines

____

10. parallel lines

____

11. the rays that form $\angle U$

____

Name ______________________________

Practice 6-2

Exploring Measuring Angles

1. Angles can be classified by the way their measures compare to 90°.

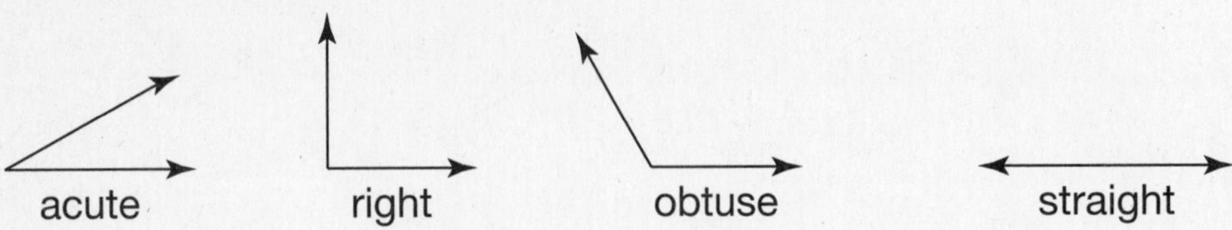

a. Which angle measure is 90°? __________

b. Which angle measure is greater than 90° and less than 180°? __________

c. Which angle measure is less than 90°? __________

d. Which angle measures 180°? __________

2. Extend the sides of each angle. Use a protractor to measure each angle.

a. __________

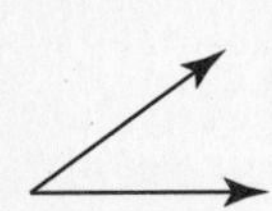

b. __________

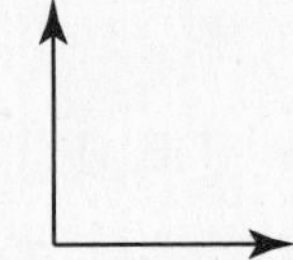

Identify each angle as acute, right, or obtuse. Extend the sides of each angle. Then measure each with a protractor.

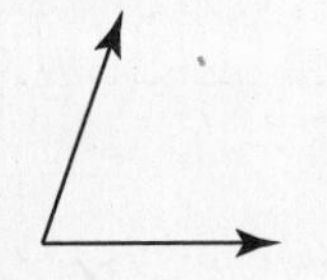

3. __________

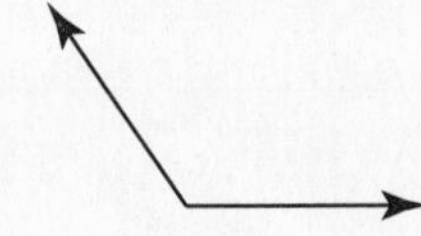

4. __________

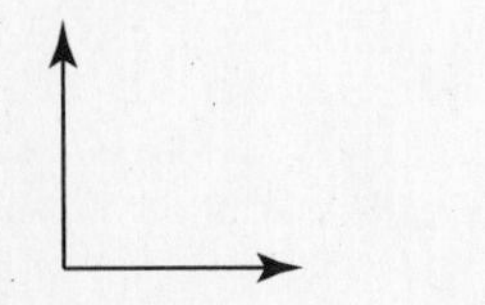

5. __________

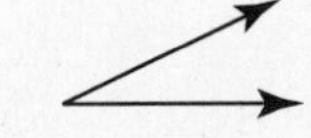

6. __________

 Use with pages 272–273.

Name ___________________________

Practice 6-3

Triangles

1. Classify each triangle as equilateral, isosceles, or scalene.

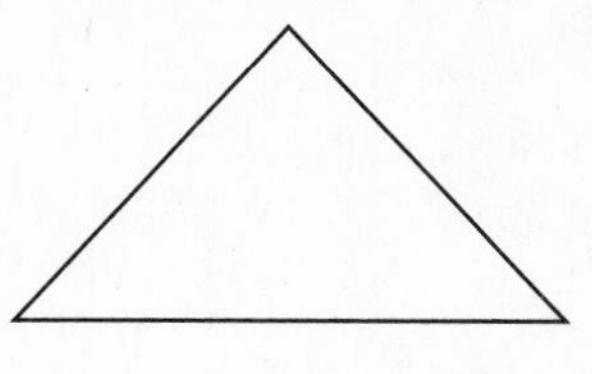
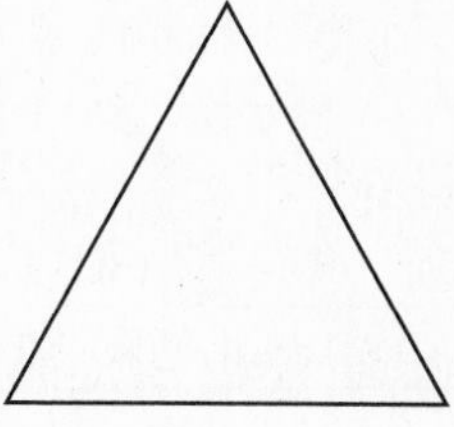

a. ______________ b. ______________ c. ______________

2. Classify each triangle as acute, right, or obtuse.

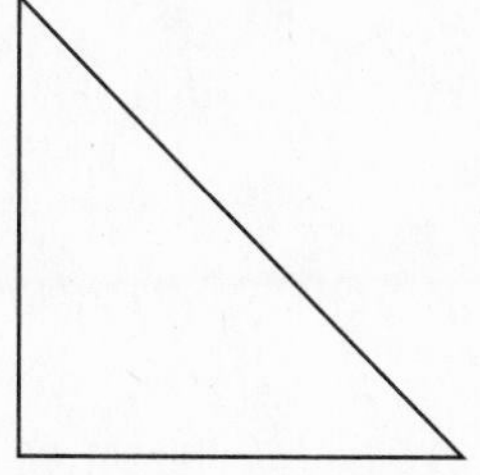
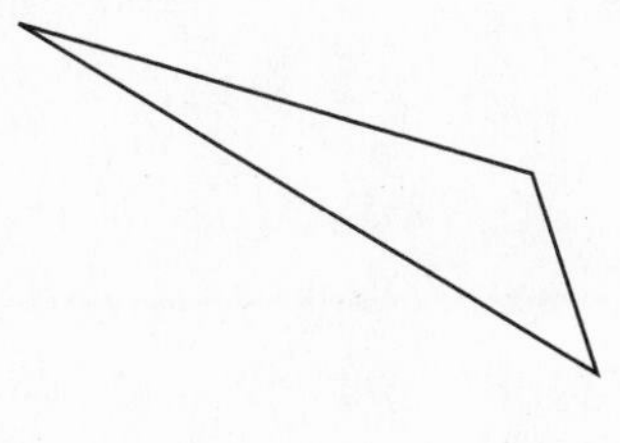
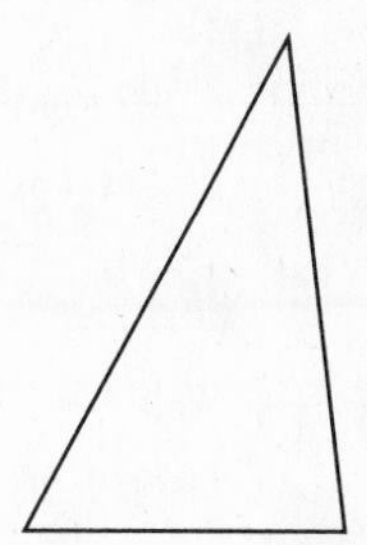

a. ______________ b. ______________ c. ______________

3. Evan drew a triangle with a 100° angle. Could it be acute, right, or obtuse? ______________

4. Rachel drew a triangle with a 90° angle. Were the other angles acute, obtuse or right? ______________

5. Tanisha drew a triangle with a 45° angle. Could it be acute, right, or obtuse? ______________

6. Draw a right, an acute and an obtuse triangle. Write whether each is scalene, isosceles or equilateral.

a. b. c.

______________ ______________ ______________

Name ______________________________

Practice 6-4

Quadrilaterals

Write the name that best describes each figure.

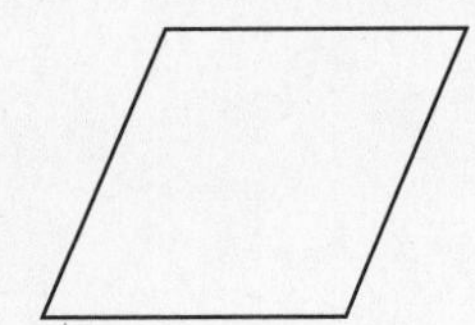

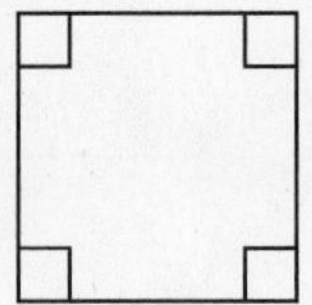

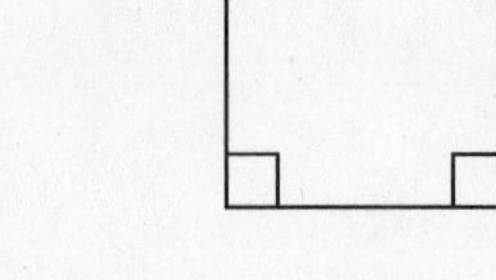

1. ____________________ **2.** ____________________

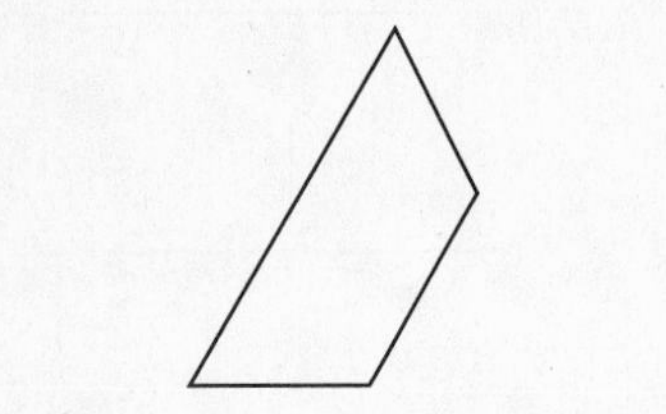

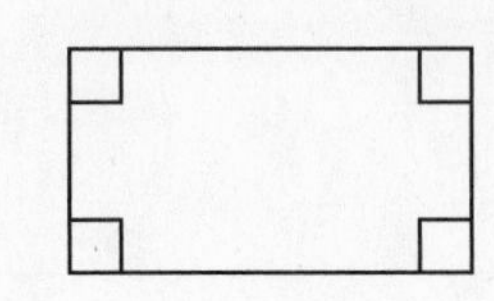

3. ____________________ **4.** ____________________

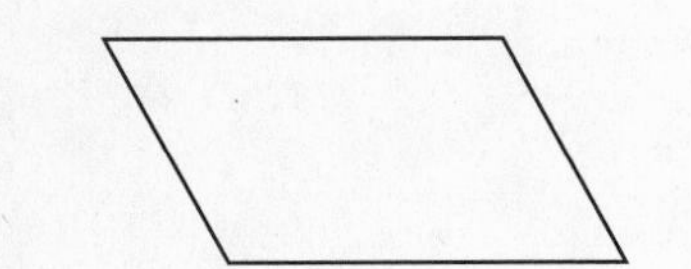

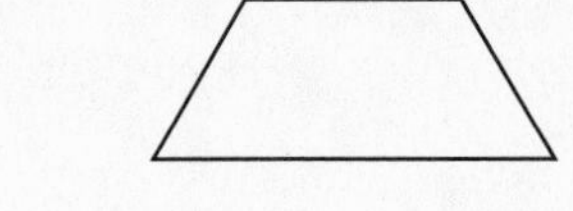

5. ____________________ **6.** ____________________

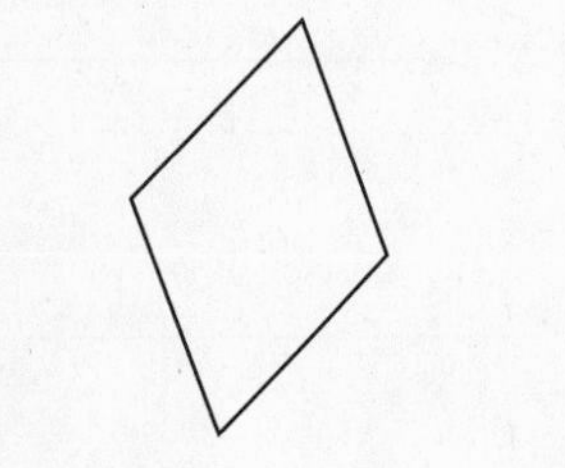

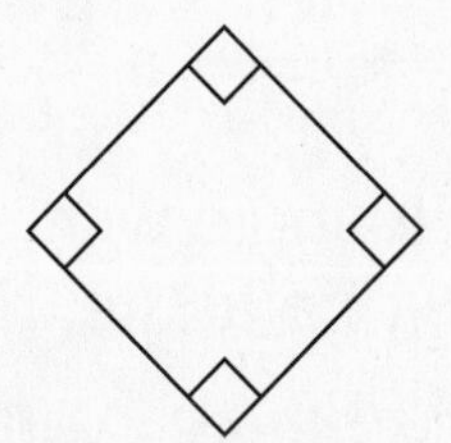

7. ____________________ **8.** ____________________

9. Ivan is making a design using a quadrilateral that has two pairs of parallel sides with all sides the same length, but with no right angles. What shape is he using? ____________________

10. You are making a design using a quadrilateral with only one pair of parallel sides. What shape could you use? ____________________

Name ______________________________

Practice 6-5

Analyze Strategies: Solve a Simpler Problem

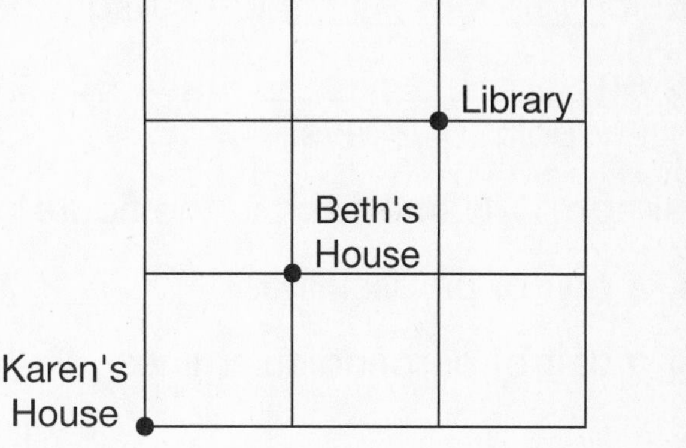

1. Karen rides her bike to school every day. How many different routes can Karen take to get to school without backtracking?

   a. How many different routes can Karen take to get to Beth's house?

   ____

   b. How many different routes can Karen take to get to the library?

   ____

   c. How many different routes can Karen take to get to school? __________

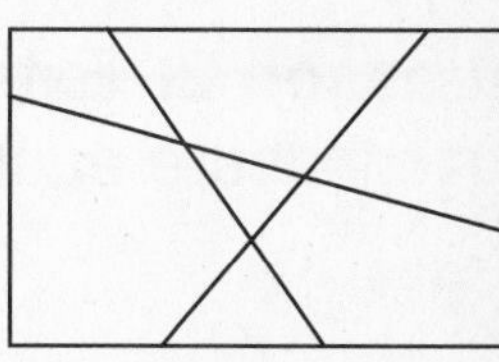

2. If you cut a piece of clay with 3 intersecting lines, you can get 7 pieces of clay. What is the greatest number of pieces you can get by cutting the clay with 5 intersecting lines?

____

Use any strategy to solve each problem.

3. If 14 students are playing musical chairs, how many times does the music have to stop for someone to win the game if one chair is removed at a time?

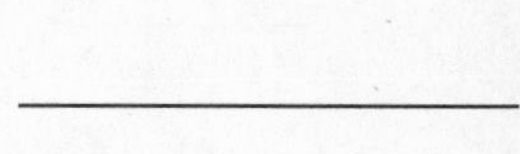

4. You're playing in a baseball tournament with 8 teams. Each team plays until they lose. What is the most number of games one team will play?

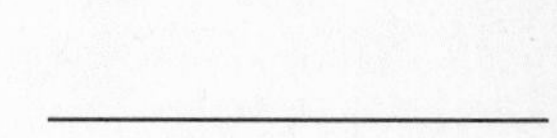

5. The Rockets beat the Tigers in a game of baseball. The Rockets scored 4 more runs than the Tigers. The total number of runs scored was 14. What was the score?

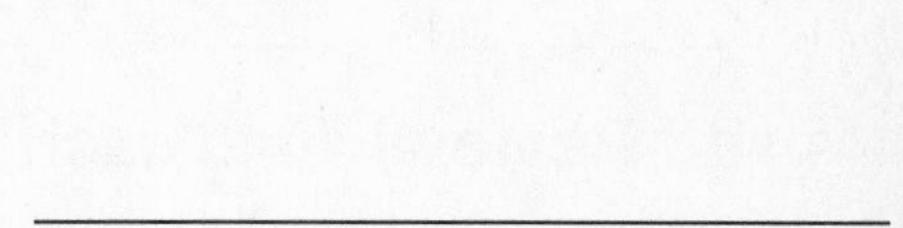

Name ________________________________

Review and Practice

Vocabulary Complete with the correct word from the list.

protractor
line
angle

1. A ______________ is used to measure angles.

2. A ______________ is a straight path that goes on forever.

3. An ______________ is formed at the shared endpoint of 2 rays.

(Lesson 1) Name each in the figure at the right.

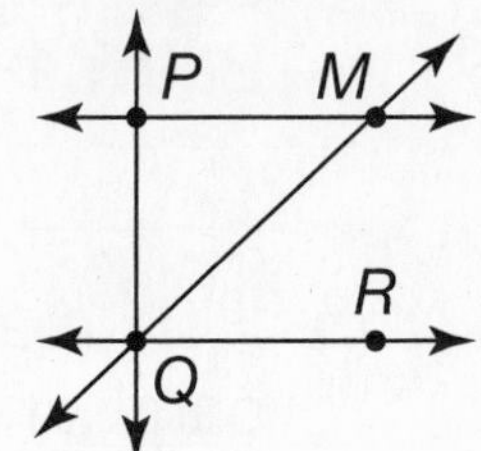

4. a pair of parallel lines ________________

5. a pair of perpendicular lines

____

6. a pair of intersecting lines

____

7. the rays that form angle *M* ________________

(Lesson 2) Extend the lines of each angle. Use a protractor to measure each angle.

8. 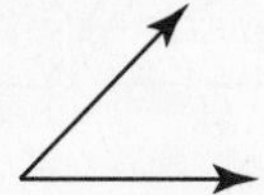 ________

9.  ________

(Lesson 3) Classify each triangle as equilateral, isosceles, or scalene. Then classify each triangle as acute, right, or obtuse.

10. 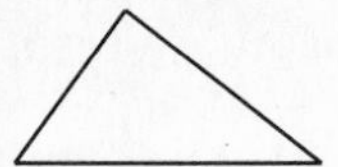 ____________, ____________

11. 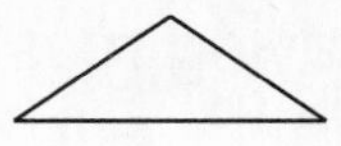 ____________, ____________

(Lesson 4) Write the name that best describes each figure.

12. 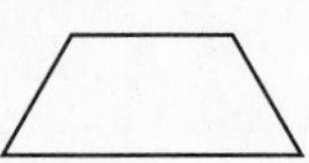 ______________

13.  ______________

14.  ______________

(Mixed Review) Find each product.

16. 50 × 70 = ________

17. 46 × 3 = ________

18. 8 × 3,000 = ________

19. 70 × 900 = ________

Name ______________________________

Practice
6-6

Similar and Congruent Polygons

Circle the polygon similar to the first one in each row.

1. 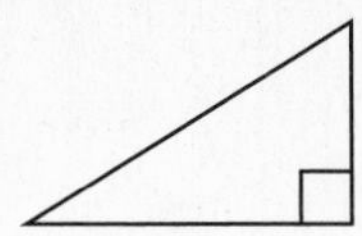 **a.**  **b.** 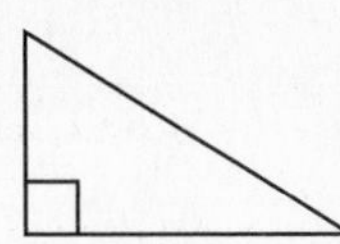 **c.** 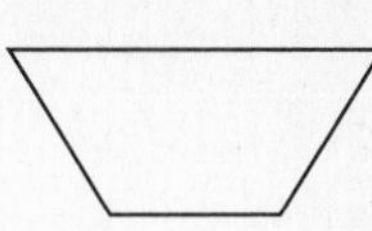

2. 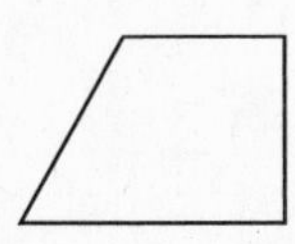 **a.** 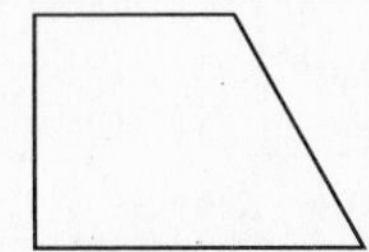 **b.** 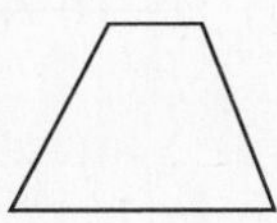 **c.** 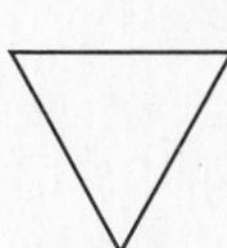

3. 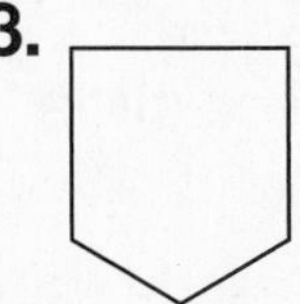 **a.** 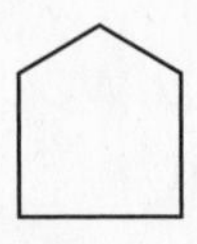 **b.** 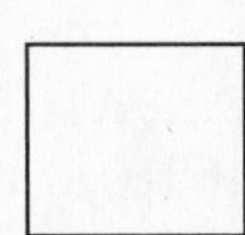 **c.** 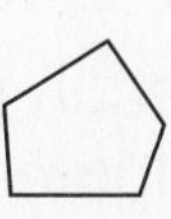

Circle the polygon congruent to the first one in each row.

4. 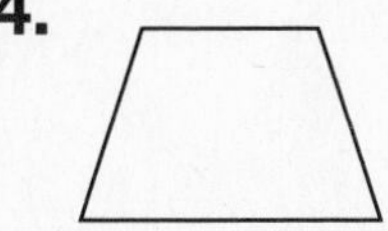 **a.** 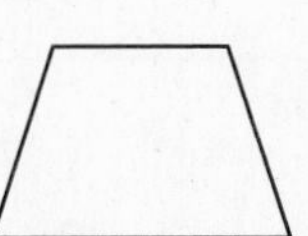 **b.** 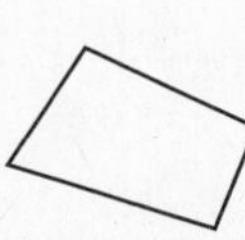 **c.** 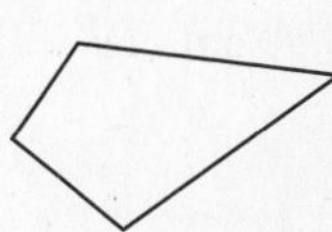

5.  **a.**  **b.** 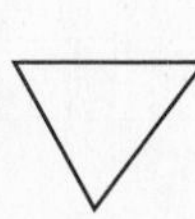 **c.** 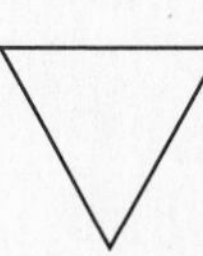

6. 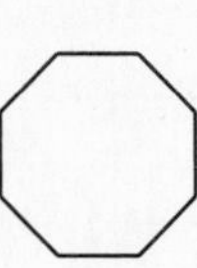 **a.** 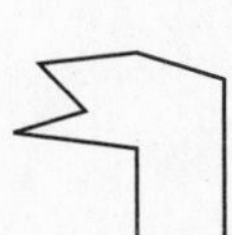 **b.** 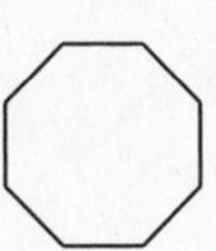 **c.** 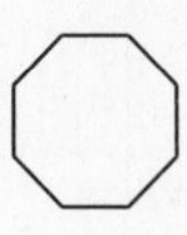

7. Are two congruent figures similar?

____

____

Name ________________________________

Practice 6-7

Exploring Congruence and Motions

Write the motion used to get from start to finish.

1. __________

2. __________

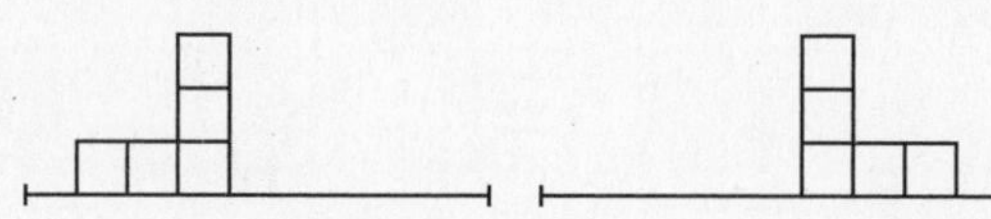

3. __________

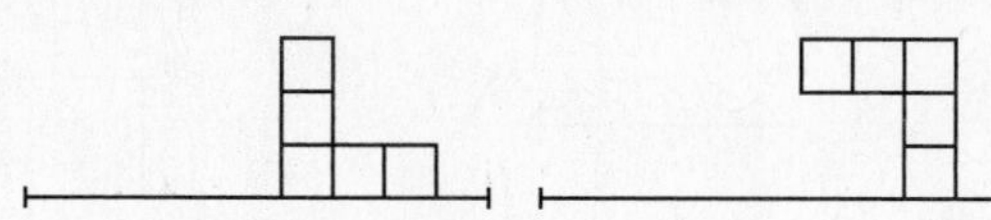

4. For each pentomino pair, write whether you would flip, turn, or slide the figures to show that they are congruent.

a.

b. 

______________________ ______________________

5. Which of the figures is congruent to ? ____

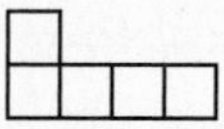

a. 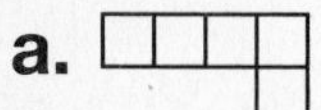

b. 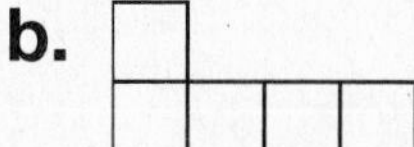

c.

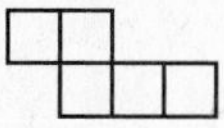

d. 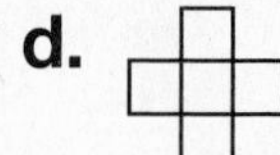

6. Which of the figures is **not** congruent to ? ____

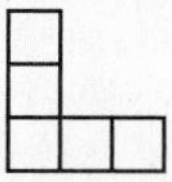

a. 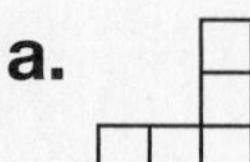

b.

c.

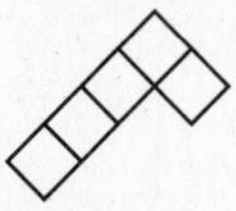

d. 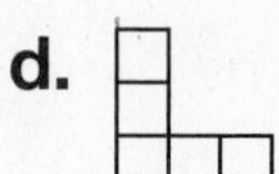

7. Which of the figures shows 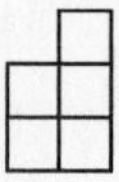 turned? ____

a. 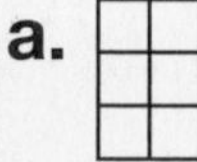

b.

c. 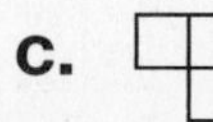

d.

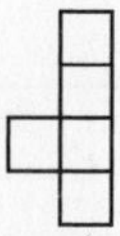

Name ________________________________

Exploring Line Symmetry

1. Explain how tracing a figure can help you find its lines of symmetry.

____

____

____

Draw all lines of symmetry.

2. 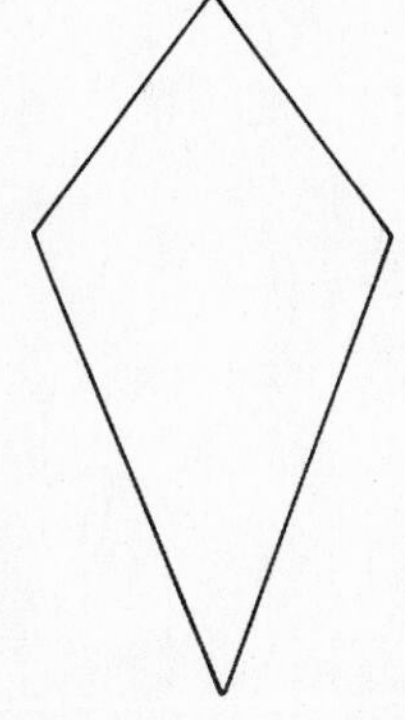

3. 

Use the line of symmetry to complete each figure.

4. 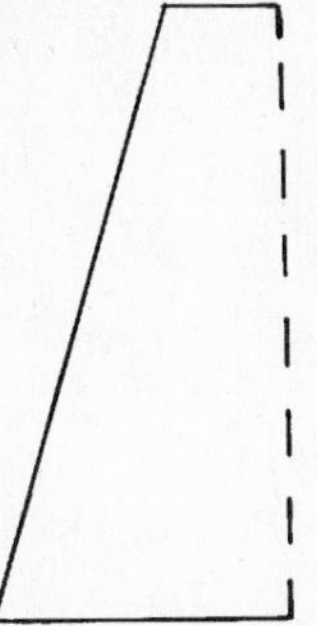

5. 

Use flips, turns, or slides. Is each pair of figures congruent? Explain.

6. 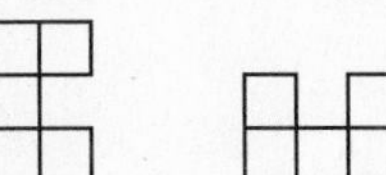

7. 

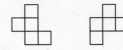

____________________ ____________________

8. Draw three hexominoes that have at least 1 line of symmetry.

Name ______________________________

Practice
6-9

Decision Making

You want to complete an art project over the weekend. You have to decide between 2 project choices. You will be working by yourself. Here are the 2 project choices:

Polygon Collage: Make a collage by drawing, cutting out, and pasting polygons. Include some similar and congruent figures.

Mask: Make a mask that is symmetrical. It should have 1 line of symmetry.

In order to decide which project to complete, you need to think about some details of the project. Answer the following questions:

1. How much time do you have to work on the project? __________

2. Do you have the materials you need for each project? __________

3. Will you be able to use either of the projects in the future?

   Polygon Collage: __________ Mask: __________

4. Which project would you enjoy completing? ____________________

5. Write an estimate of how much time each project will take.

   Polygon Collage: ____________________

   Mask: ____________________

6. Divide the time you will need for each project equally among the number of days in the weekend.

   Polygon Collage: ________ each day Mask: ________ each day

7. Think about your answers to the questions above. Which project would you choose to complete? Why?

   ____

   ____

Name ______________________

Review and Practice

Vocabulary Match each with its definition.

_____ **1.** congruent polygons

_____ **2.** pentominoes

_____ **3.** similar figures

_____ **4.** line of symmetry

a. have the same shape, but not necessarily same size

b. have the same shape and size

c. five congruent squares joined

d. separates a shape into two congruent halves

(Lesson 6) Use the figures to answer **5** and **6**.

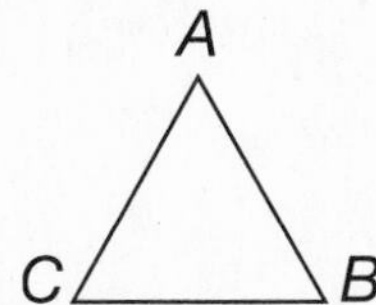

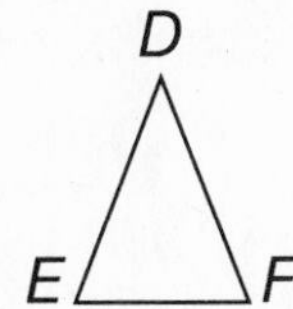

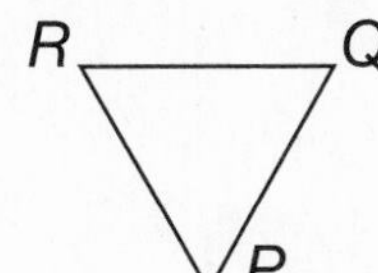

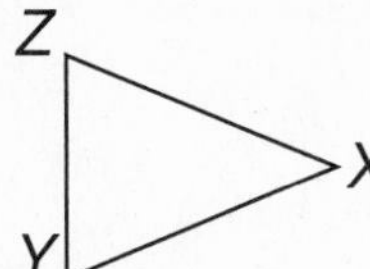

5. Which triangle is congruent to triangle *ABC*? ______________

6. Which triangle is similar to triangle *XYZ*? ______________

(Lesson 7) Use the figures to answer **7** and **8**.

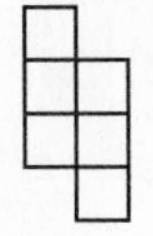
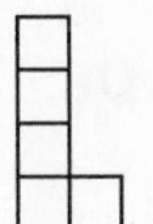
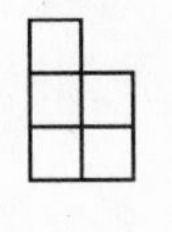
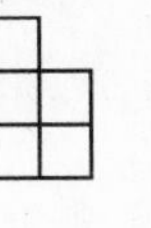
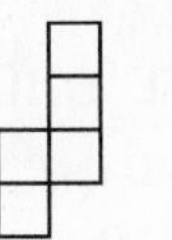
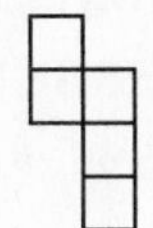
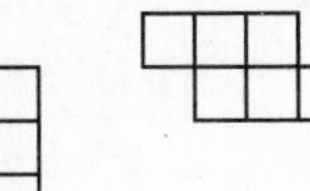

a **b** **c** **d** **e** **f**

7. Which figures are pentominoes? ______________

8. Which figures are congruent? ______________

(Lesson 8) Draw all lines of symmetry.

9.

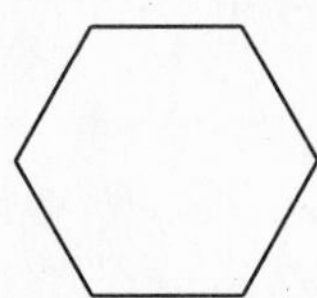

10.

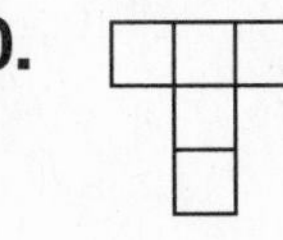

(Mixed Review) Add or subtract.

11. $\begin{array}{r} 3,248 \\ +\,2,638 \\ \hline \end{array}$

12. $\begin{array}{r} 5,733 \\ -\,2,885 \\ \hline \end{array}$

13. $\begin{array}{r} 1,911 \\ -\,992 \\ \hline \end{array}$

14. $\begin{array}{r} 3,067 \\ +\,7,864 \\ \hline \end{array}$

Name ______________________

Practice
Chapters 1–6

Cumulative Review

(Chapter 4 Lesson 13)

1. Which numbers in **2–7** are divisible by 3? __________

(Chapter 4 Lesson 14) Write prime or composite for each number.

2. 26 __________ **3.** 111 __________ **4.** 31 __________

5. 47 __________ **6.** 61 __________ **7.** 57 __________

(Chapter 5 Lessons 4 and 5) Divide.

8. $42\overline{)369}$ **9.** $85\overline{)710}$ **10.** $55\overline{)493}$

11. $34\overline{)642}$ **12.** $26\overline{)478}$ **13.** $58\overline{)944}$

(Chapter 6 Lesson 2) Identify each angle as acute, right, or obtuse. Extend the sides of each angle. Then measure each with a protractor.

14.

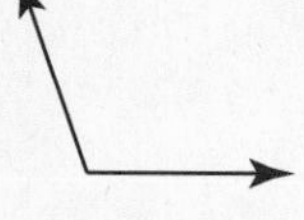

____

15.

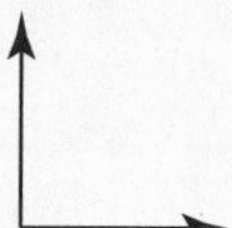

____

16.

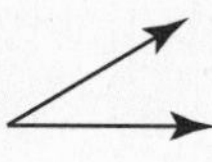

____

(Chapter 6 Lesson 6) Use the figure to answer **17–20**.

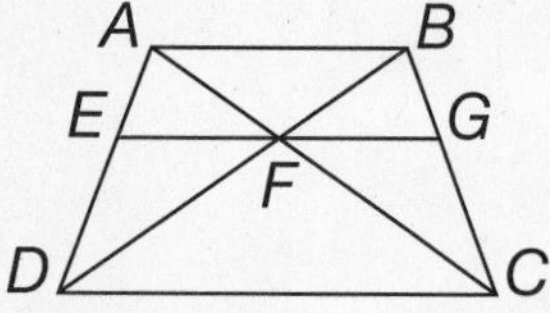

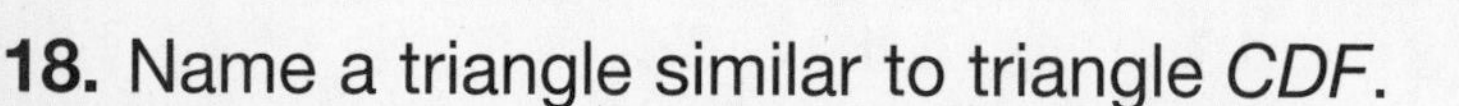

17. Name a triangle congruent to triangle *AFD*. __________

18. Name a triangle similar to triangle *CDF*. __________

19. Name a triangle congruent to triangle *ABD*. __________

20. Name a trapezoid similar to trapezoid *GFDC*. __________

Name ______________________________

Practice
7-1

Whole and Parts

Write the fraction that names each shaded part.

1. 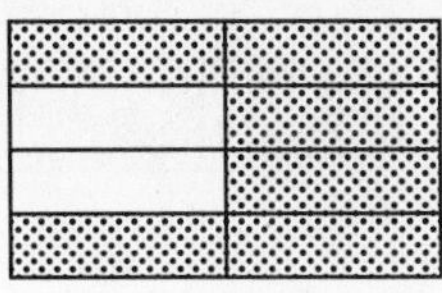

______

2. 

______

What part of each set is square?

3. 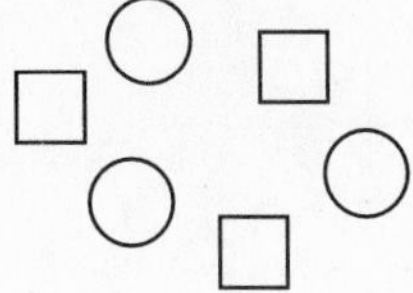

______

4. 

______

5. Which shows three fourths? ______

A. 

B. 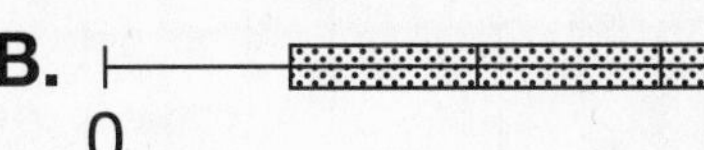

6. Estimate the fraction of the figure that is shaded. ______

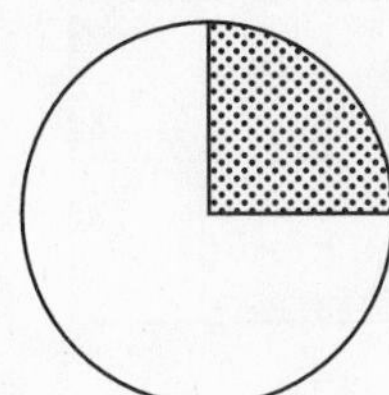

A. $\frac{1}{8}$ B. $\frac{1}{4}$ C. $\frac{1}{2}$

7. During an art contest at your school, you and a classmate each won blue ribbons for $\frac{1}{3}$ of the pieces you entered in the contest. You won 2 blue ribbons and your classmate won 3 blue ribbons. Explain how this could be.

____

____

Name ______________________

Practice
7-2

Exploring Equivalent Fractions

1. Which shadings show fractions equivalent to $\frac{2}{3}$? ________

A. 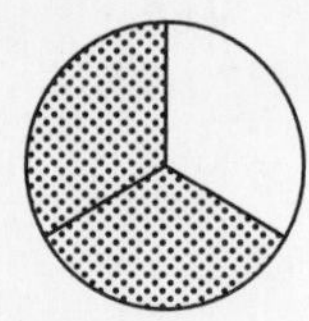

B. 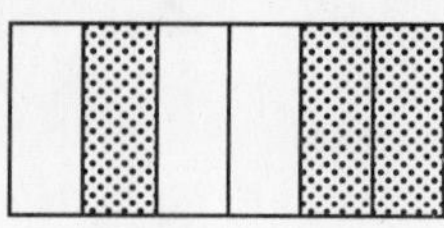

C. 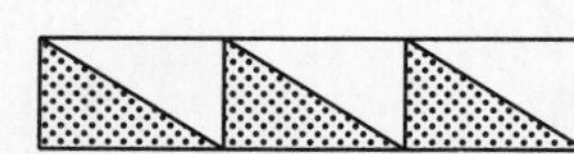

Write two fractions that name the shaded part.

2. 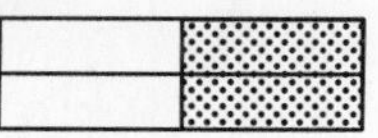

____

3. 

____

4. 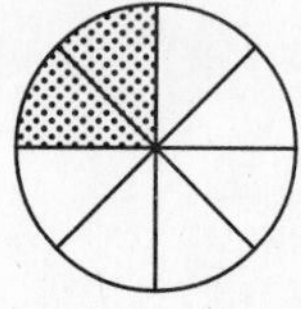

____

5. Write a fraction for the shaded part of each picture. Which fractions are equivalent to $\frac{1}{3}$?

A. 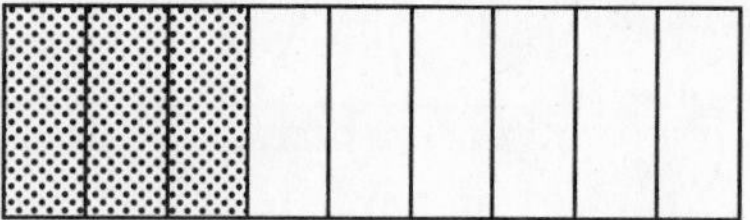

____

B. 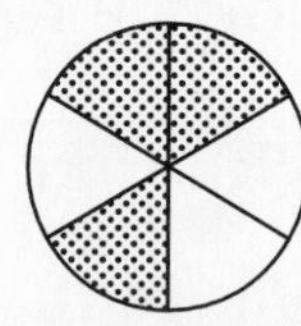

____

C. 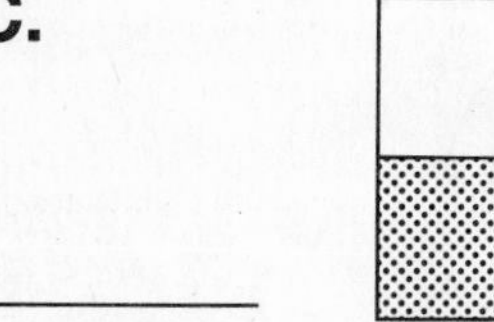

____

D. 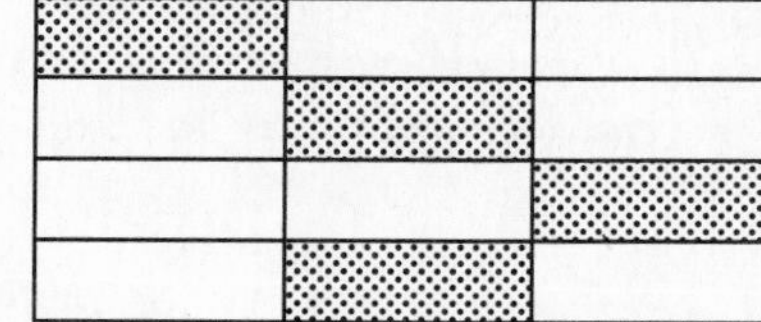

____

Fractions ____________________ are all equivalent to $\frac{1}{3}$.

6. John's mother baked a lasagna in a rectangular pan and cut it into 6 pieces. John ate 2 pieces.

a. Draw a picture to represent the lasagna and shade in the pieces that John ate.

b. Write 2 fractions that describe how much lasagna is left. ________

7. Gina said she would share half a pack of baseball cards with Joe. Joe ended up with $\frac{5}{10}$ of the pack. Did Joe get half? Explain.

____

Name ______________________

Practice
7-3

Patterns with Equivalent Fractions

Find equivalent fractions with a denominator of 8.

1. $\frac{1}{2}$ ______ 2. $\frac{3}{4}$ ______ 3. $\frac{9}{24}$ ______ 4. $\frac{25}{40}$ ______

Find equivalent fractions with a denominator of 12.

5. $\frac{2}{3}$ ______ 6. $\frac{5}{6}$ ______ 7. $\frac{8}{24}$ ______ 8. $\frac{9}{36}$ ______

Name the fractions in the box equivalent to each fraction below.

$\frac{12}{16}$	$\frac{3}{6}$	$\frac{9}{12}$	$\frac{2}{4}$	$\frac{3}{9}$	$\frac{6}{8}$	$\frac{4}{8}$	$\frac{2}{6}$	$\frac{4}{12}$

9. $\frac{1}{3}$ ______ 10. $\frac{3}{4}$ ______ 11. $\frac{1}{2}$ ______ 12. $\frac{2}{6}$ ______

Write whether each pair is equivalent. Explain how you decided.

13. $\frac{1}{4}$ and $\frac{3}{12}$

____

14. $\frac{12}{18}$ and $\frac{3}{9}$

____

15. $\frac{4}{5}$ and $\frac{12}{15}$

____

16. Three-ninths of a soccer game is over. Is this half-time? Explain.

____

Name ______________________

Practice 7-4

Greatest Common Factor

Find the greatest common factor for each pair.

1. 4 and 8 ______

2. 6 and 9 ______

3. 12 and 18 ______

4. 10 and 15 ______

5. 6 and 12 ______

6. 14 and 21 ______

7. 6 and 18 ______

8. 16 and 24 ______

9. 6 and 15 ______

10. 4 and 10 ______

11. 3 and 7 ______

12. 9 and 15 ______

13. 5 and 12 ______

14. 7 and 4 ______

15. 2 and 5 ______

16. 12 and 9 ______

17. Find two numbers that have 6 as the greatest common factor.

____

18. Find two numbers that have 10 as the greatest common factor.

____

19. Find the factors of 12 and 16.

____

____

20. Find the factors of 8 and 20

____

____

21. Could 7 be the greatest common factor of 21 and 35? Explain.

____

22. The common factors of two numbers are 2 and 4. The two numbers could be 12 and 16 or 8 and 24. Explain how.

____

____

Name ______________________________

Practice
7-5

Simplest Form

Find the simplest form for each fraction.

1. $\frac{12}{16}$ ________
2. $\frac{8}{24}$ ________
3. $\frac{3}{9}$ ________
4. $\frac{8}{16}$ ________
5. $\frac{10}{15}$ ________

6. $\frac{14}{21}$ ________
7. $\frac{12}{18}$ ________
8. $\frac{9}{27}$ ________
9. $\frac{6}{9}$ ________
10. $\frac{8}{10}$ ________

11. $\frac{7}{21}$ ________
12. $\frac{5}{15}$ ________
13. $\frac{12}{15}$ ________
14. $\frac{12}{16}$ ________
15. $\frac{15}{18}$ ________

16. $\frac{5}{25}$ ________
17. $\frac{12}{18}$ ________
18. $\frac{16}{20}$ ________
19. $\frac{6}{20}$ ________
20. $\frac{8}{48}$ ________

21. $\frac{6}{48}$ ________
22. $\frac{32}{40}$ ________
23. $\frac{35}{42}$ ________
24. $\frac{9}{45}$ ________
25. $\frac{18}{27}$ ________

Write whether each fraction is in simplest form. If it is not, find the simplest form.

26. $\frac{2}{6}$ ________
27. $\frac{3}{15}$ ________
28. $\frac{5}{6}$ ________
29. $\frac{9}{12}$ ________
30. $\frac{1}{3}$ ________

31. $\frac{2}{7}$ ________
32. $\frac{6}{10}$ ________
33. $\frac{7}{8}$ ________
34. $\frac{6}{8}$ ________
35. $\frac{5}{35}$ ________

36. Explain why a fraction whose denominator is 13 is always in its simplest form.

____

Name ______________________________

Practice 7-6

Exploring Comparing and Ordering Fractions

1. Describe how you compare two fractions whose numerators are the same.

____

____

Compare each pair of fractions. You may use fraction strips or draw pictures. Write >, < or = to complete.

2. $\frac{1}{4} \bigcirc \frac{1}{5}$
3. $\frac{3}{4} \bigcirc \frac{1}{4}$
4. $\frac{4}{7} \bigcirc \frac{4}{5}$
5. $\frac{3}{7} \bigcirc \frac{3}{9}$
6. $\frac{2}{7} \bigcirc \frac{4}{7}$
7. $\frac{1}{3} \bigcirc \frac{1}{6}$
8. $\frac{5}{8} \bigcirc \frac{8}{8}$
9. $\frac{2}{3} \bigcirc \frac{2}{5}$
10. $\frac{1}{8} \bigcirc \frac{1}{3}$
11. $\frac{1}{2} \bigcirc \frac{5}{8}$
12. $\frac{2}{3} \bigcirc \frac{10}{15}$
13. $\frac{2}{3} \bigcirc \frac{6}{7}$
14. $\frac{3}{8} \bigcirc \frac{3}{7}$
15. $\frac{6}{7} \bigcirc \frac{5}{7}$
16. $\frac{1}{6} \bigcirc \frac{1}{8}$

Order these fractions from least to greatest. Use fraction strips.

17. $\frac{3}{8}, \frac{2}{3}, \frac{4}{5}$ ________, ________, ________

18. $\frac{8}{9}, \frac{11}{12}, \frac{10}{11}$ ________, ________, ________

19. Is $\frac{1}{4}$ greater than or less than $\frac{1}{8}$? Explain.

____

____

20. Peter ate $\frac{2}{3}$ of a pizza. Jordan ate $\frac{4}{8}$ of a same size pizza.

Who ate more? ________

Name ______________________

Practice
7-7

Comparing and Ordering Fractions

Write >, < or = to complete.

1. $\frac{1}{2} \bigcirc \frac{1}{3}$ 2. $\frac{1}{2} \bigcirc \frac{2}{3}$ 3. $\frac{1}{4} \bigcirc \frac{1}{3}$

4. $\frac{1}{4} \bigcirc \frac{1}{6}$ 5. $\frac{1}{3} \bigcirc \frac{1}{5}$ 6. $\frac{2}{5} \bigcirc \frac{1}{3}$

7. $\frac{2}{5} \bigcirc \frac{2}{3}$ 8. $\frac{8}{12} \bigcirc \frac{2}{3}$ 9. $\frac{2}{3} \bigcirc \frac{4}{5}$

10. $\frac{5}{8} \bigcirc \frac{1}{2}$ 11. $\frac{1}{2} \bigcirc \frac{3}{8}$ 12. $\frac{4}{10} \bigcirc \frac{6}{15}$

13. $\frac{7}{10} \bigcirc \frac{3}{4}$ 14. $\frac{7}{10} \bigcirc \frac{2}{3}$ 15. $\frac{5}{6} \bigcirc \frac{7}{12}$

16. $\frac{3}{10} \bigcirc \frac{7}{10}$ 17. $\frac{1}{4} \bigcirc \frac{3}{10}$ 18. $\frac{1}{6} \bigcirc \frac{1}{10}$

Compare the fractions. Write them in order from least to greatest.

19. $\frac{1}{2}, \frac{1}{3}, \frac{1}{4},$ ______________

20. $\frac{2}{3}, \frac{13}{18}, \frac{7}{9}, \frac{5}{6},$ ______________

21. $\frac{3}{4}, \frac{3}{8}, \frac{3}{7},$ ______________

22. $\frac{3}{5}, \frac{1}{2}, \frac{1}{4}, \frac{2}{5},$ ______________

23. Explain how four red marbles can make up $\frac{1}{3}$ of a group of marbles and three blue marbles make up $\frac{1}{4}$ of the same group.

____

____

24. Joe has $\frac{1}{6}$ of a packet of crackers and Aaron has $\frac{3}{8}$. Who has more crackers?

____

Name ______________________

Practice 7-8

Analyze Strategies: Make a Table

Make a table or use another strategy to solve each problem.

1. For every 10 videos Video Palace rents, 5 are comedy videos. If they rent 30 videos, how many were comedy videos? ______________

2. For every 2 hours Karen does yard work, her brother, Jeff works 4 hours cleaning the house. If Jeff works in the house for 12 hours a month, how many hours would Karen work on the yard? ______________

3. José used his new telescope to view the stars. On his first night he observed 7 stars. Every night that followed he discovered 3 new stars he hadn't seen before. On the fifth night how many stars did José observe altogether? ______________

4. The local ice cream shop was selling 20 shakes in a day. Then they advertised a special on their shakes, and their sales doubled every day. On the fourth day how many shakes did they sell? ______________

5. Mrs. Gupta came home from the mall with $14. At her last stop before coming home she bought some paint and paint brushes at an art supply store for $9.50. Earlier she had purchased some overalls for $23.50. How much money did Mrs Gupta take with her to the mall? ______________

6. Lana drives 6 miles every day, and Fred drives 7 miles every day. If Fred has driven 56 miles, how many miles has Lana driven? ______________

 Use with pages 318–319.

Name ______________________________

Practice
Chapter 7
Section A

Review and Practice

Vocabulary Write true or false for each statement.

1. The denominator is the bottom number in a fraction. ______

2. A fraction is in simplest form when the GCF of the numerator and denominator is less than 3. ______

3. $\frac{2}{3}$ and $\frac{3}{4}$ are equivalent fractions. ______

(Lesson 1) Write the fraction that names each shaded part.

4. ______

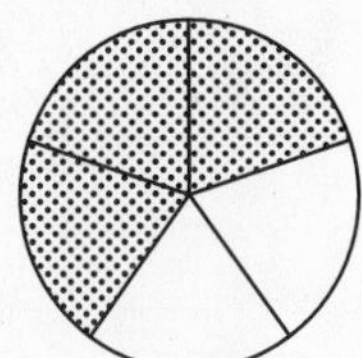

5. ______

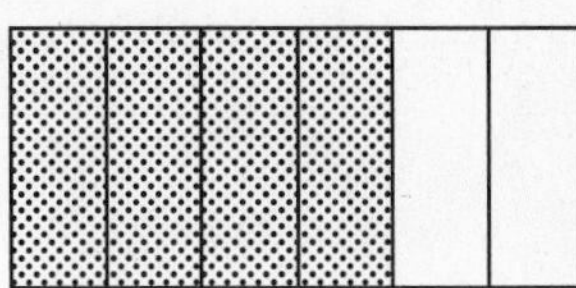

(Lessons 2 and 3) Complete.

6. $\frac{3}{4} = \frac{\square}{12} = \frac{6}{\square} = \frac{\square}{16}$

7. $\frac{5}{6} = \frac{10}{\square} = \frac{\square}{60}$

(Lesson 4) Find the greatest comon factor for each pair.

8. 12 and 8 ______

9. 20 and 9 ______

(Lesson 5) Find the simplest form for each fraction.

10 $\frac{22}{66}$ = ______

11. $\frac{36}{48}$ = ______

12. $\frac{14}{16}$ = ______

(Lessons 6 and 7) Write each set of fractions in order from least to greatest.

13. $\frac{1}{6}, \frac{2}{3}, \frac{1}{5}$ ____, ____, ____

14. $\frac{5}{6}, \frac{9}{12}, \frac{5}{8}$ ____, ____, ____

(Lesson 8) Solve. You may make a table to help.

15. On Monday, Megan found a 3-leaf plant. On Tuesday, she found a 4-leaf plant and on Wednesday she found a 5-leaf plant. If she continues to find plants in the same pattern, on what day of the week would she find a 10-leaf plant?

____

(Mixed Review) Complete each number sentence.

16. 36 ÷ ______ = 4

17. ______ ÷ 6 = 8

18. ______ × 7 = 56

Name ______________________

Practice
7-9

Exploring Mixed Numbers

Match each with its definition.

_____ **1.** mixed number

_____ **2.** improper fraction

a. a whole number and a fraction

b. a fraction greater than, or equal to, 1

Write the mixed or whole number and the improper fraction that name each shaded part.

3. 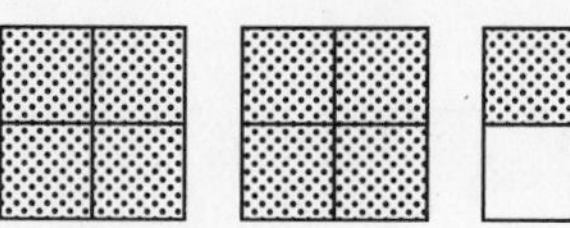

____

4. 

____

5. 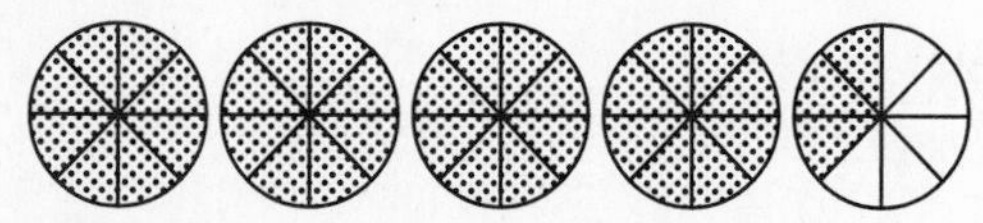

____

6. 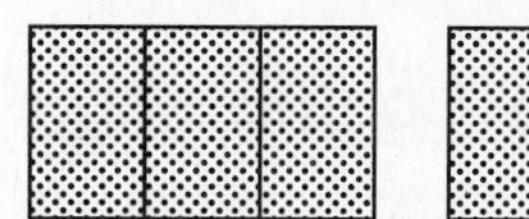 

____

7. 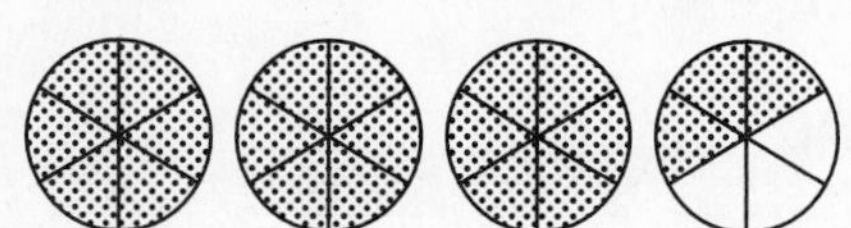

____

8. 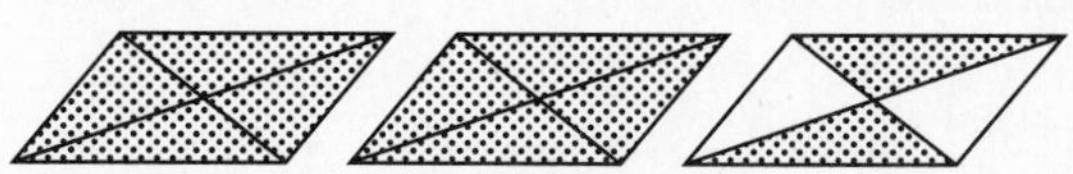

____

9. 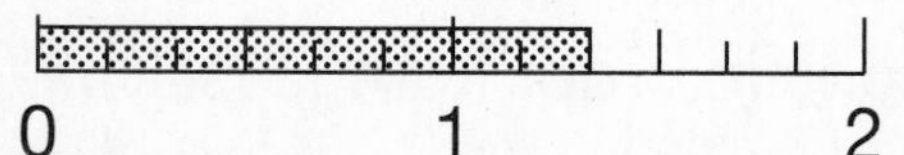

____

10. 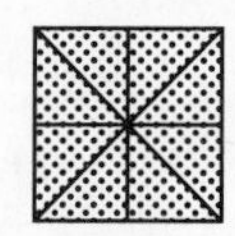 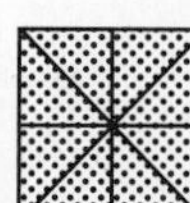 

____

Make a drawing that shows each fraction.

11. $2\frac{3}{5}$

12. $\frac{15}{3}$

13. $2\frac{2}{3}$

14. $\frac{7}{2}$

Name ___________________________

Practice 7-10

Mixed Numbers

Write each improper fraction as a mixed number in simplest form, or as a whole number.

1. $\frac{11}{3}$ = ________ **2.** $\frac{19}{5}$ = ________ **3.** $\frac{25}{3}$ = ________

4. $\frac{42}{6}$ = ________ **5.** $\frac{43}{8}$ = ________ **6.** $\frac{49}{6}$ = ________

7. $\frac{36}{4}$ = ________ **8.** $\frac{68}{9}$ = ________ **9.** $\frac{23}{4}$ = ________

10. $\frac{96}{8}$ = ________ **11.** $\frac{23}{5}$ = ________ **12.** $\frac{34}{3}$ = ________

13. $\frac{72}{5}$ = ________ **14.** $\frac{46}{6}$ = ________ **15.** $\frac{49}{7}$ = ________

Write each mixed number as an improper fraction.

16. $3\frac{1}{2}$ = ________ **17.** $5\frac{3}{4}$ = ________ **18.** $6\frac{7}{8}$ = ________

19. $5\frac{5}{12}$ = ________ **20.** $4\frac{1}{6}$ = ________ **21.** $6\frac{2}{3}$ = ________

22. $12\frac{2}{3}$ = ________ **23.** $9\frac{1}{4}$ = ________ **24.** $8\frac{2}{5}$ = ________

25. $25\frac{1}{4}$ = ________ **26.** $22\frac{1}{2}$ = ________ **27.** $6\frac{4}{5}$ = ________

28. $11\frac{3}{8}$ = ________ **29.** $16\frac{5}{6}$ = ________ **30.** $9\frac{8}{9}$ = ________

Complete.

31. $2 = \frac{\square}{20}$ **32.** $6 = \frac{\square}{3}$ **33.** $8 = \frac{\square}{5}$

34. $7\frac{1}{2} = \frac{\square}{6}$ **35.** $4\frac{3}{5} = \frac{\square}{5}$ **36.** $11\frac{1}{2} = \frac{\square}{2}$

37. The pizza at Ryan's party is divided into eighths. Ryan usually eats 3 slices and the rest of his family usually eats 13. Are 2 pizzas enough? Explain.

____

____

Name ______________________________

Practice
7-11

Exploring Comparing and Ordering Mixed Numbers

1. How do you know $2\frac{1}{3}$ is greater than $1\frac{5}{6}$ without comparing the fractions?

____

2. Can you just compare the whole numbers when comparing $1\frac{3}{4}$ and $1\frac{1}{3}$? Explain. ______________________________

____

Give a mixed number for the shaded part of each picture. Use > and < to compare each pair of mixed numbers.

3. 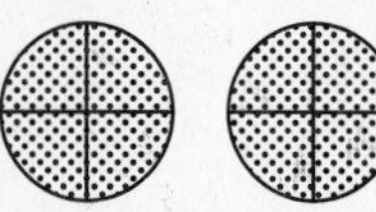 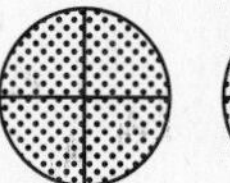 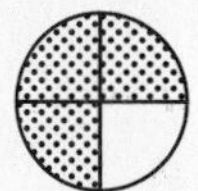 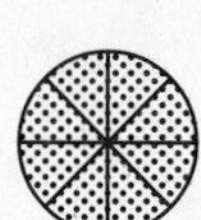 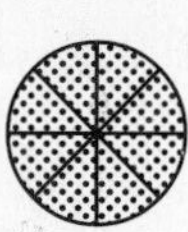 

________ ◯ ________

4. 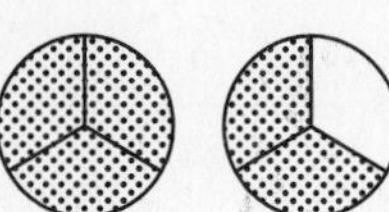 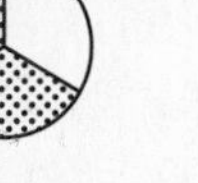  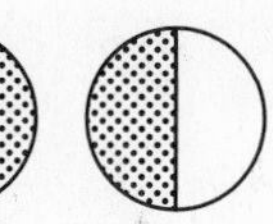

________ ◯ ________

5. 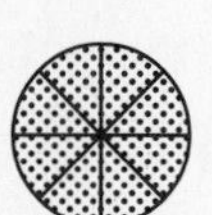 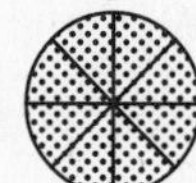 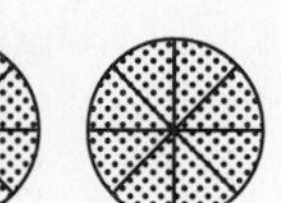  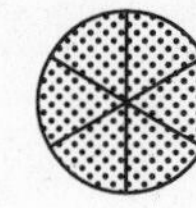 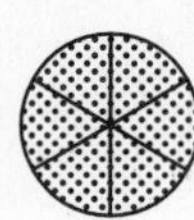 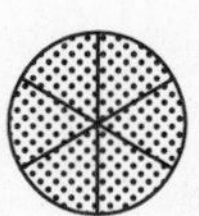

________ ◯ ________

Compare. Use > or <.

6. $4\frac{3}{8}$ ◯ $5\frac{1}{6}$ **7.** $2\frac{2}{3}$ ◯ $2\frac{1}{4}$ **8.** $3\frac{1}{8}$ ◯ $3\frac{1}{6}$

9. $2\frac{5}{8}$ ◯ $2\frac{3}{4}$ **10.** $6\frac{2}{3}$ ◯ $4\frac{7}{8}$ **11.** $3\frac{7}{10}$ ◯ $\frac{17}{4}$

Write in order from least to greatest.

12. $2\frac{1}{2}$, $\frac{9}{4}$, $\frac{8}{3}$, $1\frac{4}{5}$ ______________________________

Name ______________________________

Practice
7-12

Understanding Percent

Write the fraction and the percent shaded in each picture.

1. 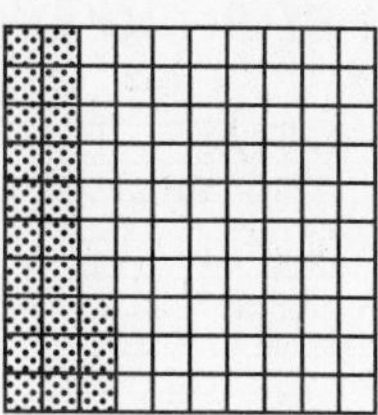

2. 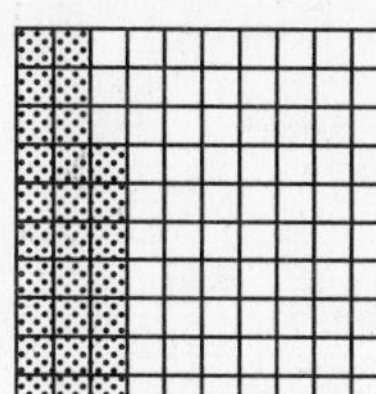

3. 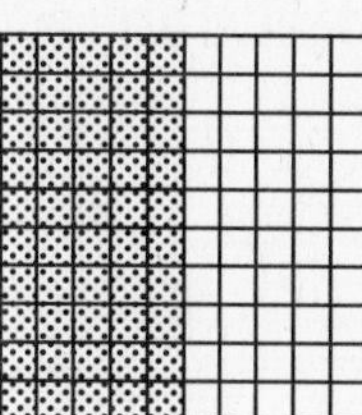

__________ __________ __________

Write each as a percent.

4. 78 out of 100 __________

5. 83 out of 100 __________

6. 55 out of 100 __________

7. $\frac{25}{100}$ __________

Write each as a hundredths fraction.

8. 82% __________

9. 6% __________

10. 59% __________

11. 60% __________

For each set, decide which does **not** belong.

12. A. 32% **B.** 32 out of 100 **C.** $\frac{3}{100}$ **D.** $\frac{32}{100}$ __________

13. A. $\frac{49}{100}$ **B.** $\frac{4}{9}$ **C.** 49 out of 100 **D.** 49% __________

Estimation Estimate the percent of each figure that is shaded.

14. 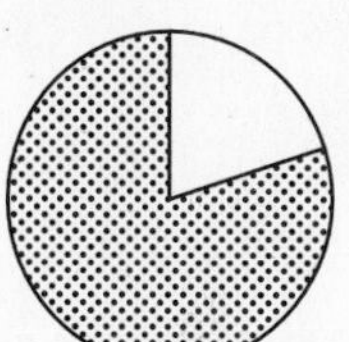

15. 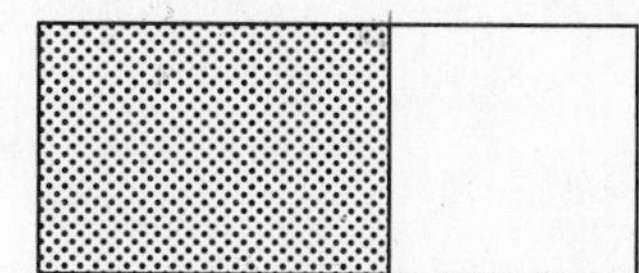

__________ __________

Name ______________________________

Practice 7-13

Connecting Fractions, Decimals and Percents

Write a fraction, a decimal, and a percent that name each shaded part.

1. 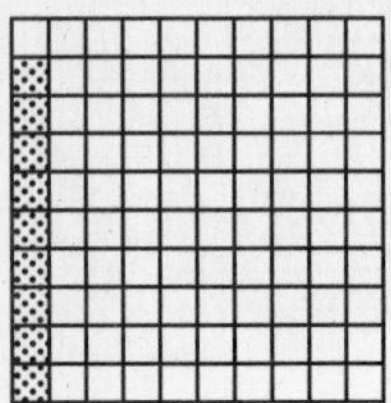

______
______
______

2. 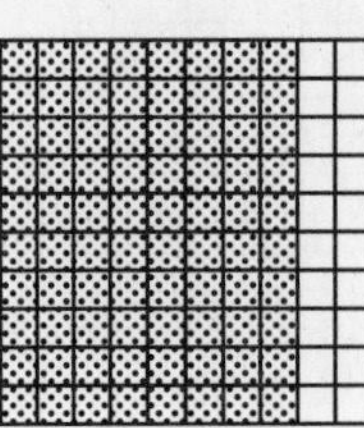

______
______
______

3. 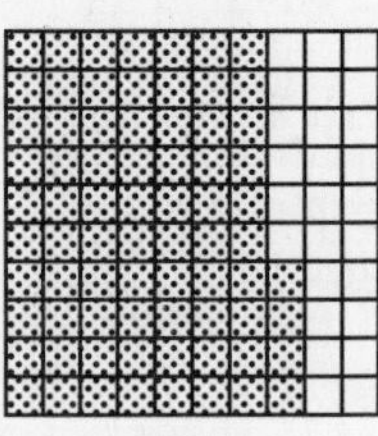

______
______
______

Write each as a percent.

4. 5 out of 100 ______

5. 89 out of 100 ______

6. 0.65 ______

7. 0.09 ______

8. $\frac{4}{100}$ ______

9. $\frac{57}{100}$ ______

Write each as a fraction and a decimal.

10. 3% ______ ______

11. 59% ______ ______

12. 35% ______ ______

13. 41% ______ ______

14. 5% ______ ______

15. 37% ______ ______

16. Which is less: $\frac{1}{3}$ or 50%? ______

17. Which is greater: 0.06 or 60%? ______

Name ______________________________

Practice
7-14

Decision Making

It's the start of football season. Suppose you read a survey of favorite teams taken at Sandburg School. You decide to survey 50 students at your own school.

Favorite Football Teams Sandburg School		Votes for Favorite Teams at Your School	
Cowboys	10%	Cowboys	5
49ers	30%	49ers	10
Steelers	25%	Steelers	20
Eagles	25%	Eagles	5
Broncos	10%	Broncos	10

1. Write fractions, decimals, and percents to describe the survey results at your school.

	Fraction	Decimal	Percent
a. Cowboys	________	________	________
b. 49ers	________	________	________
c. Steelers	________	________	________
d. Eagles	________	________	________
e. Broncos	________	________	________

2. Which team is the favorite at Sandburg School? ____________

3. Which team is the least favorite overall? ____________

4. Which team has the biggest difference between the two surveys?

____

5. Draw a circle graph for each survey.

Name ________________________________

Review and Practice

Vocabulary Match each with its example.

$2\frac{1}{5}$, $\frac{12}{7}$, 15%

1. percent ________ **2.** improper fraction ________ **3.** mixed number ________

(Lesson 9) Write the mixed or whole number and the improper fraction that name each shaded part.

4. 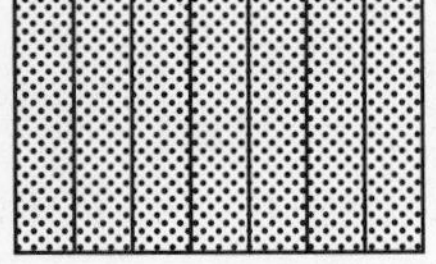 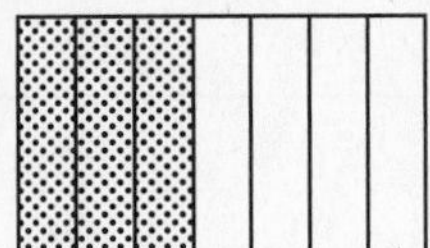

____

5. 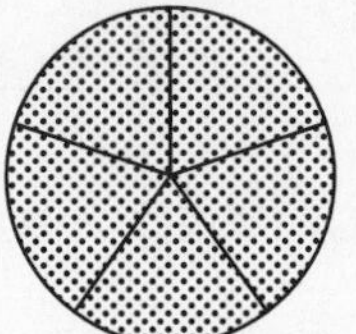 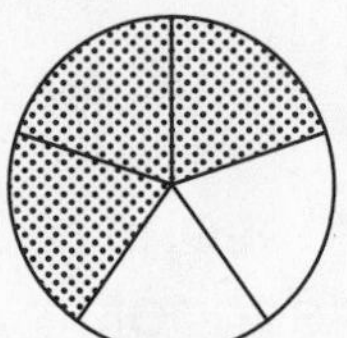

____

(Lesson 10) Write each improper fraction as a mixed number in simplest form or a whole number. Write each mixed number as an improper fraction.

6. $\frac{24}{15}$ = ________ **7.** $\frac{36}{12}$ = ________ **8.** $2\frac{4}{5}$ = ________

(Lesson 11) Write >, <, or = to complete.

9. $3\frac{2}{3}$ ◯ $1\frac{4}{5}$ **10.** $6\frac{4}{8}$ ◯ $6\frac{3}{6}$ **11.** $2\frac{6}{9}$ ◯ $2\frac{1}{5}$

(Lessons 12 and 14) Use the circle graph to answer **12** and **13**.

12. What fractional part of those surveyed favored red? __________

13. What percent favored green or blue? __________

Favorite Colors

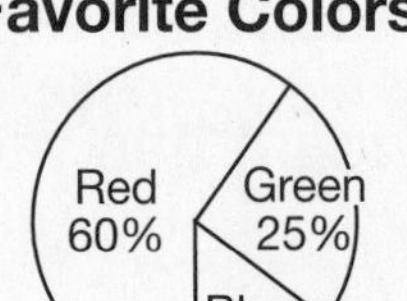

(Mixed Review) Add or subtract.

14. $69{,}294 + 13{,}920$

15. $18{,}517 - 9{,}368$

16. $806 + 736$

17. $99 - 45$

Name ______________________

Practice
Chapters 1–7

Cumulative Review

(Chapter 1 Lesson 6) Tell which operation you would use. Then solve.

1. There are 28 people on a hike. Each person carried a backpack weighing 5 pounds. How many pounds were carried in all?

____

(Chapter 3 Lesson 10) Multiply.

2. $\begin{array}{r} \$3.69 \\ \times \quad 3 \\ \hline \end{array}$ **3.** $\begin{array}{r} 37.1 \\ \times \quad 8 \\ \hline \end{array}$ **4.** $\begin{array}{r} \$9.01 \\ \times \quad 6 \\ \hline \end{array}$ **5.** $\begin{array}{r} 0.159 \\ \times \quad 7 \\ \hline \end{array}$

(Chapter 6 Lesson 3) Name each triangle by its sides and angles.

6. 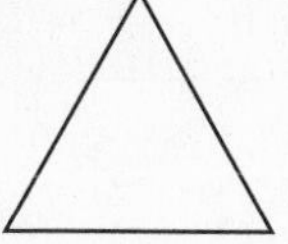

____

____

7. 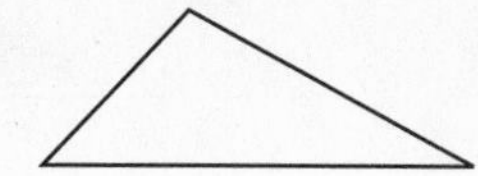

____

____

8. 

____

____

(Chapter 6 Lesson 8) Draw all lines of symmetry.

9. 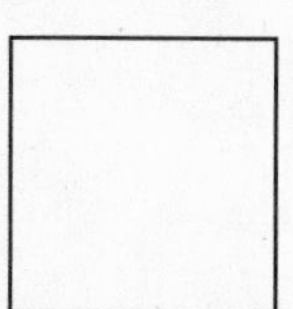

10. 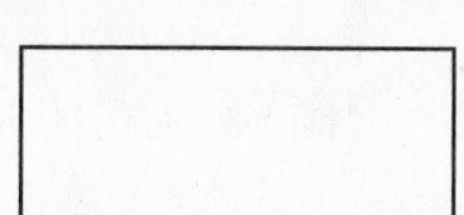

11. 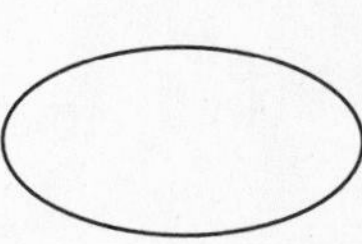

(Chapter 7 Lesson 5) Write the simplest form for each fraction.

12. $\frac{8}{16} =$ ________ **13.** $\frac{12}{32} =$ ________ **14.** $\frac{6}{14} =$ ________

15. $\frac{15}{35} =$ ________ **16.** $\frac{20}{30} =$ ________ **17.** $\frac{33}{99} =$ ________

(Chapter 7 Lesson 11) Write in order from least to greatest.

18. $2\frac{1}{4}$, $1\frac{5}{6}$, $1\frac{1}{4}$

________, ________, ________

19. $2\frac{2}{3}$, $5\frac{1}{5}$, $2\frac{1}{5}$

________, ________, ________

Name ______________________

Practice 8-1

Adding and Subtracting Fractions with Like Denominators

Find each sum or difference. Simplify.

1. $\frac{4}{6} + \frac{1}{6}$ ______

2. $\frac{7}{8} - \frac{4}{8}$ ______

3. $\frac{8}{10} - \frac{5}{10}$ ______

4. $\frac{2}{3} + \frac{2}{3}$ ______

5. $\frac{2}{6} - \frac{1}{6}$

6. $\frac{7}{8} + \frac{1}{8}$

7. $\frac{6}{9} - \frac{3}{9}$

8. $\frac{2}{7} + \frac{6}{7}$

9. $\frac{8}{9} - \frac{5}{9}$

10. $\frac{7}{8} + \frac{3}{8}$

11. $\frac{8}{10} - \frac{3}{10}$

12. $\frac{2}{12} + \frac{10}{12}$

13. $\frac{7}{8} + \frac{7}{8}$ ______

14. $\frac{6}{10} - \frac{2}{10}$ ______

15. $\frac{3}{9} + \frac{3}{9} + \frac{3}{9}$ ______

16. $\frac{2}{10} + \frac{5}{10} + \frac{6}{10}$ ______

17. $\frac{7}{12} + \frac{3}{12} + \frac{4}{12}$ ______

18. $\frac{2}{8} + \frac{4}{8} + \frac{6}{8}$ ______

19. $\frac{2}{6} + \frac{3}{6} + \frac{4}{6}$ ______

20. $\frac{1}{2} + \frac{1}{2} + \frac{1}{2}$ ______

21. $\frac{4}{5} + \frac{1}{5} + \frac{2}{5}$ ______

22. Find the sum of $\frac{8}{9}$ and $\frac{4}{9}$. ______

23. Why does $\frac{3}{9} + \frac{6}{9} = \frac{6}{9} + \frac{3}{9}$? Explain.

____

____

Name ______________________

Practice 8-2

Exploring Adding Fractions

1. $\frac{1}{2} + \frac{1}{4}$

$\frac{1}{2}$ $\frac{1}{4}$

↓

$\frac{2}{4}$ $\frac{1}{4}$

$\frac{3}{4}$

_____ $+ \frac{1}{4} =$ _____

Find each sum.

2. $\frac{2}{3} + \frac{1}{6}$

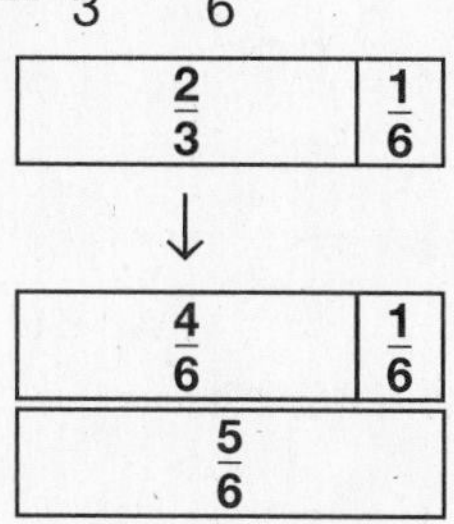

_____

3. $\frac{1}{2} + \frac{3}{8}$

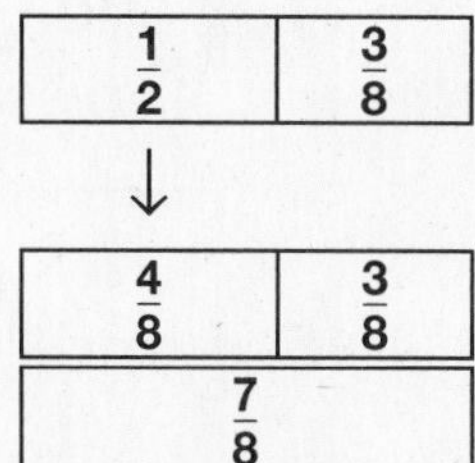

_____

4. $\frac{4}{9} + \frac{1}{3}$

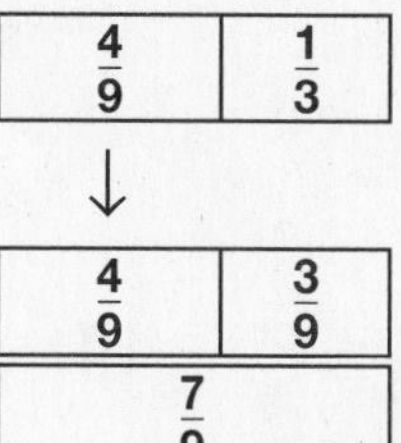

_____

Find each sum. You may use fraction strips or draw pictures to help.

5. $\frac{4}{5} + \frac{1}{10}$ _____

6. $\frac{2}{3} + \frac{2}{9}$ _____

7. $\frac{2}{5} + \frac{1}{2}$ _____

8. $\frac{1}{3} + \frac{1}{6}$ _____

9. $\frac{2}{9} + \frac{1}{3}$

10. $\frac{2}{3} + \frac{5}{6}$

11. $\frac{2}{5} + \frac{2}{3}$

12. $\frac{2}{9} + \frac{1}{3}$

13. $\frac{1}{8} + \frac{1}{2} + \frac{3}{4}$ _____

14. $\frac{2}{3} + \frac{1}{3} + \frac{5}{6}$ _____

15. $\frac{1}{2} + \frac{2}{8} + \frac{1}{4}$ _____

16. Find the sum of $\frac{2}{5}$ and $\frac{7}{10}$. _____

17. Find the sum of $\frac{1}{3}$ and $\frac{5}{9}$. _____

Name ______________________

Practice
8-3

Least Common Denominator

Find the LCD for each pair of fractions.

1. $\frac{3}{5}$ and $\frac{1}{2}$ ______ **2.** $\frac{2}{3}$ and $\frac{3}{5}$ ______ **3.** $\frac{3}{4}$ and $\frac{3}{8}$ ______ **4.** $\frac{5}{12}$ and $\frac{1}{4}$ ______

5. $\frac{1}{3}$ and $\frac{2}{5}$ ______ **6.** $\frac{1}{4}$ and $\frac{3}{10}$ ______ **7.** $\frac{4}{9}$ and $\frac{5}{12}$ ______ **8.** $\frac{3}{8}$ and $\frac{5}{12}$ ______

9. $\frac{9}{12}$ and $\frac{3}{9}$ ______ **10.** $\frac{3}{5}$ and $\frac{2}{7}$ ______ **11.** $\frac{2}{3}$ and $\frac{1}{4}$ ______ **12.** $\frac{2}{9}$ and $\frac{1}{8}$ ______

13. $\frac{1}{6}$ and $\frac{4}{9}$ ______ **14.** $\frac{1}{4}$ and $\frac{3}{9}$ ______ **15.** $\frac{2}{6}$ and $\frac{1}{8}$ ______ **16.** $\frac{2}{7}$ and $\frac{3}{4}$ ______

17. Why is the LCD of $\frac{3}{4}$ and $\frac{4}{8}$ not the product of 4 and 8?

____

18. Why is the LCD of $\frac{5}{9}$ and $\frac{7}{12}$ not the product of 9 and 12?

____

19. If you know that the least common multiple (LCM) of 3 and 7 is 21, what do you also know about the least common denominator (LCD) of $\frac{2}{3}$ and $\frac{4}{7}$?

____

20. If you know that the least common multiple (LCM) of 4 and 6 is 12, what do you also know about the least common denominator (LCD) of $\frac{3}{4}$ and $\frac{5}{6}$?

____

Name ______________________

Practice
8-4

Adding Fractions

Find each sum. Simplify.

1. $\frac{1}{4} + \frac{4}{5}$ ______ **2.** $\frac{2}{5} + \frac{2}{3}$ ______ **3.** $\frac{3}{8} + \frac{2}{3}$ ______ **4.** $\frac{2}{3} + \frac{4}{5}$ ______

5. $\frac{7}{8} + \frac{2}{3}$ **6.** $\frac{7}{12} + \frac{7}{8}$ **7.** $\frac{3}{4} + \frac{5}{12}$ **8.** $\frac{2}{5} + \frac{7}{8}$

9. $\frac{5}{9} + \frac{5}{6}$ **10.** $\frac{7}{9} + \frac{1}{2}$ **11.** $\frac{5}{6} + \frac{3}{4}$ **12.** $\frac{4}{5} + \frac{3}{4}$

13. $\frac{1}{5} + \frac{2}{3} + \frac{5}{6}$ ______ **14.** $\frac{1}{3} + \frac{1}{6} + \frac{8}{9}$ ______ **15.** $\frac{5}{8} + \frac{3}{4} + \frac{3}{10}$ ______

16. Find the sum of $\frac{1}{3}$ and $\frac{7}{8}$. ______

17. Add $\frac{3}{5}$ and $\frac{7}{10}$. ______

18. Find $\frac{1}{3} + \frac{1}{6} + \frac{1}{9} + \frac{1}{12}$ using mental math ______

19. Do you get the same sum when you use 18 rather than 9 as a common denominator for $\frac{2}{3}$ and $\frac{4}{9}$? Explain.

____

20. What extra step will you have to perform if you do not use the **least common denominator** when adding fractions? Explain your response.

____

____

Name ______________________________

Practice 8-5

Exploring Subtracting Fractions

1. $\frac{3}{4} - \frac{1}{8} = n$

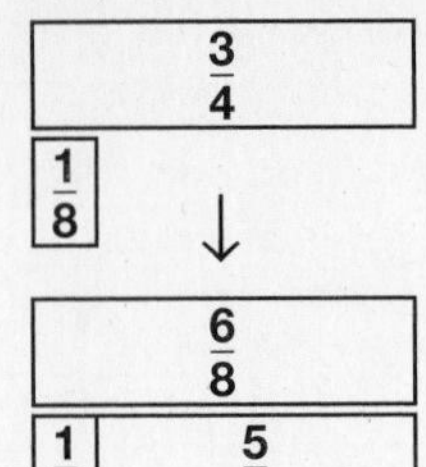

_____ $- \frac{1}{8} =$ _____

Find each difference. Simplify.

2. $\frac{9}{10} - \frac{3}{5}$

9/10
3/5

____

3. $\frac{3}{8} - \frac{1}{4}$

3/8
1/4

____

4. $\frac{5}{6} - \frac{3}{4}$

5/6
3/4

____

5. $\frac{7}{8} - \frac{1}{6}$

7/8
1/6

____

Find each difference. You may use fraction strips or draw pictures to help.

6. $\frac{4}{5} - \frac{1}{10}$ __________

7. $\frac{2}{3} - \frac{2}{9}$ __________

8. $\frac{4}{5} - \frac{8}{15}$ __________

9. $\frac{1}{3} - \frac{1}{6}$ __________

10. $\frac{3}{4} - \frac{1}{6}$ __________

11. $\frac{5}{9} - \frac{1}{3}$ __________

12. $\frac{9}{10} - \frac{3}{5}$ __________

13. $\frac{5}{6} - \frac{1}{4}$ __________

14. $\frac{7}{9} - \frac{2}{3}$

15. $\frac{5}{6} - \frac{1}{2}$

16. $\frac{5}{7} - \frac{3}{14}$

17. $\frac{1}{2} - \frac{1}{8}$

18. Find the difference of $\frac{5}{6}$ and $\frac{1}{2}$.
Write the answer in simplest form. __________

Name ______________________________

Practice
8-6

Subtracting Fractions

Find each difference. Simplify.

1. $\frac{3}{4} - \frac{1}{3} =$ ______
2. $\frac{2}{3} - \frac{1}{2} =$ ______
3. $\frac{4}{5} - \frac{3}{10} =$ ______
4. $\frac{3}{5} - \frac{1}{10} =$ ______
5. $\frac{7}{8} - \frac{1}{2} =$ ______
6. $\frac{5}{6} - \frac{2}{3} =$ ______
7. $\frac{2}{5} - \frac{1}{5} =$ ______
8. $\frac{5}{6} - \frac{3}{4} =$ ______
9. $\frac{7}{8} - \frac{2}{3} =$ ______
10. $\frac{3}{5} - \frac{1}{2}$
11. $\frac{7}{12} - \frac{1}{6}$
12. $\frac{3}{10} - \frac{1}{5}$
13. $\frac{3}{4} - \frac{2}{3}$
14. $\frac{7}{8} - \frac{1}{4}$
15. $\frac{7}{10} - \frac{2}{5}$
16. $\frac{5}{6} - \frac{3}{5}$
17. $\frac{5}{7} - \frac{1}{3}$
18. Find the difference between $\frac{5}{8}$ and $\frac{1}{6}$. ______
19. If $\frac{1}{3}$ is subtracted from $\frac{5}{6}$, will the difference be greater or less than $\frac{1}{3}$? Explain.

    ____

    ____
20. If $\frac{2}{3}$ is subtracted from $\frac{5}{6}$, will the difference be greater or less than $\frac{1}{3}$? Explain.

    ____

    ____

Name ______________________________

Practice 8-7

Analyze Word Problems: Too Much or Too Little Information

Write if each problem has too much or too little information. Solve, or if possible, tell what is needed to solve.

1. During one week, $\frac{1}{3}$ of the hotel rooms were available. The clerk took 20 additional reservations. How many rooms are still available?

____

____

2. The school is $\frac{2}{3}$ mi from the library. Jessie lives $\frac{3}{5}$ mi from school. John lives $\frac{1}{10}$ mi closer than Jessie. How far from school is John?

____

3. Cary cut a hero sandwich into 10 pieces. Only 8 pieces were eaten. His 3 sisters had ravioli. What fraction of the hero sandwich was left?

____

4. Mom built a shelf. She used $\frac{1}{2}$ a board for the shelf and $\frac{2}{5}$ of the board for the braces. How many inches of the board were left?

____

____

5. John rode with his mom in the car $\frac{1}{3}$ mi. He walked the rest of the way to Jim's house. How far did he have to walk?

____

____

6. For a recipe Lee needs $\frac{1}{3}$ cup of sugar, $\frac{3}{4}$ cup of flour, and twice as much milk as sugar. How many cups of milk does she need?

____

Name ________________________________

Practice
Chapter 8
Section A

Review and Practice

Vocabulary Write true or false.

1. The least common denominator (LCD) is the least common multiple of the two demoninators. ________

(Lesson 1) Find each sum or difference. Simplify.

2. $\frac{1}{6} + \frac{1}{6}$

3. $\frac{5}{9} - \frac{2}{9}$

4. $\frac{10}{11} - \frac{8}{11}$

5. $\frac{1}{6} + \frac{5}{6}$

6. What number must be added to $\frac{3}{7}$ to get a sum of 1? _____

(Lessons 2–4) Find each sum. Simplify.

7. $\frac{2}{3} + \frac{1}{9} =$ __________

8. $\frac{1}{4} + \frac{1}{8} =$ __________

9. $\frac{2}{5} + \frac{8}{10} =$ __________

10. $\frac{1}{20} + \frac{1}{5} =$ __________

11. On three days Wendy rode her bike $\frac{2}{5}$ mi, $\frac{1}{2}$ mi and $\frac{4}{5}$ mi. How far did she ride? ____________________

(Lessons 5–6) Find each difference. Simplify.

12. $\frac{8}{9} - \frac{1}{4}$

13. $\frac{5}{7} - \frac{1}{3}$

14. $\frac{6}{10} - \frac{1}{3}$

15. $\frac{5}{8} - \frac{2}{5}$

(Lesson 7) Write if the problem has too much or too little information. Solve if possible. Tell what is needed if you can't solve.

16. Sue needed boat line that costs \$5 for 6 ft. How much did she spend?

____

(Mixed Review) Order each list from least to greatest.

17. $\frac{3}{4}, \frac{1}{2}, \frac{4}{6}$ ________

18. $\frac{3}{5}, \frac{2}{7}, \frac{4}{8}$ ________

19. $\frac{5}{7}, \frac{5}{8}, \frac{1}{2}$ ________

Name ________________________

Practice 8-8

Exploring Adding and Subtracting Mixed Numbers

Find each sum or difference. Use fraction strips or drawings to help. Simplify.

1. 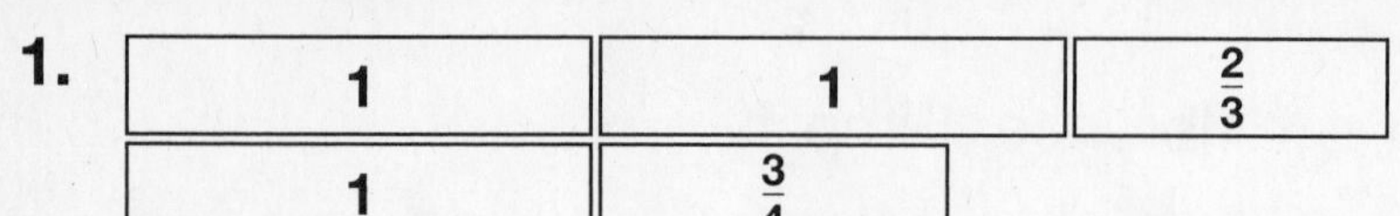

$2\frac{2}{3} + 1\frac{3}{4} =$ ________

2.

$1\frac{1}{2} - \frac{2}{3} =$ ________

3. $2\frac{2}{3} - 1\frac{1}{2}$

4. $3\frac{1}{6} + 2\frac{2}{3}$

5. $1\frac{3}{4} + \frac{1}{12}$

6. $2\frac{3}{10} + \frac{2}{5}$

7. $4 - 2\frac{1}{3}$

8. $3\frac{1}{4} - \frac{2}{16}$

9. $3\frac{1}{6} + 1\frac{2}{3} =$ ________

10. $3\frac{3}{5} - 2\frac{3}{10} =$ ________

11. Find the sum of $2\frac{1}{8}$ and $3\frac{3}{4}$. ________

12. Find the difference of $5\frac{4}{9}$ and $2\frac{1}{3}$. ________

13. How much longer is the pen than the piece of chalk? ________

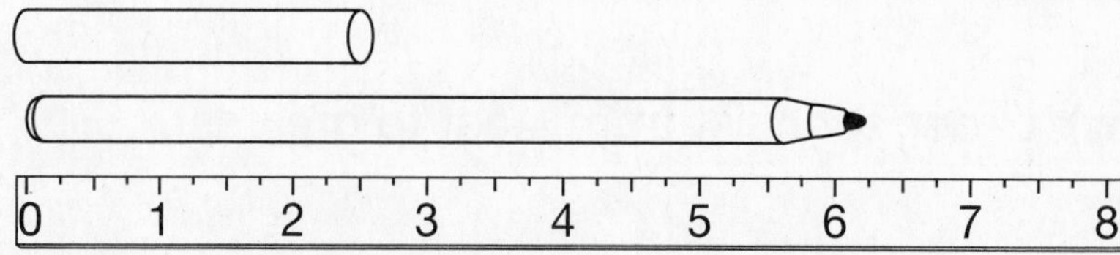

Name ______________________

Practice 8-9

Estimating Sums and Differences

Estimate each sum or difference.

1. $1\frac{1}{3} + 1\frac{1}{6}$ ______

2. $5\frac{1}{8} + 2\frac{1}{2}$ ______

3. $8\frac{1}{2} - 1\frac{1}{4}$ ______

4. $7\frac{4}{5} - 5\frac{1}{4}$ ______

5. $2\frac{3}{4} + 3\frac{2}{3}$ ______

6. $7\frac{3}{4} - 3\frac{1}{2}$ ______

7. $2\frac{1}{2} - 1\frac{1}{8}$ ______

8. $1\frac{1}{3} + 6\frac{1}{12}$ ______

9. $2\frac{3}{5} + 1\frac{2}{3}$ ______

10. $2\frac{3}{4} + 3\frac{5}{8}$

11. $4\frac{1}{4} - 1\frac{5}{6}$

12. $9\frac{1}{10} - 8\frac{4}{5}$

13. $5\frac{7}{8} + 1\frac{1}{3}$

14. $6\frac{2}{3} - 1\frac{5}{6}$

15. $9\frac{1}{4} - 5$

16. $8\frac{7}{8} + 3\frac{1}{4} + 2\frac{1}{2}$ ______

17. $4\frac{1}{5} + 3\frac{2}{3} + 8\frac{5}{8}$ ______

18. Estimate the difference between $5\frac{1}{8}$ and $2\frac{2}{3}$. ______

Name ______________________

Practice
8-10

Adding and Subtracting Mixed Numbers

Find each sum or difference. Simplify.

1. $4\frac{1}{8} + 3\frac{1}{4}$

2. $4\frac{2}{3} - 2\frac{1}{4}$

3. $5\frac{1}{2} - 1\frac{1}{5}$

4. $5\frac{1}{3} + 4\frac{1}{8}$

5. $10\frac{3}{10} + 9\frac{4}{5}$

6. $14\frac{1}{8} + \frac{1}{4}$

7. $6\frac{2}{10} - 3\frac{1}{5}$

8. $7\frac{1}{3} - 5$

9. $3\frac{2}{3} + 4\frac{1}{4}$

10. $6\frac{3}{8} - 2\frac{1}{8}$

11. $6\frac{5}{6} - 5\frac{1}{3}$

12. $6\frac{5}{6} + 2\frac{1}{3}$

13. $7\frac{2}{3} - 2\frac{1}{6} =$ ______

14. $20\frac{1}{5} + 4\frac{7}{10} =$ ______

15. $8\frac{1}{3} + 8\frac{3}{4} =$ ______

16. $4\frac{5}{8} - 1\frac{1}{2} =$ ______

17. $23\frac{3}{10} + \frac{2}{5} =$ ______

18. $9\frac{3}{8} - 8 =$ ______

19. Find the sum of $6\frac{2}{3}$ and $7\frac{3}{5}$. ______

20. Find the difference of $8\frac{7}{8}$ and $2\frac{3}{4}$. ______

21. How do you simplify $8\frac{9}{6}$?

____

Name ______________________

Practice 8-11

Adding Mixed Numbers

Find each sum. Simplify, if possible.

1. $\begin{array}{r} 2\frac{1}{8} \\ 1\frac{1}{2} \\ +\ 3\frac{3}{4} \\ \hline \end{array}$

2. $\begin{array}{r} 5\frac{1}{3} \\ 2\frac{1}{2} \\ +\ 1\frac{2}{3} \\ \hline \end{array}$

3. $\begin{array}{r} 3\frac{1}{4} \\ 4\frac{1}{2} \\ +\ 1\frac{3}{4} \\ \hline \end{array}$

4. $\begin{array}{r} 6\frac{1}{4} \\ 1\frac{1}{2} \\ +\ \frac{3}{8} \\ \hline \end{array}$

5. $\begin{array}{r} 9\frac{2}{3} \\ \frac{1}{4} \\ +\ 4\frac{5}{6} \\ \hline \end{array}$

6. $\begin{array}{r} 2\frac{1}{5} \\ 4\frac{3}{10} \\ +\ 3\frac{3}{5} \\ \hline \end{array}$

7. $\begin{array}{r} 3\frac{3}{8} \\ 2\frac{1}{2} \\ +\ 3\frac{1}{8} \\ \hline \end{array}$

8. $\begin{array}{r} 13\frac{5}{12} \\ 8\frac{1}{2} \\ +\ 11 \\ \hline \end{array}$

9. $7 + 4\frac{1}{4} + 6\frac{7}{10} =$ ________

10. $\frac{2}{5} + 4\frac{3}{10} + 1\frac{1}{5} =$ ________

11. $8\frac{1}{8} + 4\frac{7}{10} + \frac{3}{5} =$ ________

12. $3\frac{1}{7} + 21\frac{3}{4} + 3\frac{5}{7} =$ ________

13. $2\frac{1}{2} + 3\frac{1}{4} + 5\frac{1}{8} =$ ________

14. Add $\frac{1}{3}$, $3\frac{3}{5}$, and $7\frac{1}{3}$. ________

15. When adding several fractions you can combine those with common denominators first to make addition easier. How can you combine fractions first to add $2\frac{1}{5}$, $4\frac{1}{4}$, and $3\frac{3}{5}$?

____

____

____

16. Estimation What is $3\frac{5}{7} + 4\frac{1}{8} + 2\frac{3}{4}$ to the nearest whole number?

____

17. What is the sum of the answers for **1–4**? ________

Name ____________________

Practice 8-12

Subtracting Mixed Numbers

Find each difference. Simplify.

1. $6\frac{1}{3} - 2\frac{3}{4}$

2. $7\frac{3}{4} - 1\frac{3}{8}$

3. $9\frac{1}{2} - \frac{1}{3}$

4. $6\frac{3}{4} - 4\frac{1}{2}$

5. $7 - \frac{3}{5}$

6. $22\frac{1}{3} - 13\frac{3}{8}$

7. $7 - 2\frac{1}{3}$

8. $6\frac{7}{10} - \frac{5}{8}$

9. $3\frac{3}{4} - 2\frac{1}{2}$

10. $5 - 3\frac{3}{4}$

11. $17\frac{4}{9} - 11\frac{5}{6}$

12. $7\frac{1}{8} - 4\frac{4}{5}$

13. $15 - 7\frac{2}{5} =$ __________

14. $11\frac{1}{4} - \frac{5}{8} =$ __________

15. $8\frac{7}{12} - 3\frac{3}{4} =$ __________

16. $5\frac{2}{3} - 2\frac{1}{2} =$ __________

17. $8 - 2\frac{1}{3} =$ __________

18. $17\frac{1}{8} - 4\frac{1}{2} =$ __________

19. Find the difference of $13\frac{2}{5}$ and $3\frac{3}{4}$. __________

20. **Estimation** What is $4\frac{1}{8} - 2\frac{2}{3}$ to the nearest whole number? __________

21. Bridget added $\frac{1}{5}$ to both 12 and $6\frac{4}{5}$ when subtracting $12 - 6\frac{4}{5}$. Tell why.

____

____

____

____

Name ______________________________

Practice 8-13

Compare Strategies: Work Backward/Draw a Picture

Work backward or use any strategy to solve the problem.

1. Stacey, Kiesha, and Maria planned their trip to band camp. Maria had to travel 5 more miles than Kiesha. Stacey had to travel $\frac{1}{2}$ the distance Kiesha traveled. Stacey traveled 50 miles. How far did Maria travel?

   ____

2. Sven and Ryan hiked a desert trail for their scout badge. They followed the trail $1\frac{1}{4}$ miles west, then turned north for $\frac{5}{8}$ mile. Finally they headed east for $1\frac{5}{8}$ mile to join the troop for camp. The next morning they hiked back over the same trail. How many miles in all did they hike? ____________

3. Students voted to raise money for new soccer goals for their school. The goals cost $450. Students raised $\frac{1}{3}$ of the money. The school's PTA contributed $50 more than the students. Parents organized an additional fundraiser for the extra funds needed. How much did each group contribute?

   ____

4. Carly, Courtney, and Ashley went to the skating party for their school. Courtney skated three times as many laps as Ashley. Carly skated $\frac{2}{3}$ of the distance Courtney skated. Ashley skated 50 laps. How many laps did Courtney and Carly skate?

   ____

5. Max invited his friends over for pizza. Matt ate 12 slices. Cole ate half as much as Matt but twice as much as Sergio. Max ate 2 more slices than Sergio. How much pizza did Cole, Sergio, and Max each eat?

   ____

Name ______________________________

Practice
Chapter 8
Section B

Review and Practice

(Lessons 8–12) Find each sum or difference. Simplify.

1. $5\frac{1}{3} + 3\frac{1}{6}$

2. $4\frac{7}{9} - 1\frac{2}{9}$

3. $6\frac{5}{8} - 2\frac{2}{4}$

4. $8\frac{2}{3} + 1\frac{1}{9}$

5. $9 - \frac{1}{8}$

6. $7\frac{2}{5} + 1\frac{3}{10}$

7. $6\frac{2}{9} - 4\frac{2}{3}$

8. $8\frac{5}{7} - 2\frac{5}{6}$

9. $2\frac{1}{10} - 1\frac{7}{8}$

10. $13\frac{6}{9} + 12\frac{1}{5}$

11. $16\frac{4}{5} - 12\frac{3}{4}$

12. $9\frac{1}{4} + 1\frac{3}{8}$

13. Ms. Whitney bought $2\frac{1}{4}$ yd of red checked material, $1\frac{3}{4}$ yd of blue material, and 3 yd of red material. How many yards of material did she buy in all? __________

(Lesson 13) Solve. Use any strategy.

14. Leroy gave half of his crayons to a friend. He then lost 2. He had 10 left. How many crayons did he have to begin with? ____________________

15. Trish has a total of 36 colored pencils and chalks. She has 8 more pencils than chalks. How many chalks does she have? ____________________

(Mixed Review) Tell whether the each is prime or composite.

16. 6 ____________ **17.** 5 ____________ **18.** 27 ____________

19. 21 ____________ **20.** 38 ____________ **21.** 31 ____________

Name ______________________

Practice
8-14

Linear Measure

Find the length to the nearest $\frac{1}{4}$-inch.

1. __________

2. __________

Find the length to the nearest $\frac{1}{8}$-inch.

3. __________

4. __________

5. Mario broke a pane of glass in a window. The opening measured $7\frac{1}{4}$ in. by $9\frac{1}{2}$ in. At the hardware store, they sold him a pane of glass that was $7\frac{1}{4}$ in. by $9\frac{1}{2}$ in. to the nearest $\frac{1}{4}$ in. Can Mario be sure the glass will fit the window? Explain.

____

Use your ruler to draw a line segment for each length.

6. $1\frac{3}{4}$ in.

7. $2\frac{1}{8}$ in.

8. $3\frac{1}{4}$ in.

9. $1\frac{1}{8}$ in.

Name ___________________________

Practice 8-15

Feet, Yards, and Miles

Complete.

1. 12 yd = _______ ft
2. 3 mi = _________ ft
3. 192 in. = _______ ft
4. 2 mi = _________ yd
5. 180 in. = _______ ft
6. 87 in. = _______ ft _______ in.
7. 15 ft 3 in. = _______ in.
8. 21,120 ft = _______ mi
9. 7 ft 4 in. = _______ in.
10. 5 yd 2 ft = _______ ft
11. 63 in. = ______ ft ______ in.
12. 15,840 yd = _______ mi
13. 38 yd = _______ ft
14. 7 mi = _________ ft
15. 420 in. = _______ ft
16. 3 yd 1 ft = _______ ft
17. Kevin and Reggie are on the track team. Kevin's best high jump is 4 ft 9 in. Reggie's best jump is 56 in. Who has the better record? _______________
18. Complete.

a. Number of feet	21				36	45
b. Number of yards		8	6	4		

c. To change feet to yards, you must divide the number of feet by _______.

d. To change yards to feet, you must ___________ the number of yards by 3.

19. Complete.

a. Number of inches	12	24	36			
b. Number of feet				5	10	25

c. To change inches to feet you must divide the number of inches by _______.

d. To change feet to inches you must ___________ the number of feet by 12.

Name ______________________________

Practice
8-16

Analyze Word Problems: Exact or Estimate?

Decide whether you need an exact answer or an estimate. Solve.

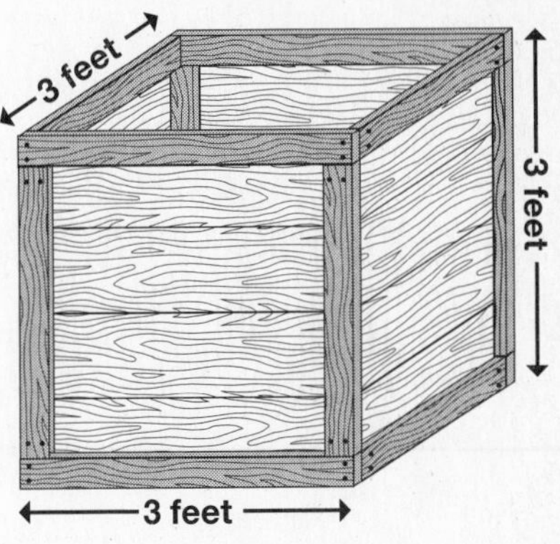

1. Kathy wants to build a storage box 3 ft wide, 3 ft high, and 3 ft deep. Would three 2 × 4's that are each 8 ft long be enough to build the box? Explain your answer.

____

____

2. If Kathy wanted to make the cage 2 ft on each side, would she have enough wood?

____

3. Carly usually does gymnastics for three hours on Monday through Friday, and for two hours on Saturday. About how many hours does she do gymnastics in a month?

____

4. Donald needs to be at school band practice by 7:30 A.M. He wants to get to school at least 15 minutes early. School is about a $\frac{1}{2}$ –hr bike ride away. What time should Donald leave for school?

____

5. Sharish saved $210 for a stereo for her room. The stereo costs $186. Sharish also wanted to purchase two CD's at $11 each. While at the store, Sharish found another CD she wanted for $13. Did Sharish have enough money to pay for everything she wanted? Tell what strategy you used.

____

____

Name ______________________

Review and Practice

(Lesson 14) Find the length to the nearest $\frac{1}{8}$-inch.

1. __________ **2.** __________

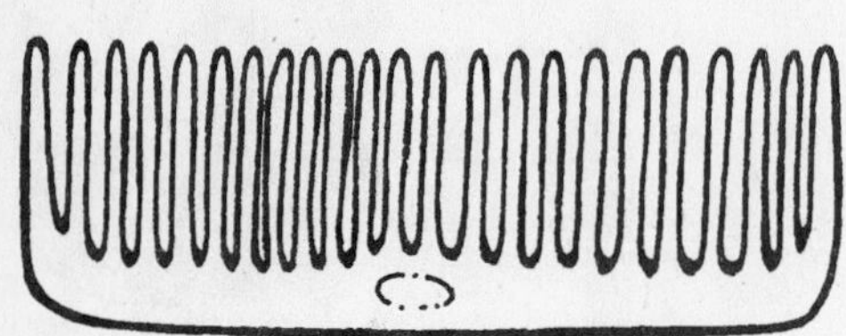

Use your ruler to draw a line segment for each length.

3. $2\frac{3}{4}$ inches

4. $3\frac{7}{8}$ inches

(Lesson 15) Complete.

5. 5 yd = _______ ft

6. 8 ft 7 in. = _______ in.

7. 137 in. = _______ ft _______ in.

8. 3 mi = _________ ft

9. 5 mi = _________ yd

10. 96 in. = _______ ft

11. 6 yd 2 ft = _______ ft

12. 15,840 ft = _______ mi

13. Which is longer, 526 ft or 150 yd? ________

(Lesson 16) Tell whether you need an exact answer or an estimate. Then solve.

14. Betty went to the library at 8:30 A.M. She wants to be at her friend's house by 10:30 A.M. It takes her about 20 minutes to walk to her friend's house. What time should she leave the library?

____

15. Philip has $12. Does he have enough money to treat himself and two friends a movie that costs $4? ______________

(Mixed Review) Divide.

16. 400 ÷ 2 ________

17. 390 ÷ 3 ________

18. 400 ÷ 20 ________

19. 100 ÷ 50 ________

Name ______________________

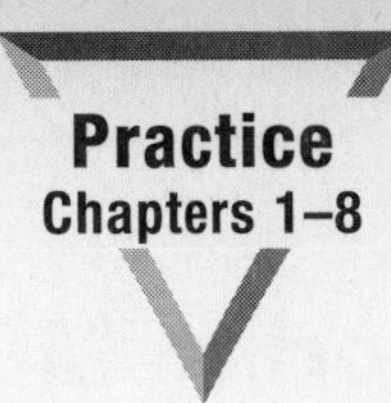

Cumulative Review

(Chapter 4 Lesson 5) Divide.

1. $6\overline{)726}$ **2.** $8\overline{)2488}$ **3.** $5\overline{)834}$

(Chapter 7 Lesson 7) Write in order from least to greatest.

4. $\frac{1}{4}, \frac{5}{6}, \frac{2}{9}$ ________, ________, ________

5. $\frac{2}{3}, \frac{1}{5}, \frac{3}{8}$ ________, ________, ________

6. $\frac{1}{2}, \frac{5}{9}, \frac{2}{5}$ ________, ________, ________

(Chapter 7 Lesson 13) Write each as a percent.

7. 12 out of 100 ________ **8.** $\frac{31}{100}$ ________

Write each as a hundredths fraction and as a decimal.

9. $\frac{15}{25} =$ ________, ________

10. $\frac{2}{50} =$ ________, ________

(Chapter 8 Lessons 4, 6, and 10) Add or subtract.

11. $\frac{1}{5} + \frac{3}{5}$ **12.** $\frac{7}{8} - \frac{3}{8}$ **13.** $\frac{4}{7} + \frac{2}{7}$ **14.** $\frac{6}{9} - \frac{2}{3}$

15. $3\frac{1}{4} + 2\frac{3}{6}$ **16.** $4\frac{7}{9} - 1\frac{2}{3}$ **17.** $5 + \frac{4}{11}$ **18.** $4 - 1\frac{2}{5}$

19. $3\frac{1}{4} - 1\frac{2}{3}$ **20.** $8\frac{1}{12} + 3\frac{4}{6}$ **21.** $4\frac{2}{3} - 1\frac{2}{8}$ **22.** $\frac{6}{7} + 3\frac{1}{6}$

Name ______________________________

Practice 9-1

Exploring Multiplication of Whole Numbers by Fractions

Use division to help you find the fraction of each number.

1. To find $\frac{3}{4}$ of 12, think:

a. $\frac{1}{4}$ of 12 is $\square$.

b. $\frac{3}{4}$ is 3 times as much as $\square$.

c. $3 \times 3 = \square$ so $\frac{3}{4}$ of 12 is $\square$.

Find each product. You may use counters to help.

2. $\frac{1}{2}$ of 20 ______ **3.** $\frac{1}{4}$ of 16 ______ **4.** $\frac{3}{4}$ of 24 ______

5. $\frac{1}{9}$ of 27 ______ **6.** $\frac{2}{9}$ of 36 ______ **7.** $\frac{1}{5}$ of 45 ______

8. $\frac{1}{3}$ of 18 ______ **9.** $\frac{4}{5}$ of 15 ______ **10.** $\frac{2}{3}$ of 15 ______

11. Find two-fifths of ten. __________

12. Find four-ninths of 27. __________

13. Find one-third of 21. __________

14. Find two-sevenths of 28. __________

15. Which of the number lines below shows $\frac{1}{5}$ of 50? ______

a.

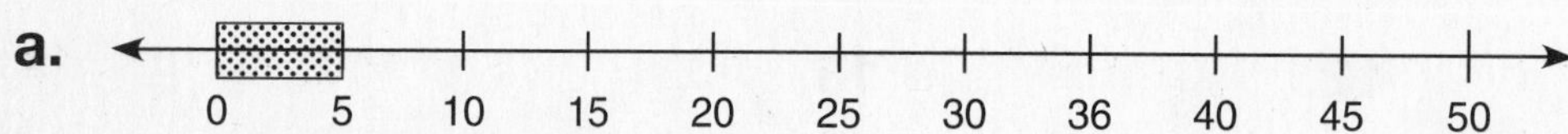

b.

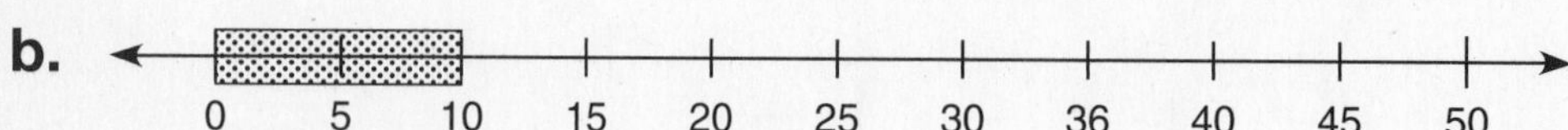

c.

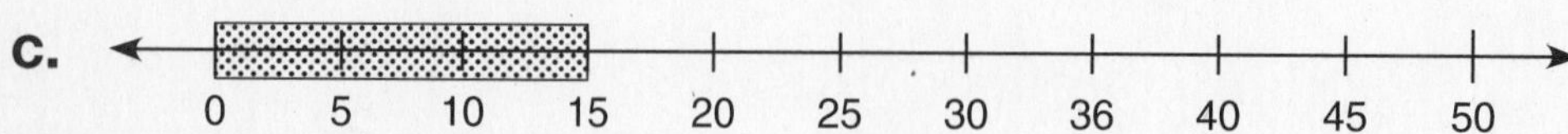

Name ______________________________

Practice 9-2

Multiplying with Fractions

Find each product. Use mental math.

1. $\frac{1}{4}$ of 28 ______ **2.** $\frac{1}{9}$ of 63 ______ **3.** $\frac{2}{5}$ of 35 ______

4. $\frac{2}{3}$ of 27 ______ **5.** $\frac{3}{8}$ of 24 ______ **6.** $\frac{4}{7}$ of 70 ______

7. $\frac{1}{3}$ of 18 ______ **8.** $\frac{1}{5}$ of 45 ______ **9.** $\frac{5}{8}$ of 32 ______

10. $\frac{1}{8}$ of 48 ______ **11.** $\frac{4}{9}$ of 54 ______ **12.** $\frac{3}{4}$ of 40 ______

13. $\frac{1}{2}$ of 18 ______ **14.** $\frac{4}{5}$ of 30 ______ **15.** $\frac{2}{7}$ of 14 ______

16. $\frac{3}{8}$ of 32 ______ **17.** $\frac{2}{7}$ of 21 ______ **18.** $\frac{4}{5}$ of 45 ______

19. Multiply one-sixth and sixty. ______

20. Multiply three-fifths and thirty. ______

21. Multiply three-fourths and forty. ______

22. Multiply two-ninths and forty-five. ______

23. Complete the table. Use patterns to help you find each product.

$\frac{1}{6}$ of 36	6	$\frac{4}{6}$ of 36	
$\frac{2}{6}$ of 36	12	$\frac{5}{6}$ of 36	
$\frac{3}{6}$ of 36		$\frac{6}{6}$ of 36	

24. How could you use the product of $\frac{1}{3}$ and 300 to find the product of $\frac{1}{6}$ and 300?

____

____

25. How could you use the product of $\frac{1}{2}$ and 200 to find the product of $\frac{1}{8}$ and 200?

____

____

Name ______________________________

Practice 9-3

Estimating Products

Use rounding, benchmarks, or compatible numbers to estimate each products.

1. $7 \times 2\frac{8}{9}$ ________ **2.** $\frac{1}{8} \times 17$ ________ **3.** $\frac{5}{8} \times 10$ ________

4. $\frac{3}{8} \times 22$ ________ **5.** $1\frac{4}{5} \times 6$ ________ **6.** $\frac{2}{9} \times 28$ ________

7. $\frac{2}{7} \times 48$ ________ **8.** $\frac{4}{9} \times 30$ ________ **9.** $\frac{4}{7} \times 15$ ________

10. $1\frac{7}{8} \times 10$ ________ **11.** $\frac{4}{5} \times 11$ ________ **12.** $3\frac{3}{4} \times 4$ ________

13. $\frac{5}{6} \times 25$ ________ **14.** $\frac{3}{8} \times 33$ ________ **15.** $2\frac{1}{9} \times 34$ ________

16. Estimate the product of $1\frac{9}{10}$ and 15. Describe your method.

____

17. Estimate the product of $\frac{2}{3}$ and 31. Describe your method.

____

18. Estimate the product of $3\frac{7}{8}$ and 25. Describe your method.

____

Use rounding, benchmarks, or compatible numbers to estimate each product. Write the letter of the estimate that is closer to the actual product.

19. $6 \times 3\frac{7}{8}$ _____ **a.** more than 24 **b.** less than 24

20. $\frac{3}{8} \times 25$ _____ **a.** more than 9 **b.** less than 9

21. $\frac{5}{9} \times 17$ _____ **a.** more than 10 **b.** less than 10

22. $2\frac{1}{7} \times 22$ _____ **a.** more than 44 **b.** less than 44

23. $3\frac{2}{3} \times 10$ _____ **a.** more than 40 **b.** less than 40

Name ___________________________

Practice 9-4

Exploring Multiplication of Fractions by Fractions

Use the drawing to help you complete each sentence.

1. $\frac{1}{3} \times \frac{1}{4}$ means $\frac{1}{3}$ of $\frac{1}{4}$

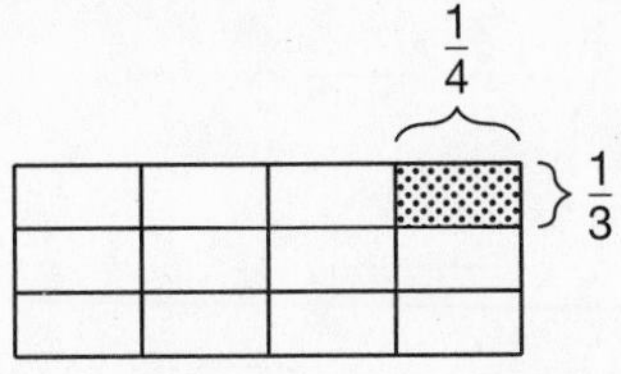

The parts of the rectangle show

that $\frac{1}{4} \times \frac{1}{3} =$ ______

2. $\frac{1}{2} \times \frac{1}{8}$ means $\frac{1}{2}$ of $\frac{1}{8}$

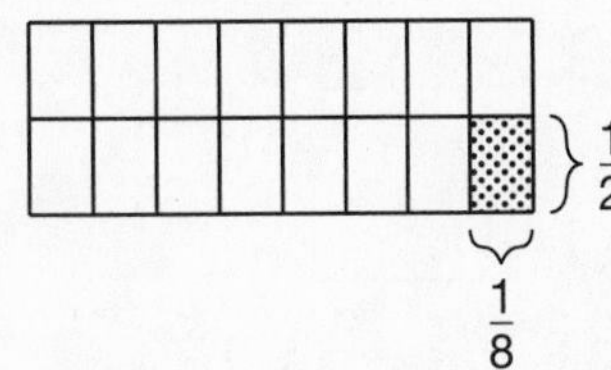

The parts of the rectangle show

that ______ $\times$ ______ $=$ ______

3. Which of the drawings below shows $\frac{1}{5} \times \frac{1}{3}$? ______

a. 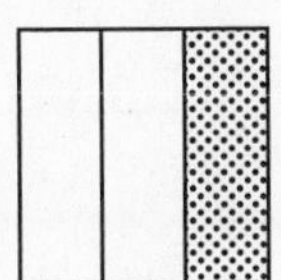

b. 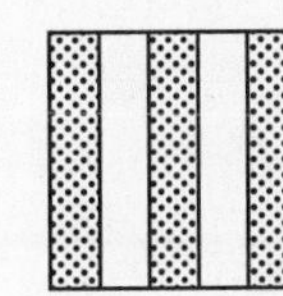

c. 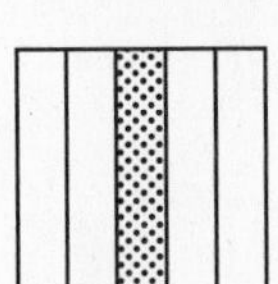

d. 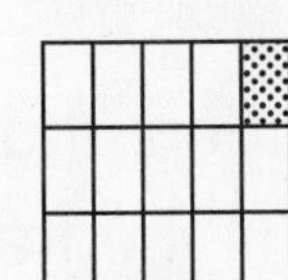

Use each drawing to help you complete each sentence.

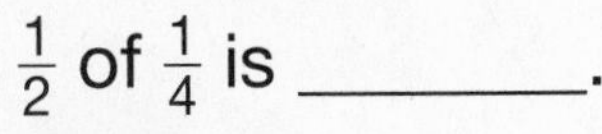

4. $\frac{1}{4}$ is shaded.

$\frac{1}{2}$ of $\frac{1}{4}$ is ________.

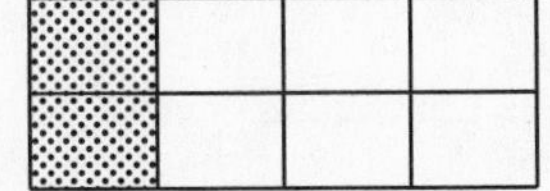

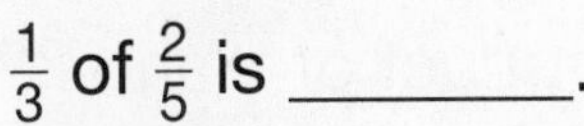

5. $\frac{2}{5}$ is shaded.

$\frac{1}{3}$ of $\frac{2}{5}$ is ________.

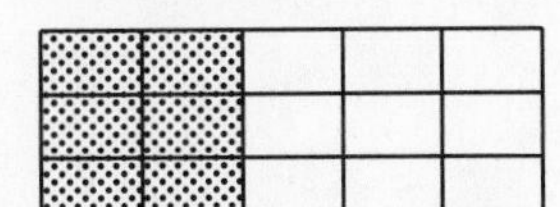

Draw pictures or use paper folding to find each product.

6. What is $\frac{1}{3} \times \frac{1}{5}$? ______

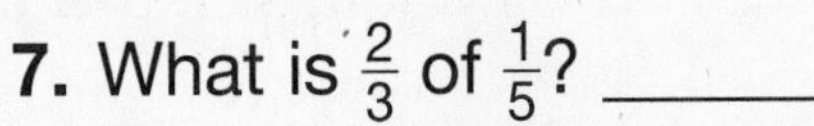

7. What is $\frac{2}{3}$ of $\frac{1}{5}$? ______

8. $\frac{1}{4} \times \frac{1}{4} =$ ______

9. $\frac{1}{6} \times \frac{1}{2} =$ ______

10. $\frac{3}{4} \times \frac{1}{3} =$ ______

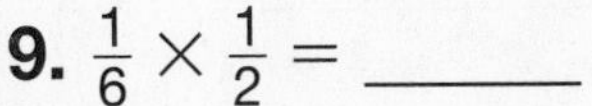

11. $\frac{1}{2} \times \frac{1}{8} =$ ______

12. $\frac{1}{3} \times \frac{1}{7} =$ ______

13. $\frac{2}{3} \times \frac{1}{7} =$ ______

Name ______________________________

Practice 9-5

Multiplying Fractions

Find each product. Simplify.

1. What is $\frac{3}{4} \times \frac{1}{3}$? ______

2. What is $\frac{7}{10} \times \frac{1}{2}$? ______

3. What is $\frac{1}{5} \times \frac{2}{3}$? ______

4. What is $\frac{2}{3} \times \frac{1}{5}$? ______

5. What is $\frac{1}{9} \times \frac{2}{3}$? ______

6. What is $\frac{2}{5} \times \frac{3}{6}$? ______

7. $\frac{1}{7} \times \frac{7}{8} =$ ______

8. $\frac{3}{8} \times \frac{1}{4} =$ ______

9. $\frac{2}{3} \times \frac{3}{5} =$ ______

10. $\frac{3}{4} \times \frac{4}{5} =$ ______

11. $\frac{1}{9} \times \frac{9}{10} =$ ______

12. $\frac{3}{7} \times \frac{1}{3} =$ ______

13. $\frac{1}{2} \times \frac{3}{5} =$ ______

14. $\frac{1}{3} \times \frac{3}{8} =$ ______

15. $\frac{5}{6} \times \frac{1}{4} =$ ______

16. $\frac{2}{5} \times \frac{1}{2} =$ ______

17. $\frac{1}{6} \times \frac{6}{7} =$ ______

18. $\frac{2}{9} \times \frac{1}{2} =$ ______

19. $\frac{4}{9} \times \frac{9}{12} =$ ______

20. $\frac{1}{7} \times \frac{5}{7} =$ ______

21. $\frac{11}{12} \times \frac{6}{11} =$ ______

22. $\frac{1}{2}$ is multiplied by a fraction and the product is $\frac{3}{8}$. What is the fraction? ______

23. $\frac{4}{5}$ is multiplied by a fraction and the product is $\frac{4}{15}$. What is the fraction? ______

24. What is the product of $\frac{2}{3}$ and $\frac{3}{3}$? ______

25. Multiply $\frac{1}{2}$ and $\frac{2}{2}$. ______

26. Multiply $\frac{3}{4}$ and $\frac{4}{4}$. ______

27. Multiply $\frac{2}{5}$ and $\frac{5}{5}$. ______

28. Multiply $\frac{8}{8}$ and $\frac{7}{8}$. ______

29. If $\frac{3}{4}$ is multiplied by itself, will the product be greater than $\frac{3}{4}$? Explain.

____

____

 Use with pages 412–413.

Name ______________________________

Practice 9-6

Analyze Word Problems: Overestimating and Underestimating

Use overestimating and underestimating to solve the problem.

1. Paula's class washed 22 cars on Saturday afternoon. Each customer paid $4.25 for a car wash. Did the class earn the $75 they need for a field trip?

   a. Can the problem be solved with an estimate or does it require an exact answer? ______________

   b. Should you overestimate or underestimate? Why?

   ____

   ____

   c. Did the class earn enough?

   ____

   ____

   d. If the field trip costs $80 instead of $75, how can the class be sure that they earned enough? How do you know?

   ____

   ____

Estimate to solve. Tell whether you overestimated or underestimated. Explain your reasoning.

2. Marlene invited 34 people to a party. She will serve salad, corn, and $\frac{1}{4}$-pound burgers. How many pounds of meat should she buy?

   ____

   ____

Name ____________________

Practice
Chapter 9
Section A

Review and Practice

Vocabulary Fill-in each blank with a word from the word bank.

factor   unit fraction   whole number   numerator   denominator

1. The ____________ is the top number of a fraction.
2. A ____________ has a 1 as the numerator.
3. One ____________ of 8 is 4. Others are 1, 2, and 8.

(Lessons 1 and 2) Find each product.

4. $\frac{1}{3}$ of 24 ______
5. $\frac{1}{9}$ of 36 ______
6. $\frac{10}{11} \times 22 =$ ______
7. $\frac{5}{6} \times 18 =$ ______
8. Find two-thirds of thirty. ______

(Lesson 3) Estimate each product. Use rounding, benchmarks, or compatible numbers.

9. $\frac{3}{4} \times 18$ ________
10. $3\frac{2}{5} \times 32$ ________
11. $2\frac{7}{20} \times 41$ ________
12. $\frac{6}{11} \times 12$ ________
13. $\frac{1}{8}$ of a small box of detergent cleans 1 load of laundry. How many loads could you wash with 5 boxes of detergent?

____

(Lessons 4 and 5) Find each product.

14. $\frac{8}{9} \times \frac{1}{4} =$ ______
15. $\frac{5}{7} \times \frac{3}{4} =$ ______
16. $\frac{6}{10} \times \frac{5}{12} =$ ______
17. $\frac{3}{8} \times \frac{8}{9} =$ ______

Complete.

18. $\frac{1}{3}$ of ______ $= \frac{1}{9}$
19. $\frac{1}{6}$ of ______ $= \frac{5}{42}$

(Mixed Review) Round each to the nearest whole number.

20. $2\frac{1}{3}$ ______
21. $6\frac{3}{8}$ ______
22. 5.75 ______
23. 6.09 ______
24. $14\frac{7}{8}$ ______
25. 2.49 ______

Name ____________________

Practice
9-7

Multiplying Whole Numbers by Fractions

Complete.

1. $\frac{5}{8} \times 3 = \frac{\square}{8} = 1\frac{7}{8}$

2. $\frac{2}{7} \times 5 = \frac{\square}{7} = 1\frac{3}{7}$

3. $\frac{3}{5} \times 9 = \frac{\square}{5} = \square$

4. $\frac{3}{4} \times 7 = \frac{\square}{4} = \square$

5. $\frac{3}{4} \times 8 = \frac{\square}{\square} = \square$

6. $5 \times \frac{8}{10} = \frac{\square}{\square} = \square$

7. $9 \times \frac{5}{9} = \frac{\square}{\square} = \square$

8. $4 \times \frac{9}{12} = \frac{\square}{\square} = \square$

Find each product.

9. $\frac{7}{6} \times 6 =$ ______

10. $\frac{2}{3} \times 9 =$ ______

11. $\frac{8}{9} \times 7 =$ ______

12. $\frac{3}{7} \times 49 =$ ______

13. $\frac{1}{3} \times 96 =$ ______

14. $\frac{9}{8} \times 11 =$ ______

15. $\frac{4}{5} \times 30 =$ ______

16. $\frac{2}{9} \times 54 =$ ______

17. $\frac{4}{3} \times 24 =$ ______

18. $\frac{8}{7} \times 63 =$ ______

19. $\frac{6}{7} \times 28 =$ ______

20. $\frac{3}{5} \times 60 =$ ______

21. Explain how you can find the product of 5 and $\frac{3}{4}$.

____

22. Complete. $4 \times \frac{3}{4} = 3$, so $\frac{3}{4} \times 4 = \square$.

23. James says that he knows all the answers to the following problems are mixed numbers, even without solving them. Explain how he knows.

$\frac{3}{5} \times 248$ $\frac{5}{9} \times 366$ $\frac{7}{8} \times 450$

____

____

Name ____________________

Practice 9-8

Multiplying Whole Numbers and Mixed Numbers

Complete.

1. $8\frac{2}{3} \times 7 = \frac{\square}{3} \times 7$

2. $4\frac{1}{8} \times 6 = \frac{\square}{8} \times 6$

3. $4 \times 5\frac{1}{3} = 4 \times \frac{\square}{3}$

4. $9 \times 6\frac{7}{8} = 9 \times \frac{\square}{8}$

5. $7\frac{7}{8} \times 3\frac{3}{4} = \frac{\square}{8} \times \frac{\square}{4}$

6. $3\frac{4}{7} \times 2\frac{7}{9} = \frac{\square}{7} \times \frac{\square}{9}$

Find each product. Simplify. Use estimation to check.

7. $7\frac{8}{9} \times 3 =$ ________

8. $8 \times 2\frac{2}{3} =$ ________

9. $2\frac{3}{4} \times 12 =$ ________

10. $2\frac{7}{9} \times 4 =$ ________

11. $2\frac{7}{8} \times 8 =$ ________

12. $4 \times 3\frac{1}{6} =$ ________

13. $10 \times 4\frac{1}{8} =$ ________

14. $3\frac{5}{6} \times 7 =$ ________

15. $\frac{2}{3} \times 1\frac{7}{10} =$ ________

16. $2\frac{1}{4} \times \frac{8}{9} =$ ________

17. $3\frac{1}{2} \times \frac{7}{8} =$ ________

18. $5\frac{2}{3} \times \frac{2}{5} =$ ________

19. $3\frac{1}{2} \times 2\frac{2}{5} =$ ________

20. $3\frac{3}{8} \times 4\frac{1}{3} =$ ________

21. $\frac{2}{9} \times 4\frac{3}{8} =$ ________

22. $4\frac{5}{7} \times 2\frac{8}{9} =$ ________

23. Find the product of $2\frac{1}{3}$ and $3\frac{1}{8}$. ________

24. Find the product of $4\frac{2}{3}$ and $7\frac{5}{6}$. ________

25. Find the product of $1\frac{3}{7}$ and 9. ________

26. Multiply $2\frac{2}{3}$ and $7\frac{3}{8}$. ________

27. Multiply $3\frac{9}{10}$ and $2\frac{2}{5}$. ________

28. Multiply $8\frac{6}{7}$ and $3\frac{2}{7}$. ________

Name ____________________

Practice 9-9

Compare Strategies: Logical Reasoning/Draw a Picture

Use logical reasoning to solve the problem.

1. Rosa, Gina, Bryan, and Patrick are each wearing their favorite color shirt: blue, pink, green, or red. No one likes a color that begins with the same letter as his or her name. Neither Gina nor Bryan likes red. Gina's pink shoes match her shirt. Which person is wearing each color?

	Rosa	**Gina**	**Bryan**	**Patrick**
Red				
Green				
Blue				
Pink				

Use logical reasoning or any strategy to solve each problem.

2. Luis said, "Guess my birthday. I was born in a summer month whose name does not begin with J. The day is a 2-digit number that is a multiple of 7. My birthday is close to the middle of the month." When is Luis's birthday?

____

3. Amy's ancestors came to America in the 1800s. Amy asked her mom what the exact year was. Her mom said, "The digit in the tens place is half the digit in the hundreds place. The digit in the ones place is 3 more than the digit in the tens place." What year did they come to America?

____

4. LaVonne goes to bed at 9:00. She has 2 hours of homework. Dinner will take 30 minutes, and washing the dishes will take 15 minutes. She wants to watch $1\frac{1}{2}$ hours of TV and work on the computer for 45 minutes.

   a. What time should she start doing all these things? ____________

   b. What strategy did you use to solve this problem?

   ____

Name ________________________________

Practice 9-10

Exploring Division of Fractions

Complete the drawings to find each quotient.

1. How many $\frac{1}{2}$'s are in 3? ________

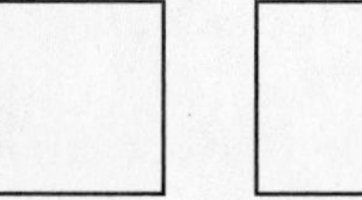

2. How many $\frac{1}{3}$'s are in 2? ________

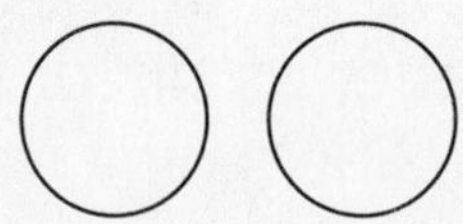

3. How many $\frac{1}{4}$'s are in 4? ________

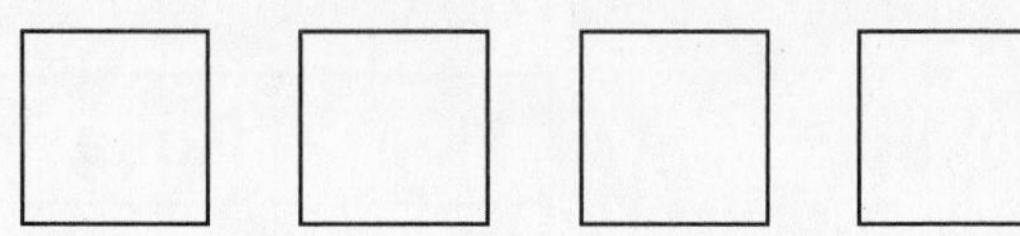

4. How many $\frac{1}{6}$'s are in 5? ________

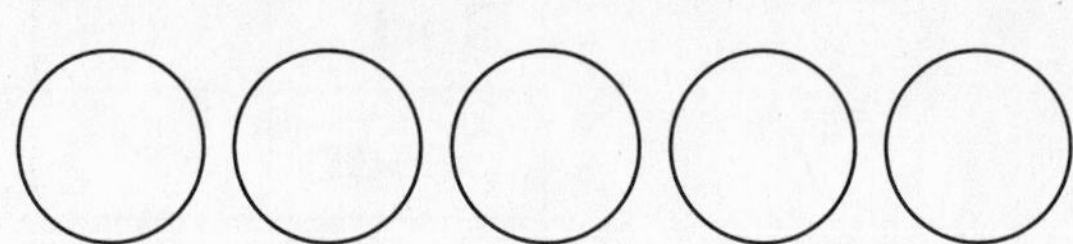

Find each quotient.

5. How many $\frac{1}{2}$'s are in 9? ________

6. How many $\frac{1}{6}$'s are in 5? ________

7. How many $\frac{1}{4}$'s are in 14? ________

8. $10 \div \frac{1}{8} =$ ________

9. $11 \div \frac{1}{4} =$ ________

10. $4 \div \frac{1}{11} =$ ________

11. $6 \div \frac{1}{3} =$ ________

12. $8 \div \frac{1}{10} =$ ________

13. $15 \div \frac{1}{4} =$ ________

14. $9 \div \frac{1}{6} =$ ________

15. $12 \div \frac{1}{5} =$ ________

16. $7 \div \frac{1}{4} =$ ________

17. $7 \div \frac{1}{7} =$ ________

18. Cheesy Pizza cuts all large pizzas into twelfths. How many pieces of pizza would Alicia get if she orders 3 large pizzas? ________________

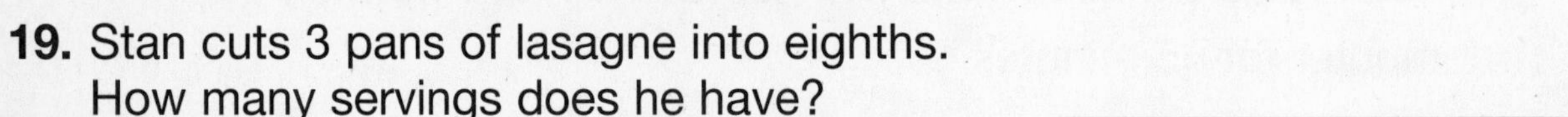

19. Stan cuts 3 pans of lasagne into eighths. How many servings does he have? ________________

20. For a fruit plate, Jay cuts 6 apples into sixths. How many pieces of apple does he have? ________________

Name ___________________________________

Practice
Chapter 9
Section B

Review and Practice

(Lessons 7 and 8) Find each product. Simplify.

1. $\frac{2}{3} \times 9 =$ ________ **2.** $\frac{7}{9} \times \frac{9}{10} =$ ________

3. $\frac{5}{8} \times \frac{4}{5} =$ ________ **4.** $\frac{2}{7} \times \frac{1}{4} =$ ________

5. $2\frac{1}{2} \times 6 =$ ________ **6.** $\frac{1}{7} \times 6\frac{2}{9} =$ ________

7. $2\frac{2}{5} \times \frac{4}{6} =$ ________ **8.** $2\frac{2}{7} \times 1\frac{3}{4} =$ ________

9. Kim can walk $\frac{2}{3}$ of a mile in 15 minutes. How far can she walk in $\frac{1}{3}$ of the time? ___________

(Lesson 9) Solve each problem.

10. Phil, Mel, Shel, and Cal are a pharmacist, machinist, secretary, and chef. No one has an occupation that begins with the same letter as his or her name. Neither Phil nor Mel is a chef. Cal is a secretary. What is the occupation of each person?

____

____

11. What fraction of an hour is 40 minutes? ________

(Lesson 10) Find each quotient.

12. $4 \div \frac{1}{3} =$ ________ **13.** $5 \div \frac{1}{4} =$ ________

14. $20 \div \frac{1}{10} =$ ________ **15.** $17 \div \frac{1}{2} =$ ________

16. $18 \div \frac{1}{5} =$ ________ **17.** $13 \div \frac{1}{7} =$ ________

18. How many $\frac{1}{4}$'s are in 9? ________

19. How many $\frac{1}{3}$'s are in 12? ________

(Mixed Review) Find each sum.

20. $\frac{6}{9} + \frac{1}{9} =$ ________ **21.** $\frac{2}{5} + \frac{3}{5} =$ ________

22. $\frac{1}{8} + \frac{5}{8} =$ ________ **23.** $\frac{2}{7} + \frac{3}{7} =$ ________

Name ____________________

Practice
Chapters 1–9

Cumulative Review

(Chapter 5 Lesson 10) Divide. Round each answer to the nearest cent if needed.

1. $16\overline{)\$7.26}$ **2.** $28\overline{)\$244.88}$ **3.** $35\overline{)\$68.34}$

(Chapter 7 Lesson 3) Write each as an equivalent fraction with a denominator of 12.

4. $\frac{2}{3}$ ________ **5.** $\frac{12}{24}$ ________

6. $\frac{5}{6}$ ________ **7.** $\frac{3}{4}$ ________

(Chapter 8 Lesson 12) Find each difference.

8. $3\frac{1}{4} - 2\frac{3}{6}$ **9.** $3\frac{5}{9} - 1\frac{2}{3}$ **10.** $5\frac{6}{7} - \frac{4}{5}$

11. $3\frac{3}{4} - 1\frac{1}{3}$ **12.** $6\frac{1}{3} - 3\frac{4}{6}$ **13.** $4\frac{2}{5} - 1\frac{2}{8}$

(Chapter 8 Lesson 15) Complete.

14. 12 yd = ________ ft **15.** 2 mi = ________ ft

16. 13 ft 7 in. = ________ in. **17.** 3 yd 2 ft = ________ ft

18. 34 in. = ________ ft ________ in.

(Chapter 9 Lessons 7 and 8) Find each product.

19. $\frac{4}{5} \times 15 =$ ________ **20.** $\frac{3}{7} \times \frac{7}{8} =$ ________

21. $\frac{7}{9} \times \frac{3}{14} =$ ________ **22.** $\frac{1}{6} \times \frac{3}{4} =$ ________

23. $3\frac{1}{2} \times 16 =$ ________ **24.** $2\frac{4}{5} \times 2\frac{1}{7} =$ ________

25. $3\frac{1}{3} \times 3\frac{3}{8} =$ ________ **26.** $4\frac{1}{6} \times \frac{2}{3} =$ ________

Name ________________________________

Practice
10-1

Exploring Estimating and Measuring Length

Draw a line to match each distance estimate to the most appropriate unit of measurement listed.

1. The distance covered by driving from St. Louis, Missouri to Louisville, Kentucky
2. The distance between 2 leaves on the same branch of a tree
3. The distance you cover when crossing a parking lot
4. The distance between two rows of desks in a classroom

a. centimeters
b. decimeters
c. meters
d. kilometers

Choose the most appropriate unit of measure to estimate the length or height of each. Write cm, dm, or m.

5.  __________

6.  __________

7.  __________

8.  __________

Choose the most appropriate unit of measure to estimate the length or height of each. Write m or km.

9. 

____

10. 

____

11. 

____

12. 

____

Name ____________________

Practice
10-2

Millimeters

Complete.

1. 90 mm = ________ cm

2. 3 dm = ________ mm

3. 1,400 mm = ________ cm

4. 6 m = ________ dm

5. 50 cm = ________ mm

6. 200 cm = ________ dm

7. 9 m = ________ dm

8. 8,000 mm = ________ m

9. 40 mm = ________ cm

10. 3,000 mm = ________ dm

11. 200 cm = ________ dm

12. 4,000 mm = ________ cm

13. 900 cm = ________ mm

14. 50 dm = ________ mm

15. 6 m = ________ cm

16. 7,000 mm = ________ m

17. 20 m = ________ cm

18. 8 cm = ________ mm

19. 17 cm = ________ mm

20. 5 m = ________ mm

21. 100 cm = ________ m

22. 6 dm = ________ cm

23. The width of a hockey puck is 44 mm. Is this length shorter or longer than 5 cm? Explain.

____

24. Old Faithful, Yellowstone National Park's most famous geyser, shoots a spray of steam and hot water 50 m into the air. Is this height greater or less than 5,000 mm? Explain.

____

Name ______________________

Practice
10-3

Centimeters, Meters, and Decimals

Complete.

1. 0.42 m = ________ cm

2. 76 cm = ________ m

3. 388 cm = ________ m

4. 56 m = ________ cm

5. 6.76 m = ________ cm

6. 552 cm = ________ m

Write each measurement, first in centimeters only and then in meters only.

7. 6 m 80 cm ______________________

8. 5 m 29 cm ______________________

9. 6 m 17 cm ______________________

10. 8 m 67 cm ______________________

Write the longer distance.

11. The length of a football field (91 m) or the distance from the pitcher's mound to home plate (1,844 cm)

____

12. The length of a kangaroo's hop (7.6 m) or the length of a frog's jump (1,000 cm)

____

13. The length of the longest dinosaur (3,000 cm) or the length of the ocean liner Queen Elizabeth II (293.5 m)

____

14. The height of the Eiffel Tower in Paris (300.5 m) or the height of the Empire State Building in New York City (38,100 cm)

____

Name ________________________________

Practice
10-4

Millimeters, Centimeters, and Decimals

Complete.

1. 4.7 cm = __________ mm

2. 46 cm = __________ mm

3. 42 cm = __________ mm

4. 80 mm = __________ cm

5. 3 mm = __________ cm

6. 49 m = __________ cm

7. 9.78 cm = __________ mm

8. 32.1 cm = __________ mm

9. 4,321 cm = __________ m

10. 82.4 mm = __________ cm

11. 9.10 m = __________ cm

12. 849.2 cm = __________ mm

13. Which length is the longest?

____

A. 94 mm

B. 9.4 cm

C. 9.40 m

14. Which length is the longest?

____

A. 6.7 m

B. 67 cm

C. 670 m

15. Which length is the shortest?

____

A. 0.19 m

B. 1.9 cm

C. 190 mm

16. Which length is the shortest?

____

A. 6,205 mm

B. 6.205 m

C. 62.05 cm

17. Which two lengths are equal?

____

A. 2.3 m

B. 230 cm

C. 230 mm

18. Which two lengths are equal?

____

A. 4,867 mm

B. 486.7 cm

C. 48.67 m

Name ______________________________

Practice
Chapter 10
Section A

Review and Practice

Vocabulary Fill in each blank with the correct word.

meter decimeter centimeter

1. One tenth of a meter is equal to 1 ____________.
2. 1,000 millimeters is equal to one ____________.
3. One meter is equal to 100 ____________.

(Lesson 1) Circle the most appropriate unit of measure to estimate each.

4. length of a golf club mm m km
5. thickness of a dime mm cm dm
6. distance to a museum dm m km

(Lesson 2) Complete.

7. 8 m = ________ cm
8. 500 cm = ________ m
9. 90 dm = ________ m
10. 3,000 mm = ________ m

(Lesson 3) Write each measurement, first in centimeters only and then in meters only.

11. 9 m 15 cm ____________________
12. 4 m 30 cm ____________________
13. 12 m 8 cm ____________________

(Lesson 4) Complete.

14. 2.5 mm = ________ cm
15. 6.3 cm = ________ mm
16. 16.03 m = ________ cm
17. 9.8 m = ________ cm

(Mixed Review) Find each product.

18. $3 \times \frac{3}{5} =$ ________
19. $\frac{2}{3} \times \frac{6}{7} =$ ________
20. $3.58 \times 10 =$ ________
21. $46.17 \times 100 =$ ________
22. $\begin{array}{r} 2.75 \\ \times 0.0004 \\ \hline \end{array}$
23. $\begin{array}{r} 3.22 \\ \times 0.005 \\ \hline \end{array}$
24. $\begin{array}{r} 5.86 \\ \times 0.00003 \\ \hline \end{array}$

Name ______________________

Practice 10-5

Exploring Perimeter of Polygons

Write a multiplication number sentence describing the perimeter of each polygon.

1. 7 cm 7 cm 7 cm

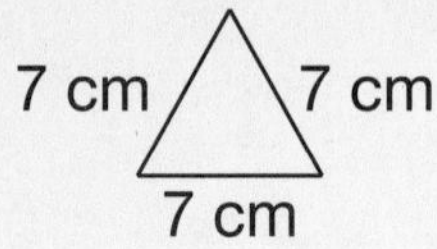

2. 8 yd 8 yd 8 yd 8 yd

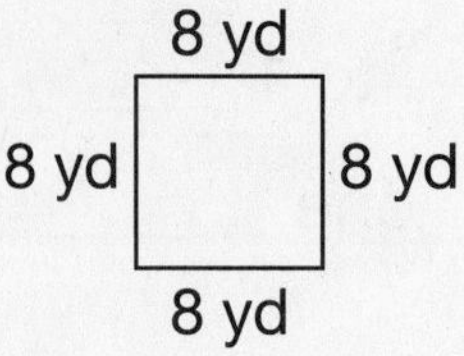

3. 3 m 3 m 3 m 3 m 3 m 3 m

______________________ ______________________ ______________________

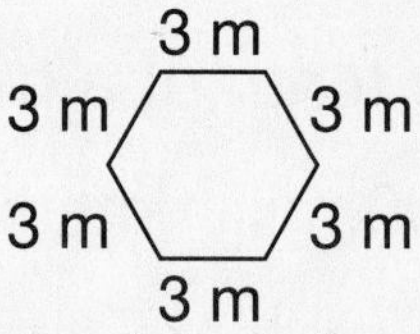

Find each perimeter.

4. 5 dm 7 dm 9 dm

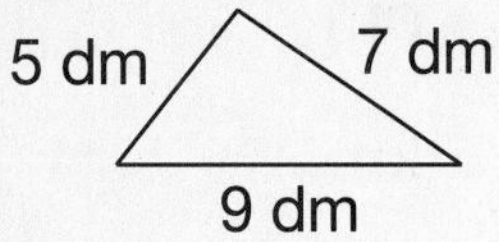

5. 2 ft

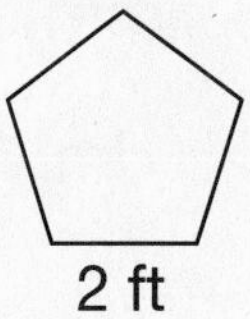

6. 20 mm 40 mm

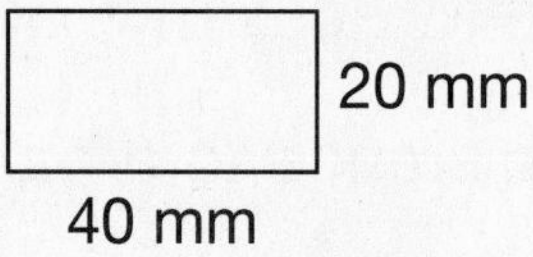

__________ __________ __________

7. 2 m 5 m 7 m 2 m 2 m 4 m

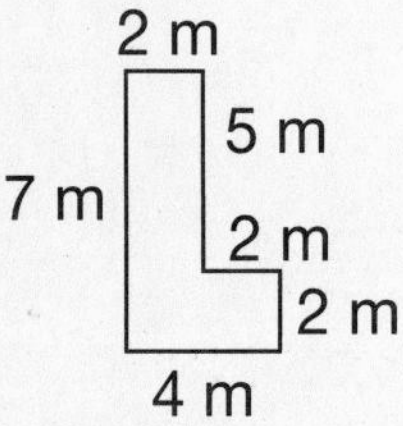

8. 4 m 5 m 3 m 6 m 1 m 3 m 2 m 2 m

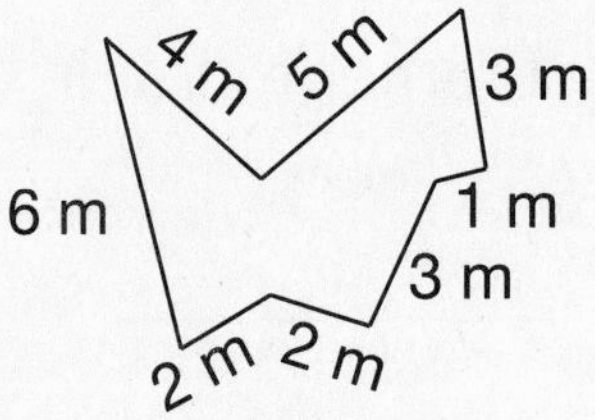

9. 4 km

__________ __________ __________

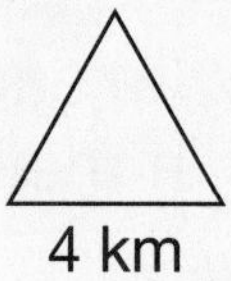

10. a regular pentagon with sides of 9 cm __________

11. a triangle with sides of 8 dm, 8 dm and 10 dm __________

12. a regular hexagon with sides of 5 mm __________

13. an equilateral triangle with sides of 4 cm __________

14. When finding the perimeter of a regular polygon, will you get the same answer if you add each side as when you multiply the length of one side by the total number of sides? Explain.

____

____

Name ______________________________

Practice 10-6

Exploring Perimeter of Rectangles

Use the formula $P = 2 \times (l + w)$ to find the perimeter of each rectangle. Fill in the missing numbers.

1.

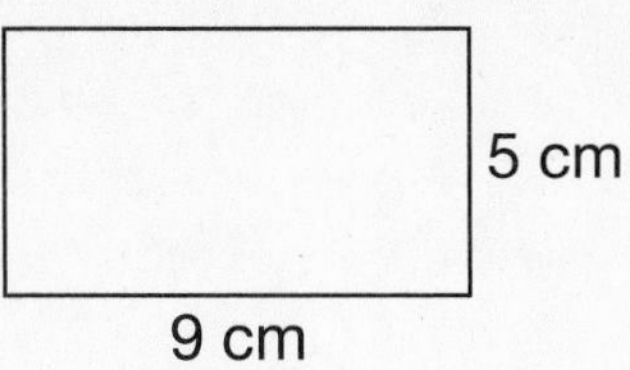

$P = 2 \times ($ _____ $+$ _____ $)$

$P = 2 \times ($ _____ $)$

$P =$ _____ cm

2.

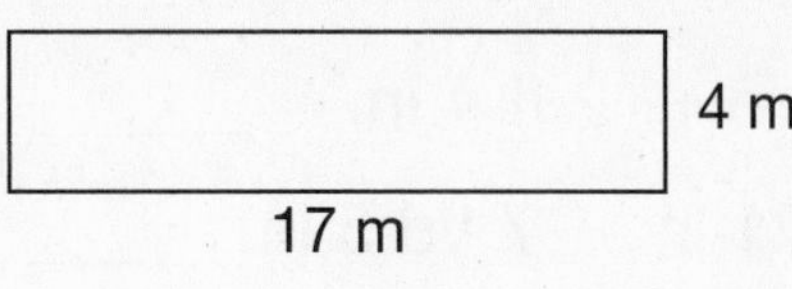

$P = 2 \times ($ _____ $+$ _____ $)$

$P = 2 \times ($ _____ $)$

$P =$ _____ m

Find the perimeter of each rectangle.

3.

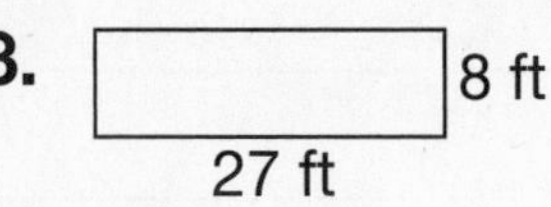

____

4.

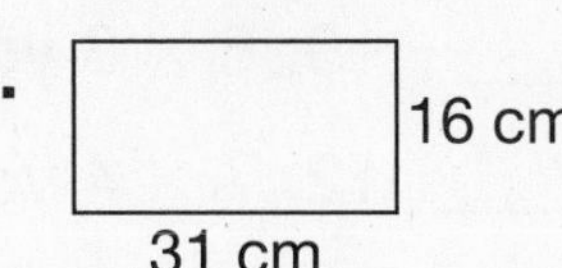

____

5.

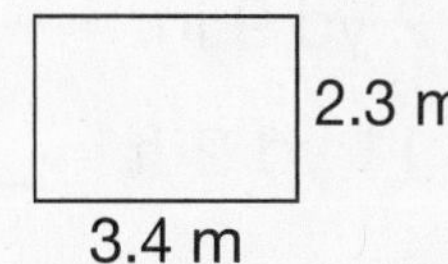

____

6. $l = 26$ ft

$w = 24$ ft

$P =$ __________

7. $l = 246$ mi

$w = 93$ mi

$P =$ __________

8. $l = 4.25$ m

$w = 3.85$ m

$P =$ __________

Estimate the perimeter of each rectangle.

9.

47.6 m

118.5 m

____

10.

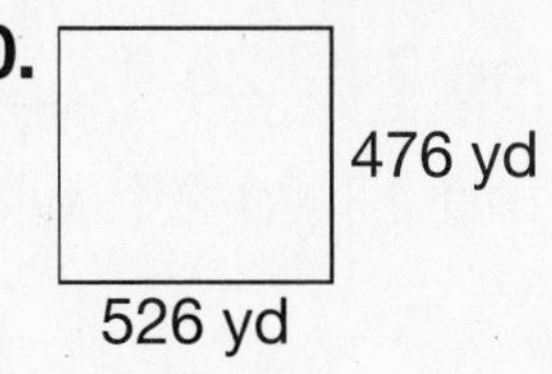

____

11.

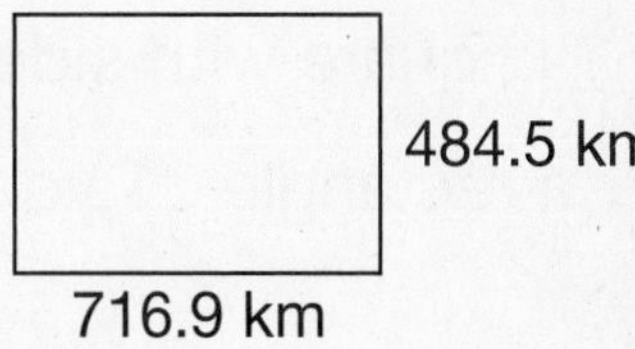

____

12. What is the perimeter of a rectangular rose garden 5.3 meters long and 3.7 meters wide? __________

Name ______________________________

Practice 10-7

Converting Units to Find Perimeter

Find each sum.

1. 3 yd 2 ft + 2 yd 1 ft = __________
2. 8 ft 8 in. + 2 ft 4 in. = __________
3. 6 yd 31 in. + 7 yd 5 in. = __________
4. 3 yd 2 ft + 5 yd 2 ft = __________
5. 9 ft 3 in. + 8 ft 11 in. = __________
6. 11 yd 1 ft + 3 yd 2 ft = __________

Find each product.

7. 3 × 4 ft 6 in. = __________
8. 2 × 6 ft 5 in. = __________
9. 5 × 2 yd 9 in. = __________
10. 6 × 3 yd 2 ft = __________
11. 4 × 11 yd 2 ft = __________
12. 7 × 4 yd 9 in. = __________

13. Find the perimeter of a bird house 2 ft 7 in. by 1 ft 5 in. __________

14. Find the perimeter of a square sandbox with sides measuring 7 ft 8 in. __________

Find each perimeter.

15. a rectangle 6 ft 10 in. long and 4 ft 11 in. wide __________
16. a square with sides measuring 2 mi 25 ft __________
17. a rectangle 31 yd 2 ft long and 17 yd 2 ft wide __________

18. Which rectangle has the greater perimeter? Explain how you know.

a.

3 ft 2 in.

3 ft 3 in.

b.

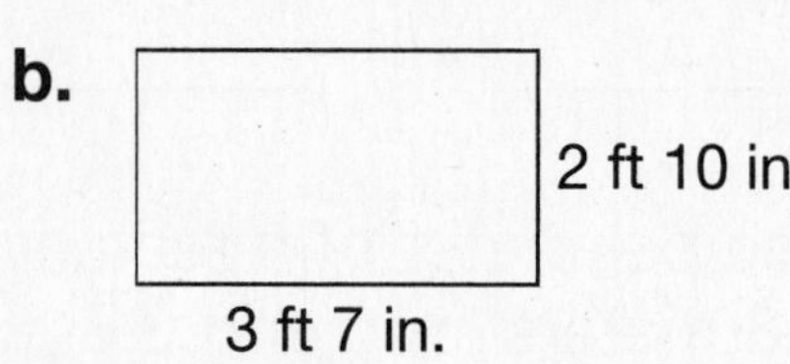

____

Name ___________________________________

Practice 10-8

Exploring Area of Rectangles

Use the formula $A = l \times w$ to find the area of each rectangle. Fill in the missing numbers.

1. 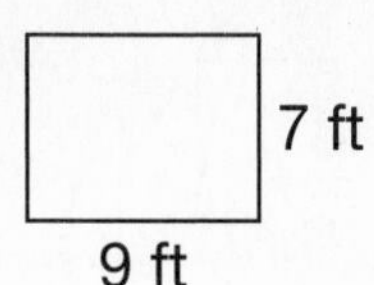

$A =$ _____ $\times$ _____

$A =$ _________ ft^2

2. 6 yd, 8 yd

$A =$ _____ $\times$ _____

$A =$ _________ yd^2

Find the area of each square.

Use the formula $A = s^2$ to find the area of each square. Fill in the missing numbers.

3. 11 in., 11 in.

a. $A =$ _________ ^{2}

b. $A =$ _________

4. 17 cm, 17 cm

a. $A =$ _________ ^{2}

b. $A =$ _________

Find the area of each rectangle.

5. $l = 14$ mi
$w = 8$ mi

$A =$ _________

6. $l = 3.9$ m
$w = 5$ m

$A =$ _________

7. $l = 16$ m
$w = 0.5$ m

$A =$ _________

8. $s = 13$ cm

$A =$ _________

9. $l = 18$ ft

$w = 12$ ft

$A =$ _________

10. $s = 15$ yd

$A =$ _________

11. A rectangle has an area of 91 m^2 and a length of 13 m. What is its width? _________

12. A square has an area of 144 cm^2. What is the measure of its side? _________

Name ______________________

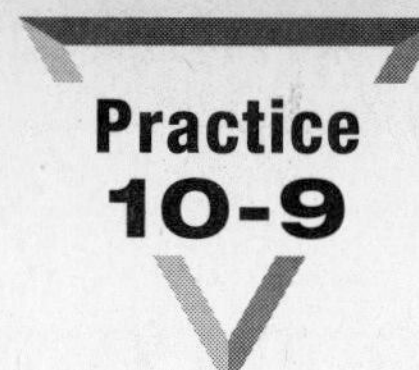

Decision Making

You would like to participate in an after-school activity. The following is a list of things you might do.

Activity	Cost	Time
Sports Team	$50 for uniform	3:45 P.M. – 5 P.M., Mon., Wed., Fri., Sat.
Dance Class	$12.75 a class	3:45 P.M. – 5 P.M., Tue., Thur.
Music Lesson	$30 a week	3 P.M. – 4 P.M., Mon., Wed.
Arts and Crafts	$40 a month	12 P.M. – 5 P.M., Sat.

1. Which activity is the most expensive for a month? the least?

____

2. If you wanted to participate in as many activities as you could, which activities could you choose? Explain.

____

____

3. How much would it cost in a month to participate in these activities? Find the cost for each.

____

____

4. a. Which activities would you choose?

____

____

b. How much would it cost for one month?

____

Name ______________________

Practice
Chapter 10
Section B

Review and Practice

Vocabulary Write a definition for each word.

1. perimeter ______________________

____

2. area ______________________

____

(Lessons 5–7) Find each perimeter.

3. 3 in., 7 in., 5 in.

4. 2 cm, 9 cm

5.

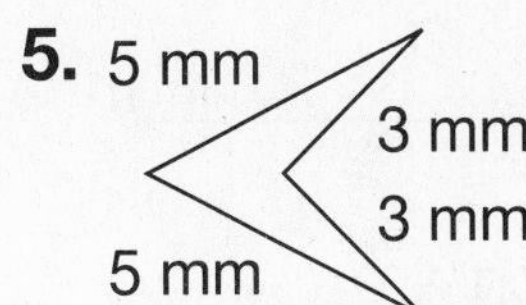

6. $\frac{1}{3}$ in., $\frac{1}{3}$ in.

7. 3 ft 2 in., 14 ft 3 in.

8. 20 mm, 40 mm

(Lesson 8) Find each area.

9. 5 ft, 5 ft

10. 50 cm, 80 cm

11.

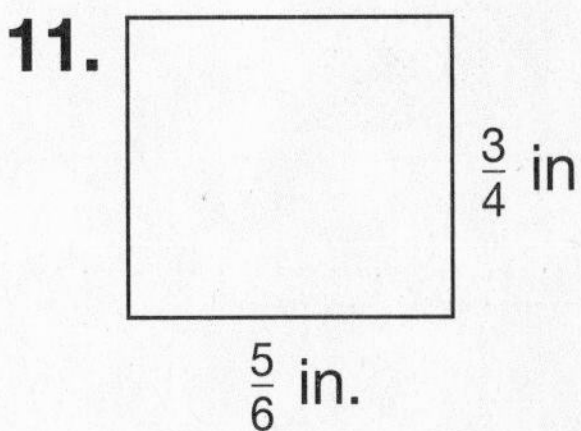

(Mixed Review) Complete.

12. 300 × ________ = 1,800

13. 36,000 ÷ ________ = 4,000

14. 16 × ________ = 320

15. 45,000 × ________ = 50

Name ______________________________

Practice 10-10

Exploring Area of Right Triangles

Use the formula $A = \frac{1}{2} \times (b \times h)$ to find the area of each right triangle. Fill in the missing numbers.

1.

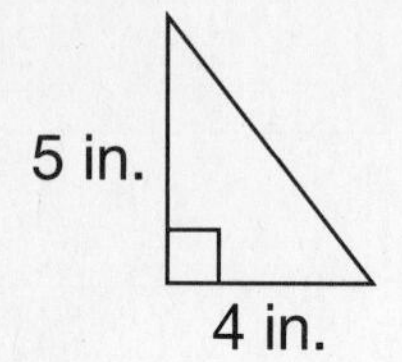

$A = \frac{1}{2} \times ($ ______ $\times$ ______ $)$

$A = \frac{1}{2} \times ($ ______ $)$

$A =$ __________ in^2

2.

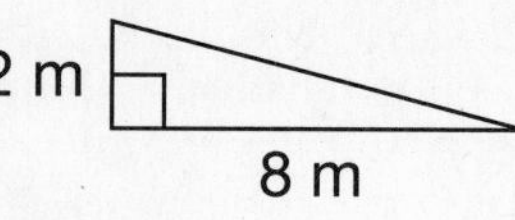

$A = \frac{1}{2} \times ($ ______ $\times$ ______ $)$

$A = \frac{1}{2} \times ($ ______ $)$

$A =$ __________ m^2

Find each area.

3.

____

4.

____

5.

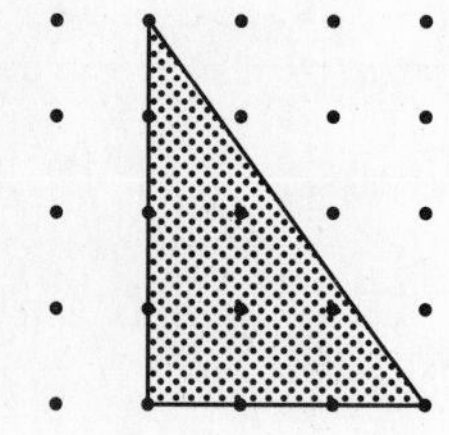

____

6.

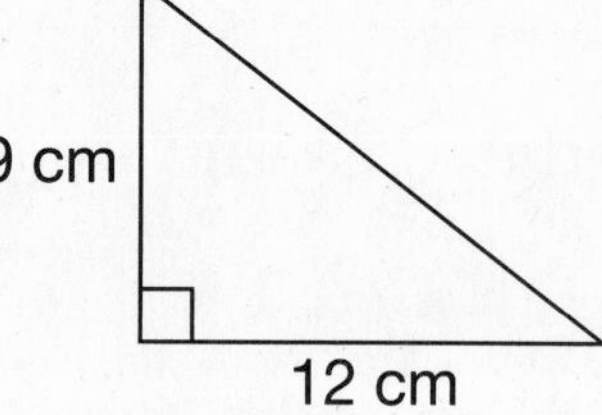

____

7.

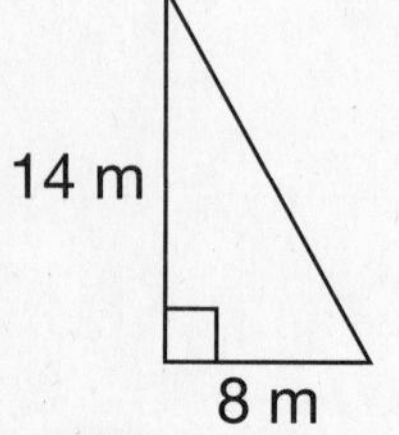

____

8.

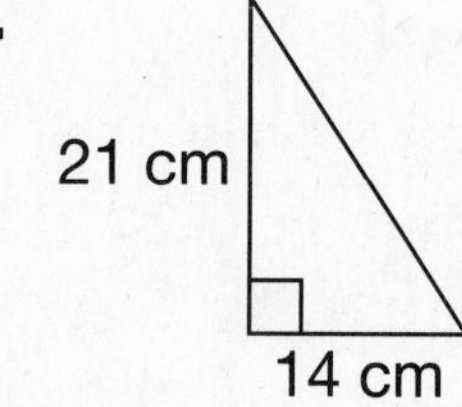

____

Name ______________________________

Practice
10-11

Exploring Area of Triangles

Use the formula $A = \frac{1}{2} \times (b \times h)$ to find the area of each triangle. Fill in the missing numbers.

1.

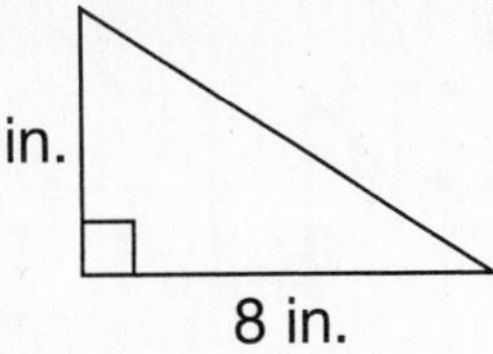

$A = \frac{1}{2} \times (\_\_\_\_ \times \_\_\_\_)$

$A = \frac{1}{2} \times (\_\_\_\_)$

$A = \_\_\_\_\_\_$ in^2

2.

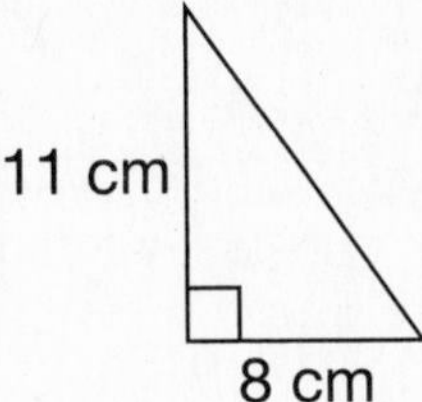

$A = \frac{1}{2} \times (\_\_\_\_ \times \_\_\_\_)$

$A = \frac{1}{2} \times (\_\_\_\_)$

$A = \_\_\_\_\_\_$ cm^2

Find each area.

3.

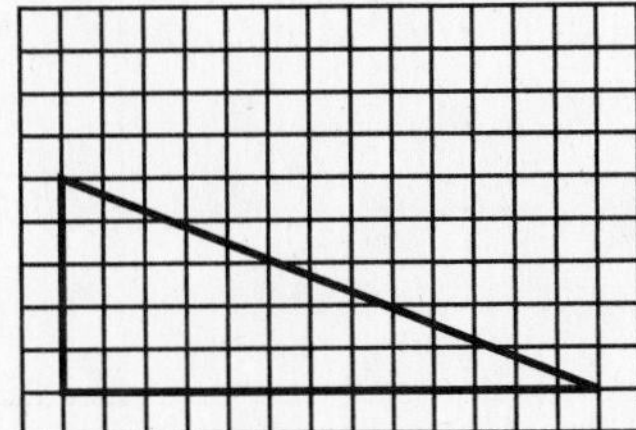

$A = \_\_\_\_\_\_$ units^2

4.

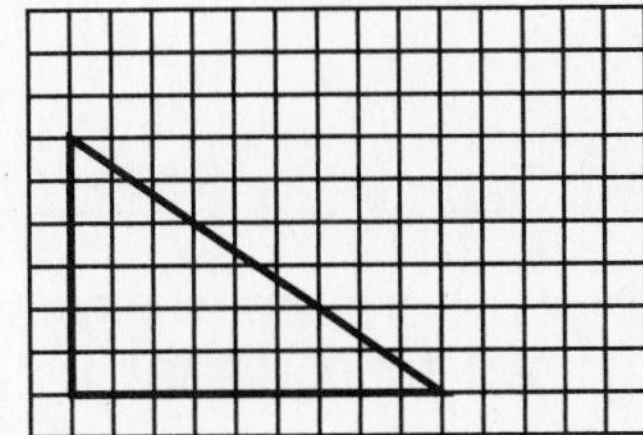

$A = \_\_\_\_\_\_$ units^2

5.

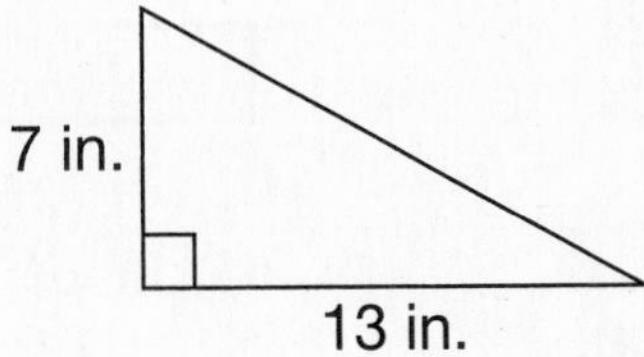

$A = \_\_\_\_\_\_$ in^2

6.

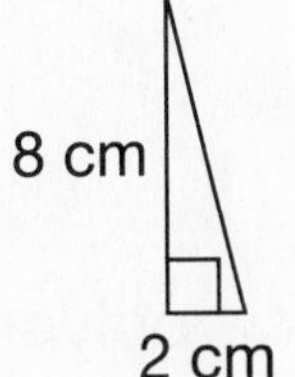

$A = \_\_\_\_\_\_$ cm^2

7. Alyson planted a garden area in the shape of a triangle. The base was 9 ft and the height was 7 ft. What was the area of the triangular garden? ______________

8. Rosey embroidered triangles on a pillow cover. Each triangle has a base of 2 in. and a height of 3 in. What is the area of each triangle? ______________

Name ______________________________

Practice 10-12

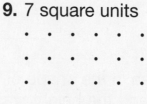

Exploring Area of Other Polygons

Find each area.

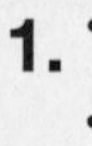

1. 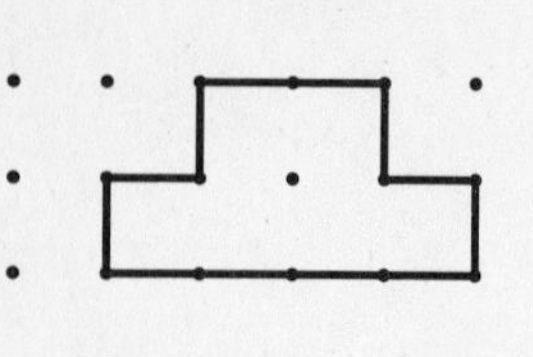
____

2. 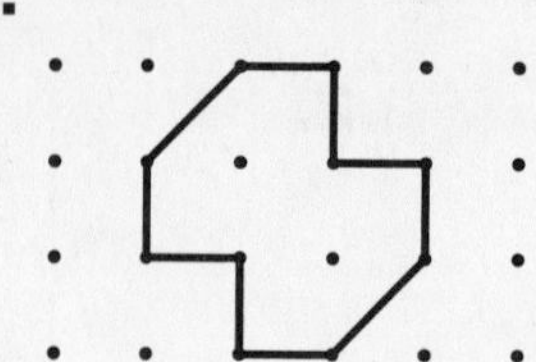
____

3. 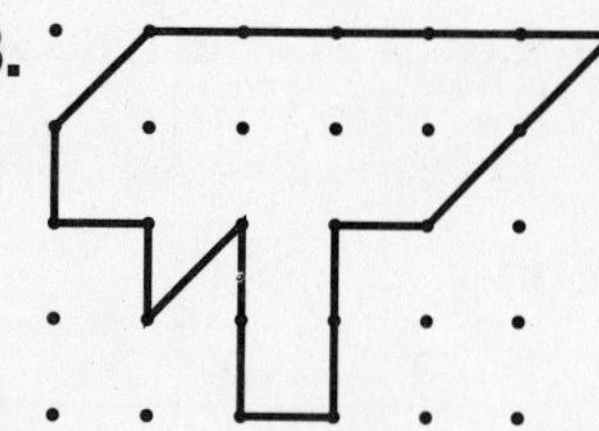
____

Find each area.

4. 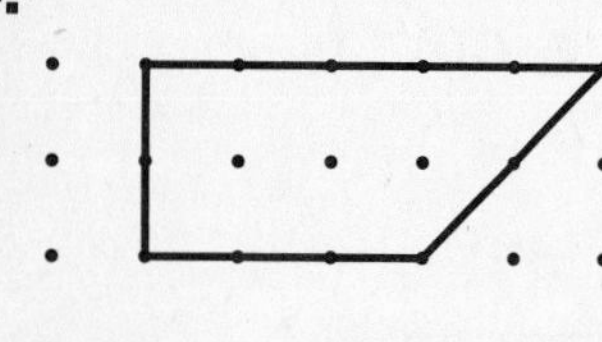
____

5. 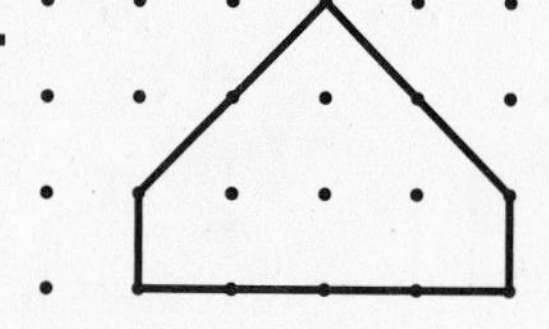
____

6. 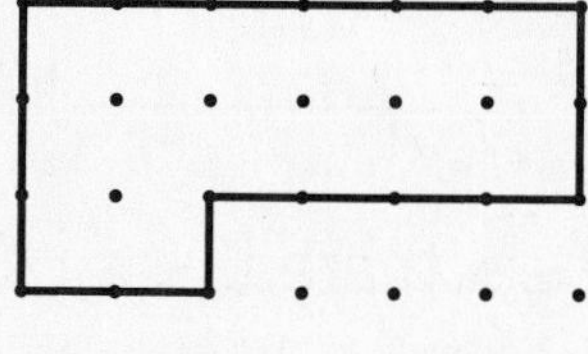
____

7. Order the figures from least to greatest area. ____, ____, ____, ____

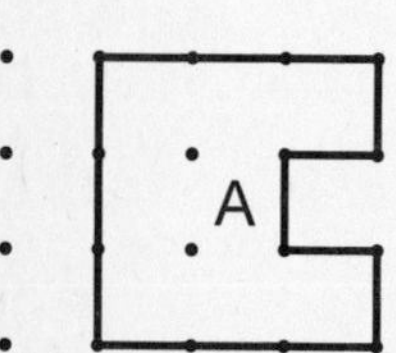

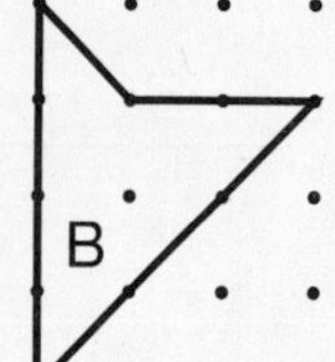

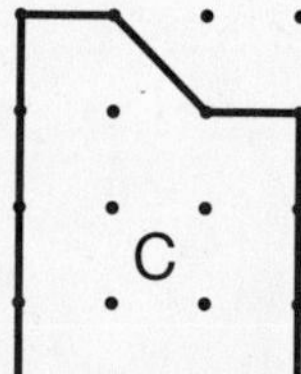

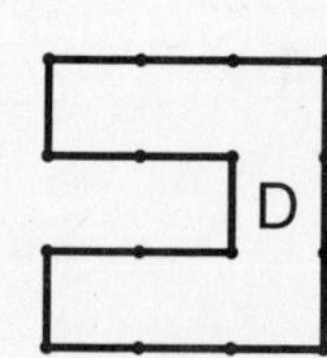

On dot paper below, draw a polygon with each area.

8. 6 square units

9. 7 square units

10. $4\frac{1}{2}$ square units

Name ______________________________

Practice 10-13

Exploring Area of Parallelograms

Use the formula $A = b \times h$ to find the area of each parallelogram. Fill in the missing numbers.

1. 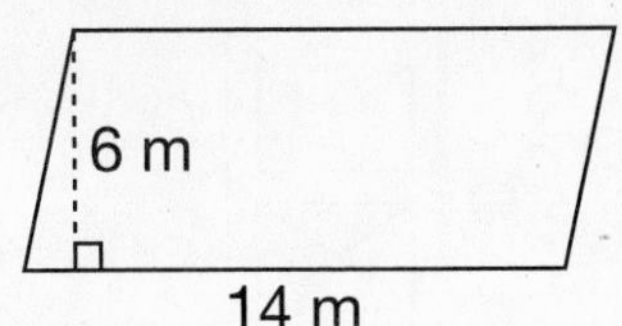

$A =$ ________ $\times$ ________

$A =$ ________ m^2

2. 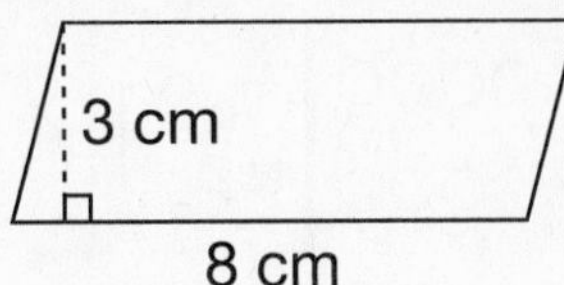

$A =$ ________ $\times$ ________

$A =$ ________ cm^2

Find each area.

3. 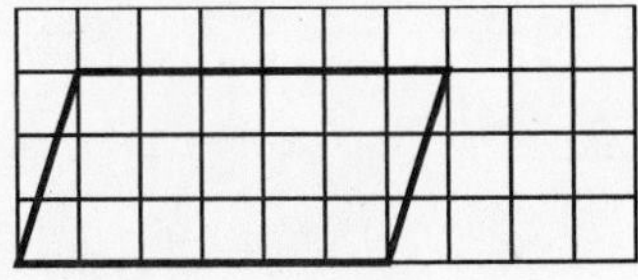

____

4. 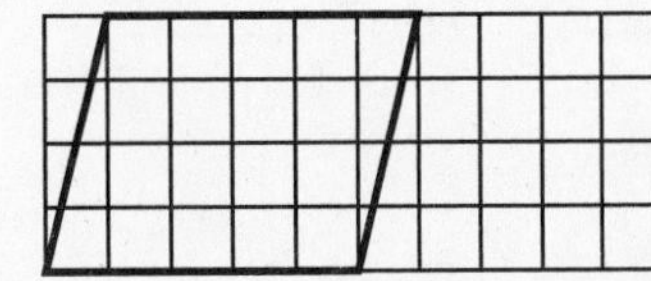

____

5. 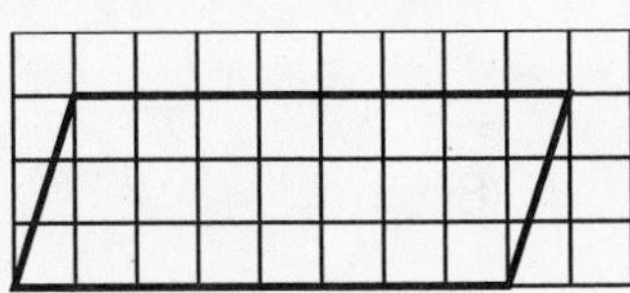

____

6. 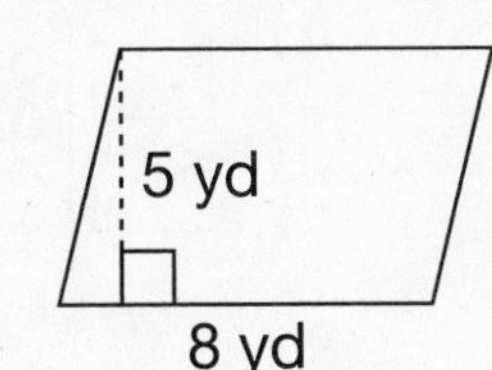

____

7. 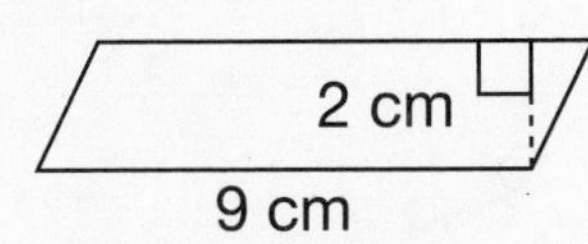

____

8. 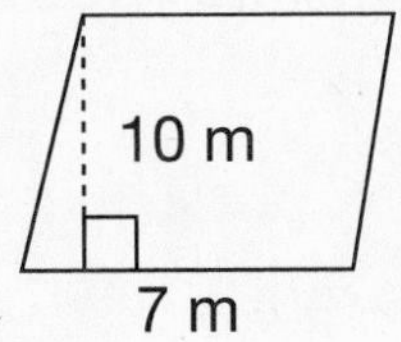

____

Find each missing base or height.

9. 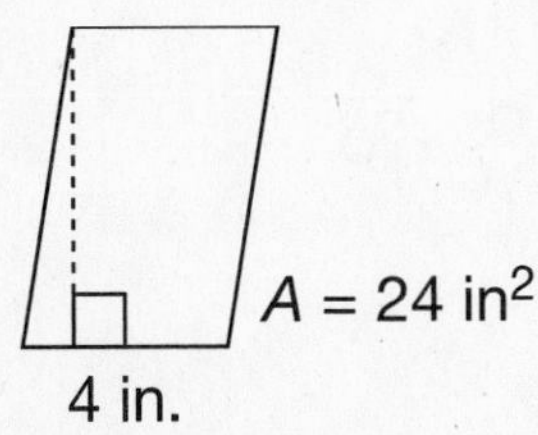

____

10. 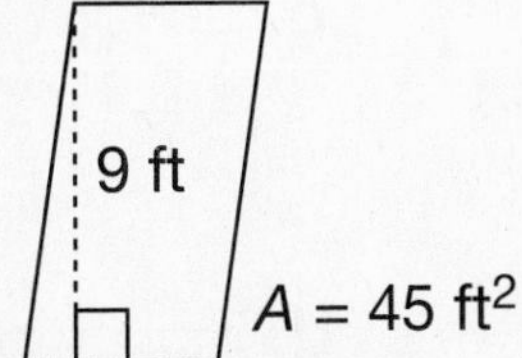

____

11. 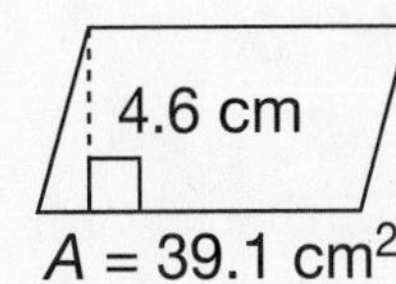

____

Name ______________________

Practice 10-14

Exploring Algebra: Balancing Equations

Find the number of counters in each envelope. Fill in the missing numbers.

1.

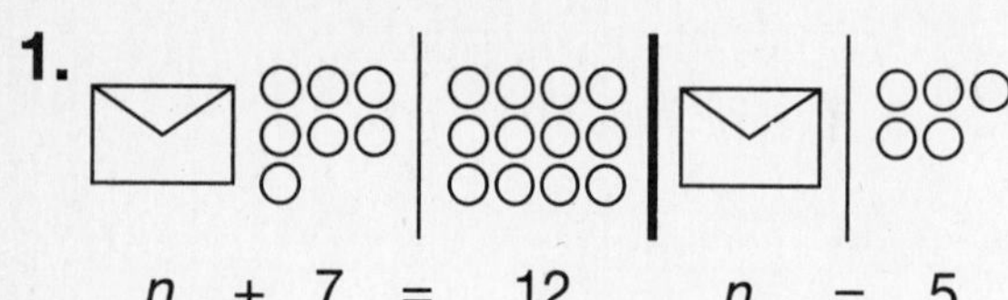

$n + 7 = 12$ $n = 5$

Find the value of n.
Subtract 7 from both sides.

a. $n + 7 -$ _____ $= 12 -$ _____

b. $n =$ _____

c. Check _____ $+ 7 = 12$

2.

$3 \times n = 18$ $n = 6$

Find the value of n.
Divide both sides by 3.

a. $(3 \times n) \div$ _____ $= 18 \div$ _____

b. $n =$ _____

c. Check $3 \times$ _____ $= 18$

Use counters to find the number of counters in each envelope.

3. $6 + n = 15$

$n =$ _____

4. $2 \times n = 10$

$n =$ _____

5. $8 = 4 + n$

$n =$ _____

Match each equation with its model. Then find the value of n.

6. $n + 8 = 21$

$n =$ _____

a.

7. $2 \times n = 20$

$n =$ _____

b.

8. $n + 8 = 15$

$n =$ _____

c.

9. $2 \times n = 32$

$n =$ _____

d.

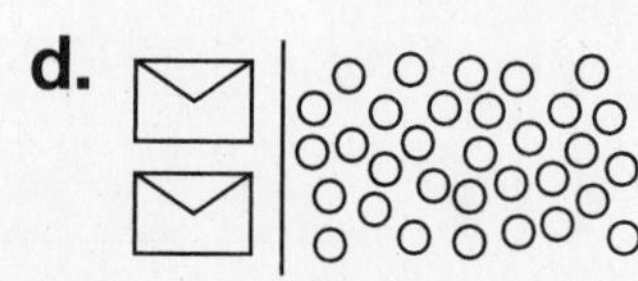

Name ______________________________

Practice
10-15

Analyze Strategies: Look for a Pattern

Look for a pattern to solve the problem.

1. The bells at Madison Middle School ring at 8:25, 9:15, 10:05, and 10:55. If this pattern continues, when will the next 4 bells ring?

   a. How much time elapses between the first 2 bells? __________

   b. How much time elapses between the 2nd and 3rd bells? __________

      the 3rd and 4th bells? __________

   c. What is the pattern? ______________________________

   d. Continue the pattern. When will the next 4 bells ring?

      ____

Look for a pattern or use any strategy to help solve each problem.

2. Kimberly is planning to make 1 beaded necklace on Monday, 2 beaded necklaces on Tuesday, 4 on Wednesday, and 8 on Thursday. If this pattern continues, how many necklaces will she make on Sunday? ____________________

3. Kineesha packed these things for a trip: a white blouse, a pink blouse, a blue blouse, white shorts, a red skirt, and blue jeans. How many different outfits can Kineesha wear? ____________________

4. To be sure to have enough baked potatoes, Stu is preparing 3 for every pair of guests. If he has invited 48 people, how many potatoes will he bake? ____________________

5. Aimee's clock was 5 minutes slow on May 1, 7 minutes slow on May 2, 10 minutes slow on May 3, 14 minutes slow on May 4, and 19 minutes slow on May 5. If this pattern continues, what is the first day the clock will be more than an hour slow? ____________________

Name ____________________

Practice 10-16

Exploring Circumference

Use the formula $C = \pi \times d$ to find the circumference of each circle. Fill in the missing numbers.

1. 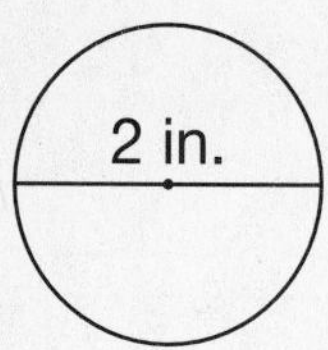

$C = 3.14 \times$ ________

$C =$ ________ in.

2. 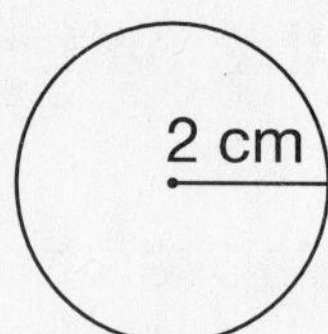

$C = 2 \times 3.14 \times$ ________

$C =$ ________ cm

Find each circumference. Use 3.14 for π.

3. $C =$ ________

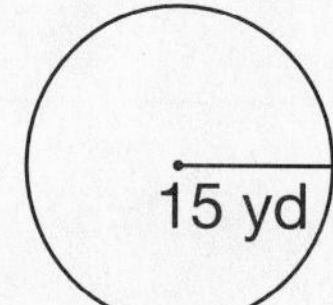

4. $C =$ ________

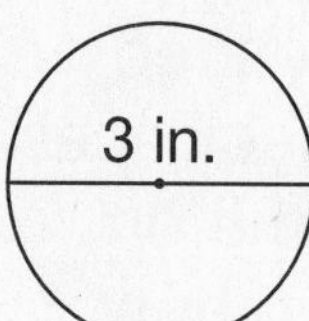

5. $C =$ ________

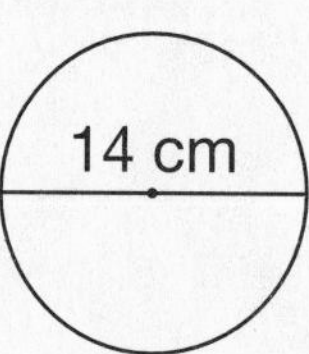

Find each diameter to the nearest hundredth. Use 3.14 for π.

6. $C = 16$ ft

$d =$ ________

7. $C = 22$ in.

$d =$ ________

8. $C = 48$ mm

$d =$ ________

Find each radius to the nearest hundredth. Use 3.14 for π.

9. $C = 52$ in.

$r =$ ________

10. $C = 73$ ft

$r =$ ________

11. $C = 62$ m

$r =$ ________

Name ____________________

Review and Practice

Vocabulary Draw an example of each on a separate sheet of paper.

1. diameter **2.** radius **3.** height of a triangle

(Lessons 10–13) Find the area of each figure.

4.
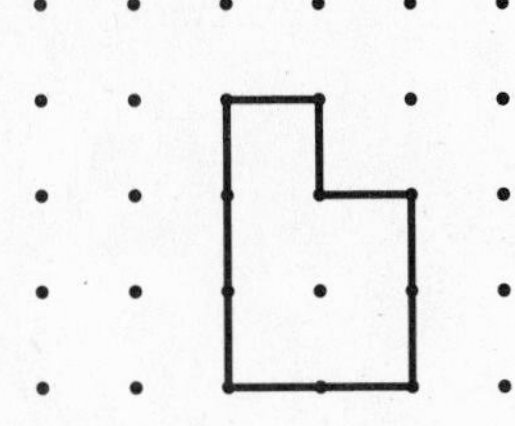

____

5.
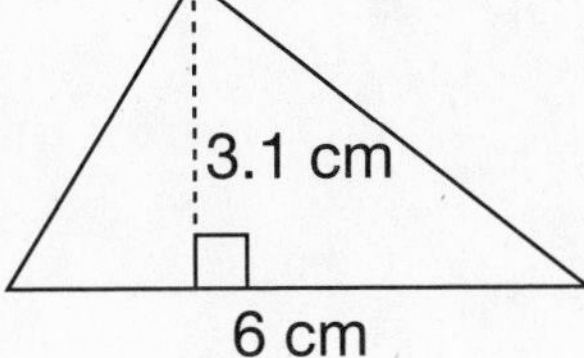

____

6.
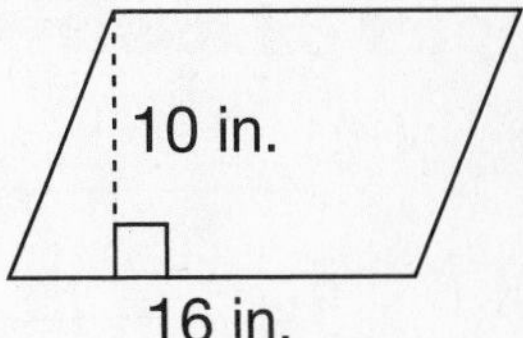

____

(Lesson 14) Find the value of *n*. You may use counters to help.

7. $n + 8 = 11$

$n =$ ____________

8. $5 + n = 13$

$n =$ ____________

(Lesson 16) Find each circumference. Use 3.14 for π.

9.
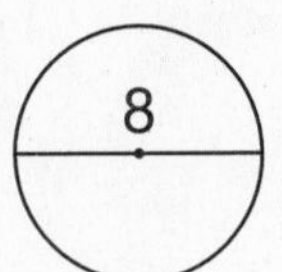

$C =$ ____________

10.
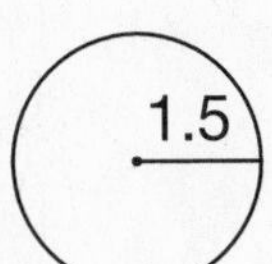

$C =$ ____________

11.
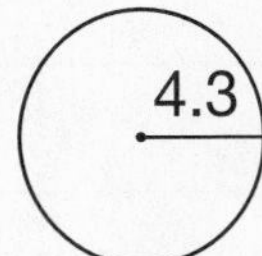

$C =$ ____________

(Mixed Review) Divide.

12. $7\overline{)945}$ **13.** $6\overline{)735}$ **14.** $5\overline{)862}$

Name ______________________

Cumulative Review

(Chapter 3 Lesson 13) Find each product. Round to the nearest cent where necessary.

1. $\begin{array}{r} 16.2 \\ \times\ 2.4 \\ \hline \end{array}$

2. $\begin{array}{r} \$38.15 \\ \times\ 5.7 \\ \hline \end{array}$

3. $\begin{array}{r} \$4.02 \\ \times\ 53 \\ \hline \end{array}$

4. $\begin{array}{r} 3.041 \\ \times\ 7.8 \\ \hline \end{array}$

(Chapter 8 Lesson 15) Complete.

5. 6 yd = __________ ft

6. 9 ft 3 in. = __________ in.

7. 28 in. = __________ ft __________ in.

8. 133 in. __________ ft __________ in.

(Chapter 9 Lesson 5) Find each product.

9. $\frac{3}{4} \times \frac{2}{7} =$ __________

10. $\frac{2}{3} \times \frac{9}{21} =$ __________

11. $\frac{3}{8} \times \frac{8}{7} =$ __________

12. $\frac{6}{10} \times \frac{20}{30} =$ __________

(Chapter 9 Lesson 10) Find each quotient.

13. $6 \div \frac{1}{2} =$ __________

14. $9 \div \frac{1}{4} =$ __________

15. $15 \div \frac{1}{3} =$ __________

16. $8 \div \frac{1}{10} =$ __________

(Chapter 10 Lesson 4) Complete.

17. 38 mm = __________ cm

18. 18 cm = __________ mm

19. 9.3 m = __________ cm

20. 472 cm = __________ m

(Chapter 10 Lesson 8) Find each area.

21. a square with sides that measure 12 feet ______________

22. a rectangle with length 1.5 m and width 5 m ______________

Name ______________________________

Practice 11-1

Exploring Solids

Complete the table comparing a pyramid and a prism.

	Solid	Number of Bases	Shape of Side Faces
1.			
2.			

Write the name of the solid suggested in each drawing.

3.

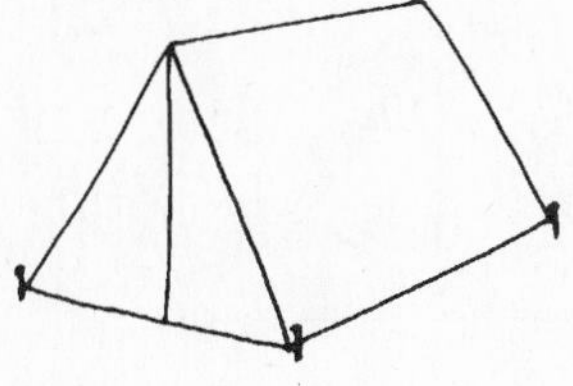

____

4.

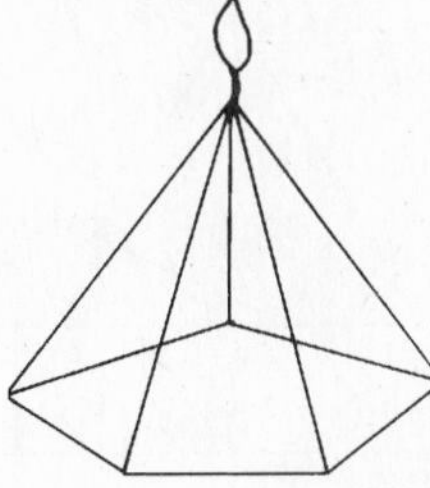

____

5.

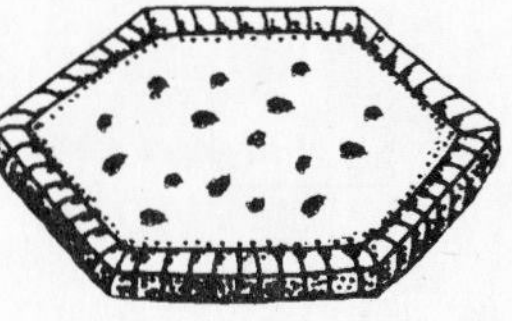

____

6.

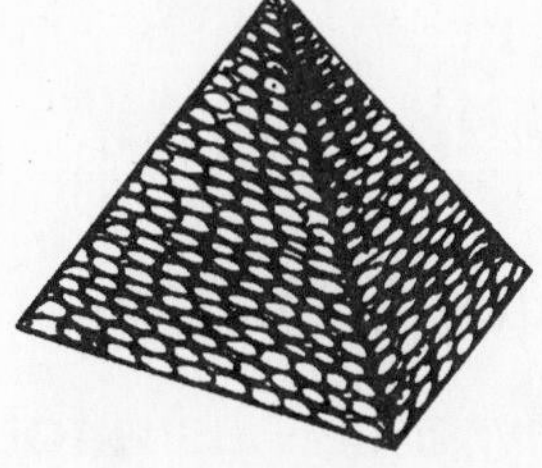

____

Decide if each statement is true *always*, *sometimes*, or *never*.

7. A pyramid has 2 bases. ____________________

8. A prism has 2 bases. ____________________

9. A pyramid has 4 faces. ____________________

10. A pentagonal pyramid has 5 triangular faces. ____________________

11. A triangular prism has 3 square faces. ____________________

12. The side faces of a pyramid are triangles. ____________________

Name ______________________________

Practice 11-2

Exploring Patterns with Solids

Complete the rule you discovered for prisms. Then solve the problems.

1. For any prism, number of ________ + number of vertices = number of edges + ________.
2. A pentagonal prism has 7 faces and 10 vertices. How many edges does it have? ________
3. An octagonal prism has 16 vertices and 24 edges. How many faces does it have? ________
4. A hexagonal prism has 8 faces and 18 edges. How many vertices does it have? ________
5. Complete the table.

Pyramid			
Edges of Base	3		
Number of Vertices			
Total Number of Edges			

Decide if each statement is true or false.

6. A hexagonal pyramid has a total of 13 edges.

____

7. A pyramid with 7 edges on its base has a total of 14 edges.

____

8. The number of edges on the base of a pyramid is twice the total number of edges.

____

Name ________________________________

Practice 11-3

Exploring Nets

Circle the design or designs that form a net for the solid described.

1. cube

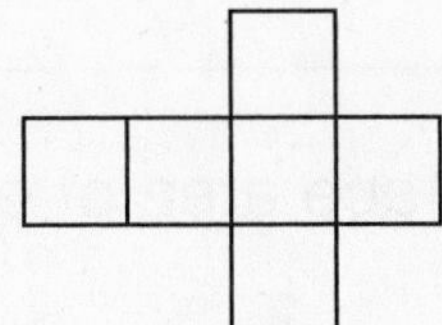

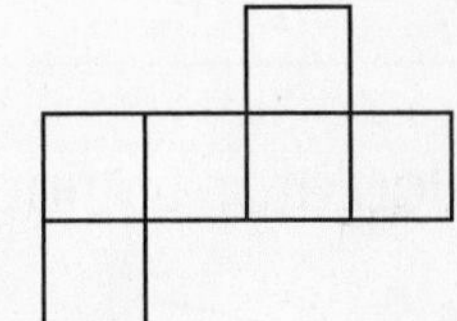

2. triangular pyramid

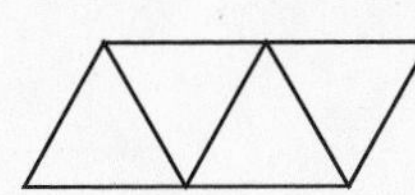

3. square pyramid

4. rectangular prism

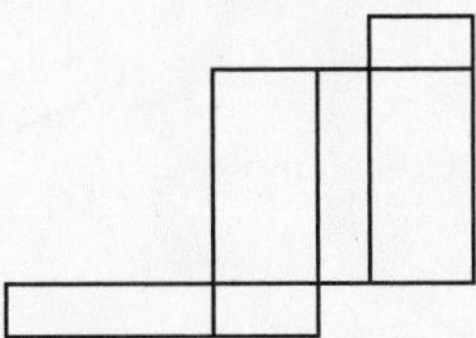

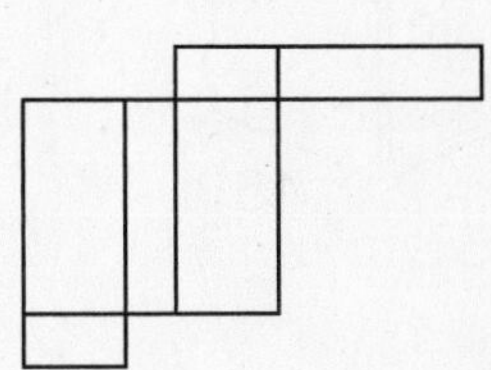

5. Design a net for a pyramid. Draw your net below.

Name ______________________

Practice 11-4

Exploring Surface Area

1. Write the formula to find the surface area of any rectangular prism.

____

____

Use a calculator to find the surface area of each figure.

2.

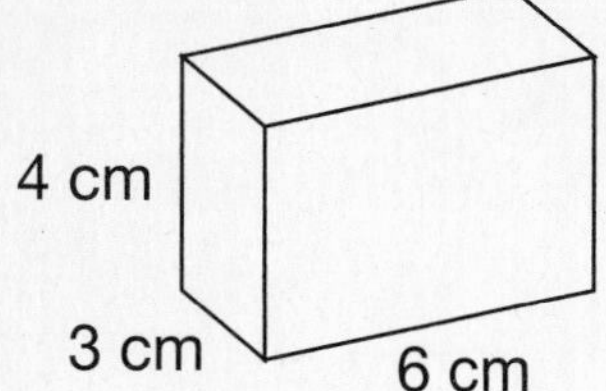

____

3.

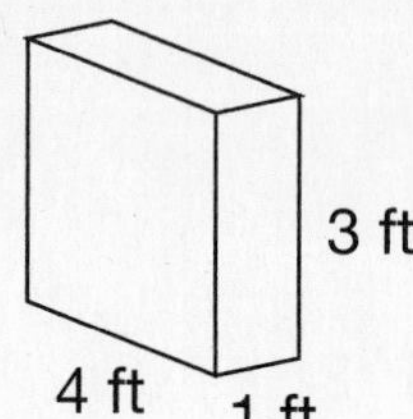

____

4.

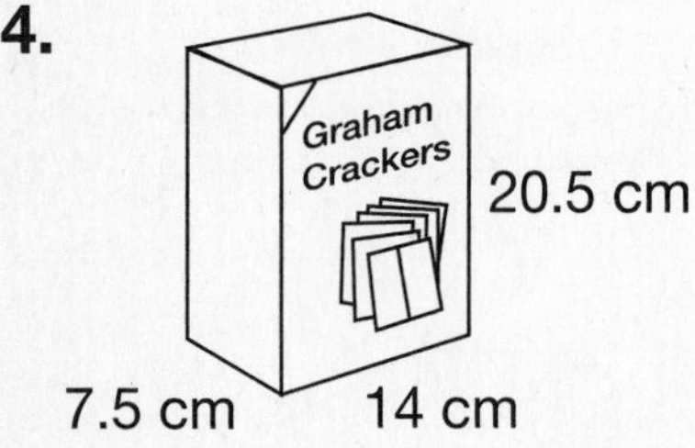

____

5.

____

6.

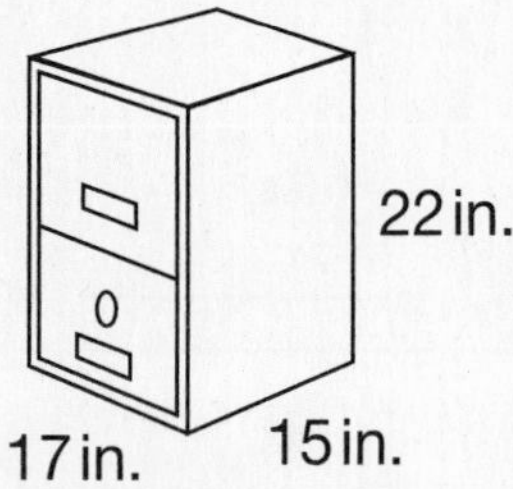

____

7.

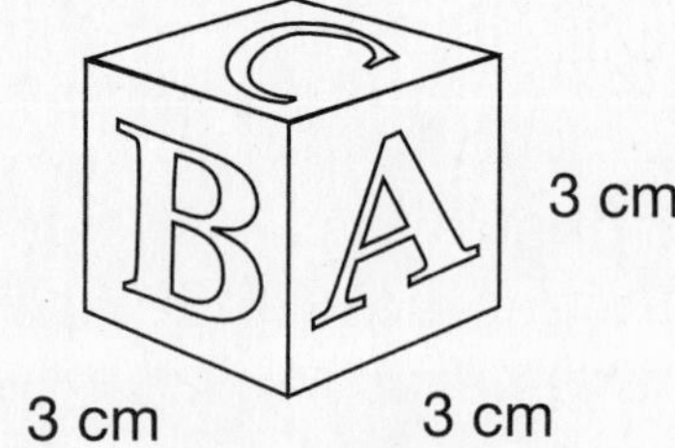

____

8. A gallon of paint covers about 400 ft^2. How many gallons would you need to paint the walls of a room 10 ft wide, 14 ft long, and 8 ft tall?

____

9. Suppose you have a 3 ft by 3 ft by 4 ft toy box with a lid. You want to paint the inside and outside of the box. What is the total surface area that you have to paint?

____

Name ___________________________

Practice 11-5

Decision Making

You want to build several bookcases.

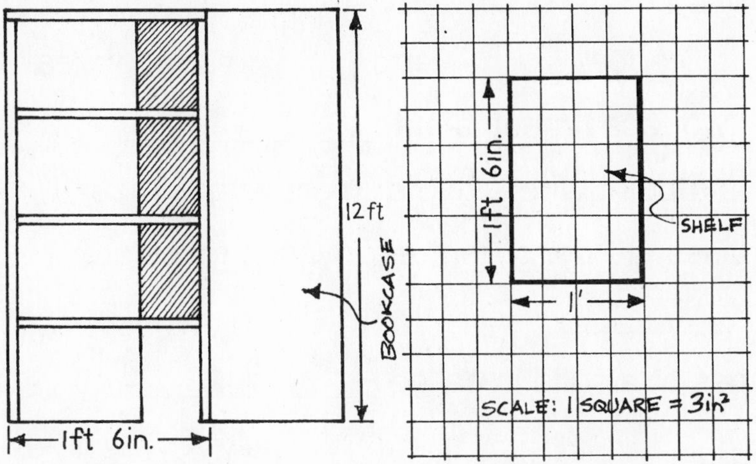

1 ft by 12 ft boards cost $16. Each additional foot costs $1.75. You have $40 to spend on wood.

1. Into what geometric figures will the board be cut? ______________

2. How much wood can you afford?

____

3. What length of wood will you need for:

a. the 2 sides? ______________

b. the 3 shelves? ______________

c. the top? ______________

4. How many bookcases can you make with the wood you can afford? ______________

5. Can you make another book-case with the leftover wood? ______________

6. Should you buy any boards less than 12 ft long? Explain your reasoning.

____

____

7. How much more money would you need to make another bookcase? ______________

Name ______________________

Practice
Chapter 11
Section A

Review and Practice

Vocabulary Use a word from the list to complete each sentence. Not all words will be used.

pyramid prism edge vertex surface area

1. A line segment where two faces meet is a(n) ____________.

2. A(n) ____________ is a point where two or more edges meet.

3. A solid figure whose bases are congruent and whose faces are rectangles is a(n) ____________.

4. The total area of all faces of a solid is called ____________.

(Lessons 1 and 2) Complete.

5. The base of a pentagonal prism has ________ sides.

6. A solid with rectangular faces and a triangular base is a ____________ prism.

7. A heptagonal prism has ________ faces.

(Lesson 3) Name the solid each net makes.

8. 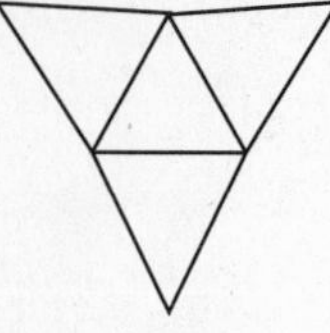

____

9. 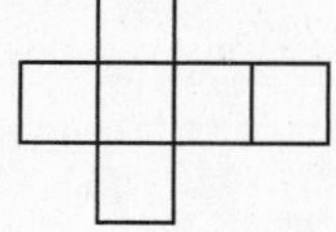

____

10. 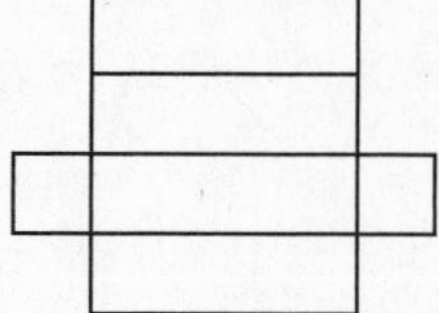

____

(Lesson 4) Find the surface area of each figure.

11. 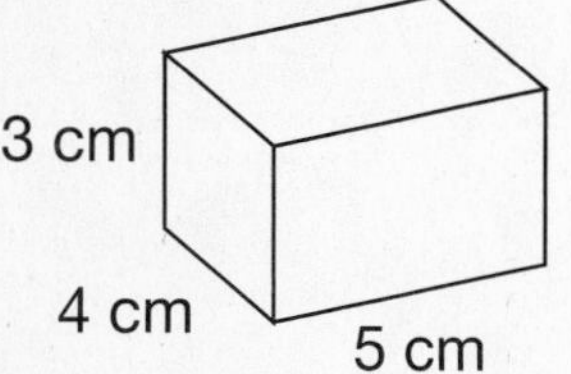

____

12. 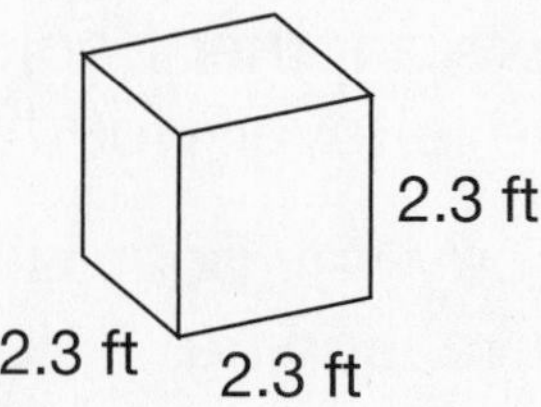

____

(Mixed Review) Write the simplest form for each fraction.

13. $\frac{21}{35} =$ __________

14. $\frac{33}{36} =$ __________

Name ___________________________

Practice 11-6

Ounces, Pounds, and Tons

Complete. Check the reasonableness of your answer.

1. 4 lb = ________ oz

2. 1 T = ________ lb

3. 6,000 lb = ________ T

4. 32 oz = ________ lb

5. 112 oz = ________ lb

6. 5 T = ________ lb

7. 5 lb 3 oz = ________ oz

8. 40 oz = ________ lb ________ oz

9. 3 T 21 lb = ________ lb

10. 100 oz = ________ lb ________ oz

11. 20,000 lb = ________ T

12. 4 T 100 lb = ________ lb

13. 9 lb 5 oz = ________ oz

14. 2,340 lb = ________ T ________ lb

15. 7 T 15 lb = ________ lb

16. 82 oz = ________ lb ________ oz

17. Which is less, 2 T or 2,600 lb? Explain.

____

18. Which is less, 50 ounces or 4 lb? Explain.

____

19. Which is greater, 3 T or 5,999 lb? Explain.

____

20. Which is greater, 5 lb 9 ounces or 90 ounces? Explain.

____

21. Estimate the number of pounds in 700 ounces. ________________

22. Estimate the number of tons in 19,680 pounds. ________________

Name ______________________________

Practice 11-7

Grams and Kilograms

Use mental math to change to kilograms or grams.

1. 3 kg = __________ g

2. 2,500 g = __________ kg

3. 6.8 kg = __________ g

4. 4,301 g = __________ kg

5. 0.022 kg = __________ g

6. 1.542 kg = __________ g

7. 35,000 g = __________ kg

8. 89,901 g = __________ kg

9. 77 g = __________ kg

10. 100 kg = __________ g

11. 2.21 kg = __________ g

12. 2 g = __________ kg

13. 978 g = __________ kg

14. 6,082 g = __________ kg

15. 0.23 kg = __________ g

16. 20.4 kg = __________ g

17. How many kilograms?

227 g

____

18. How many grams?

15 kg

____

19. How many kilograms?

4.5 g

____

20. How many grams?

12.35 kg

____

21. Apples cost $2.20 per kilogram. You need 500 g of apples to put in a fruit salad. How much money will you need to buy the apples?

____

Name ______________________________

Practice
11-8

Temperature

Write each temperature in Celsius and Fahrenheit.

1.

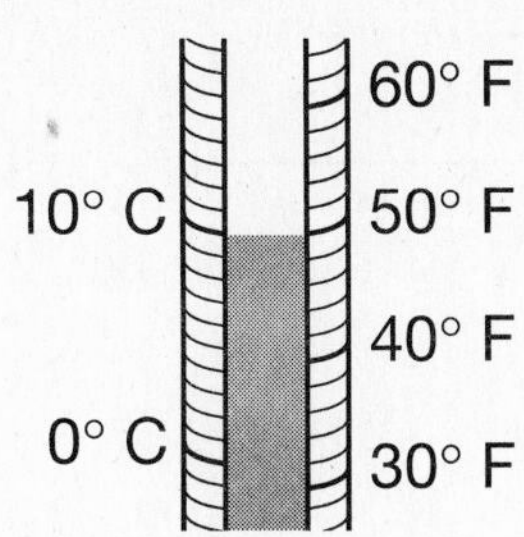

____

2.

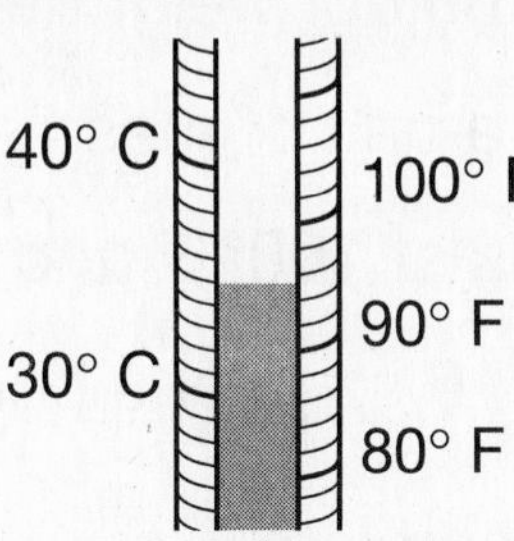

____

3.

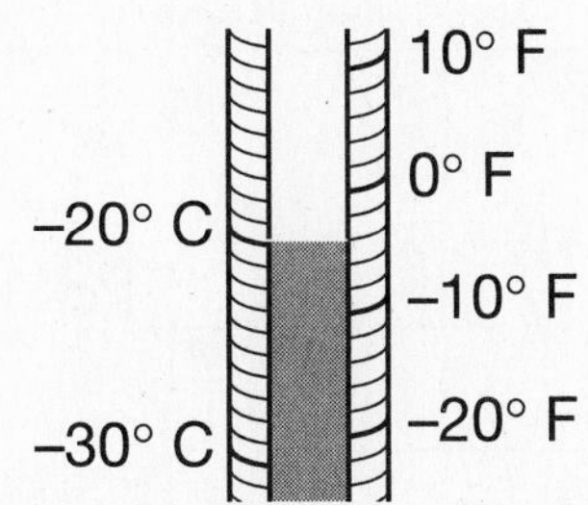

____

4.

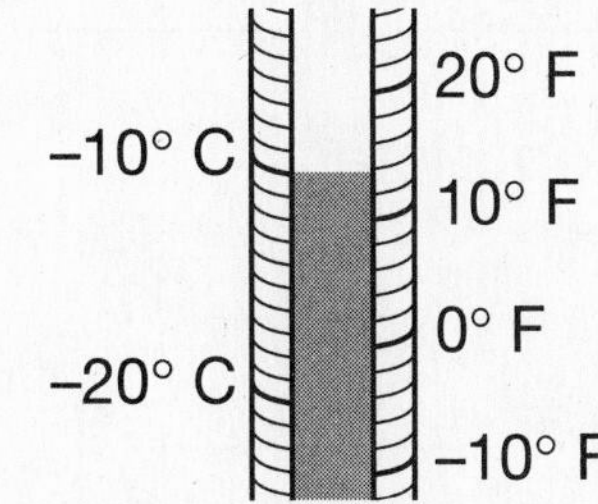

____

5.

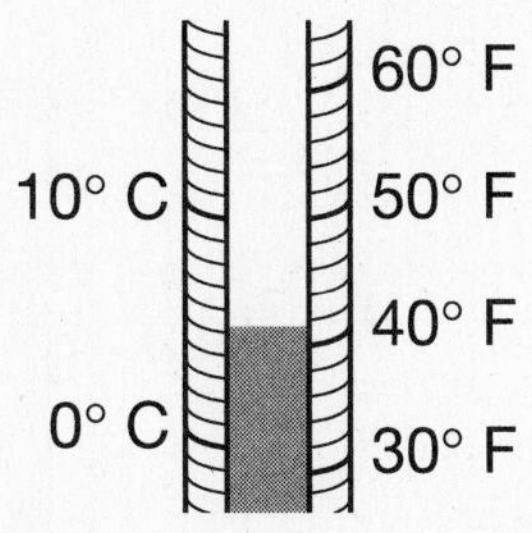

____

6.

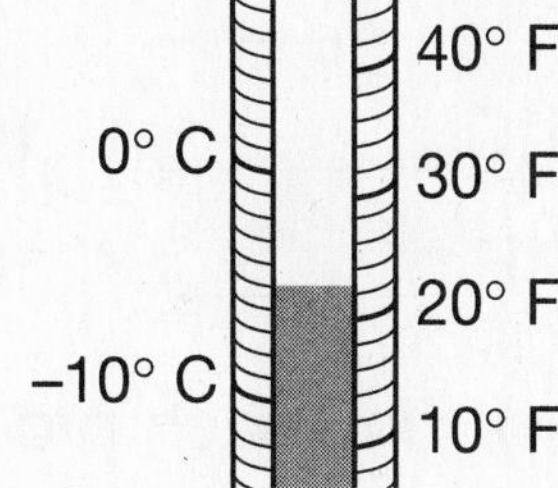

____

Find each change in temperature.

7. 22°C to 36°C __________

8. 18°F to 32°F __________

9. 40°F to 12°F __________

10. –2°C to –30°C __________

11. –5°C to 14°C __________

12. 86°F to 101°F __________

13. Which decrease in temperature would feel cooler: 35°C or 35°F? Explain.

____

____

Name ______________________________

Practice
Chapter 11
Section B

Review and Practice

Vocabulary Write true or false for each statement.

1. A ton is a unit of weight equal to 2,000 lb. __________
2. A gram is a unit of mass equal to 1,000 kg. __________
3. Water boils at 100° F and 212°C. __________
4. There are 16 oz in one pound. __________

(Lesson 6) Complete.

5. 80 oz = __________ lb **6.** 8 T = __________ lb

7. 54 oz = ______ lb ______ oz **8.** 31 lb = __________ oz

(Lesson 7) Complete.

9. 1.45 kg = __________ g **10.** 34,980 g = __________ kg

11. 0.0008 kg = __________ g **12.** 204 g = __________ kg

(Lesson 8) Use the thermometer to find each change in temperature.

13. 35°C to 42°C ________ **14.** 32°F to –4°F ________

15. –7°C to 15°C ________ **16.** 50°F to 83°F ________

17. 18°F to 37°F ________ **18.** 28°C to –1°C ________

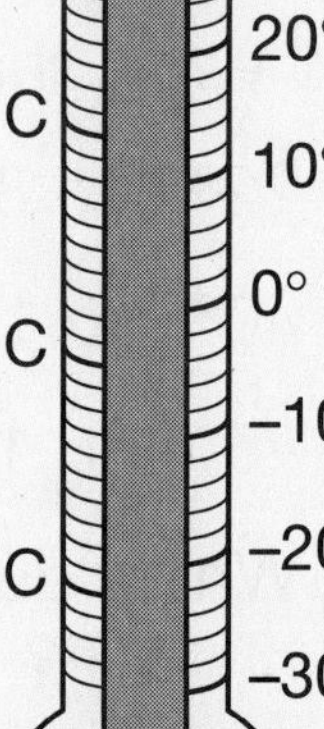

(Mixed Review) Find each product or quotient.

19. $\begin{array}{r} 819 \\ \times\ 26 \\ \hline \end{array}$ **20.** $\begin{array}{r} 271 \\ \times\ 38 \\ \hline \end{array}$ **21.** $\begin{array}{r} 358 \\ \times\ 46 \\ \hline \end{array}$

22. $16\overline{)58}$ **23.** $12\overline{)37}$ **24.** $15\overline{)72}$

Name ______________________________

Practice
11-9

Exploring Volume

Find each volume.

1.

_______ units^3

2.

_______ units^3

3.

_______ units^3

4.

_______ units^3

Complete.

4. l = 10 cm

w = 5 cm

h = 5 cm

V = [ ]

5. l = 8 in.

w = 3 in.

h = 5 in.

V = [ ]

6. l = 10 ft

w = 10 ft

h = 8.5 ft

V = [ ]

7. l = 6 ft

w = 8 ft

h = 11 ft

V = [ ]

8. Use mental math to estimate the volume of a box whose dimensions are 11 m × 17 m × 13 m. _______

Name ___________________________

Practice 11-10

Customary Units of Capacity

Complete.

1. 1 pt = ☐ qt

2. 2 qt = ☐ c

3. $\frac{1}{2}$ gal = ☐ fl oz

4. $\frac{1}{2}$ c = ☐ tbsp

5. 24 fl oz = ☐ pt

6. 20 pt = ☐ gal

Use the drawings to answer **7–12**.

7. ☐ pt of mayonnaise

8. ☐ qt of apple cider

9. ☐ c of milk

10. ☐ c of maple syrup

11. ☐ oz of vinegar

12. ☐ pt of barbecue sauce

13. Nathan says 2 gallons is greater than 200 fl oz. Is he correct? Explain.

____

____

Name ______________________

Practice
11-11

Metric Units of Capacity

Complete.

1. 8,000 mL = ☐ L
2. 750 mL = ☐ L
3. 3 L = ☐ mL
4. 3.75 L = ☐ mL
5. 36 mL = ☐ L
6. 4 L = ☐ mL
7. 40 L = ☐ mL
8. 400 L = ☐ mL
9. 0.4 L = ☐ mL
10. 1.75 L = ☐ mL
11. 480 mL = ☐ L
12. 50 mL = ☐ L
13. 0.22 L = ☐ mL
14. 0.059 L = ☐ mL
15. 16 mL = ☐ L
16. 1 mL = ☐ L
17. 0.71 L = ☐ mL
18. 1.6 L = ☐ mL
19. 4,360 mL = ☐ L
20. 621 mL = ☐ L

Use the drawings to answer **21–24**.

75 mL

3.5 L

50 mL

0.25 L

21. ☐ mL of milk
22. ☐ mL of juice
23. ☐ L of perfume
24. ☐ L of vanilla

Name ____________________

Practice 11-12

Connecting Volume, Mass, and Capacity

Write the number for each.

1. 1,800 mL of water would fill a(n) ☐ cm^3 container.

2. 2.9 kg of water would fill a(n) ☐ mL container.

3. 1.25 L water has a mass of ☐ kg.

4. A 50 cm^3 container can hold ☐ L.

5. Complete.

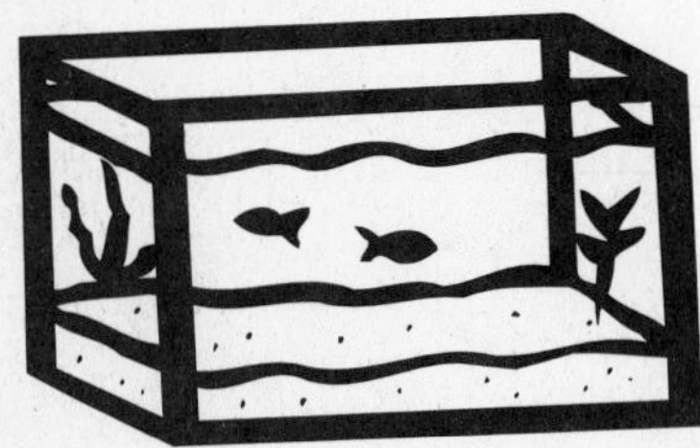
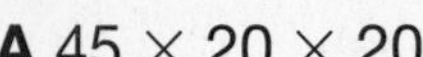

A 45 × 20 × 20 **B** 25 × 22 × 26 **C** 15 × 12 × 10 **D** Mass = 20.5kg

	Volume (cm^3)	Amount of Water (L)	Amount of Water (mL)	Mass of Water (kg)	Mass of Water (g)
Aquarium A					
Aquarium B					
Aquarium C					
Aquarium D					

6. Describe how you can calculate the amount and mass of water an aquarium can hold if you know its dimensions.

____

Name ______________________________

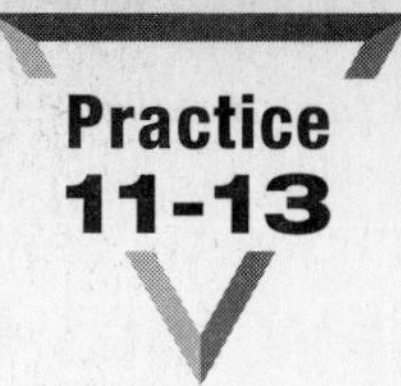

Compare Strategies: Solve a Simpler Problem/Draw a Picture

Use Solve a Simpler Problem to solve the problem.

1. Mr. Mansfield likes to make pancakes for visitors. His basic recipe makes enough for 2 adults and 1 child. The recipe calls for 2 cups of flour and 2 eggs. Mr. Mansfield wants to know how much flour he needs to make pancakes for 10 adults and 5 children.

   a. How much flour will he need to make pancakes for 4 adults and 2 children? ______________

   b. How much flour will he need to make pancakes for 6 adults and 3 children? ______________

   c. How many people could he serve if he used 8 cups of flour? ______________

   d. How much flour will he need to make pancakes for 10 adults and 5 children? ______________

   e. Describe the pattern you see.

   ____

   ____

   ____

Use Solve a Simpler Problem or any strategy to solve each problem.

2. Regina plants her tomato garden in rows of 6 and labels her plants with letters of the alphabet. For example, the plants in the first row were labeled A–F. In which row is plant W located?

   ____

3. Mrs. Maynor has an interesting doll collection. Half of her dolls are baby dolls and $\frac{2}{3}$ of these are antique. The other half are fashion and rag dolls. All 15 of her fashion dolls are quite new but they only make up $\frac{1}{10}$ of the collection. How many antique baby dolls does she have?

   ____

Name ___________________________

Review and Practice

Vocabulary Write a definition for each word.

1. mass ___________________________

____

2. volume ___________________________

____

(Lesson 9) Find each volume.

3.

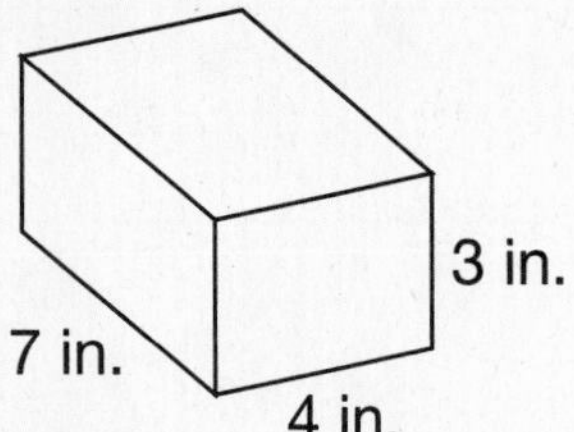

____

4.

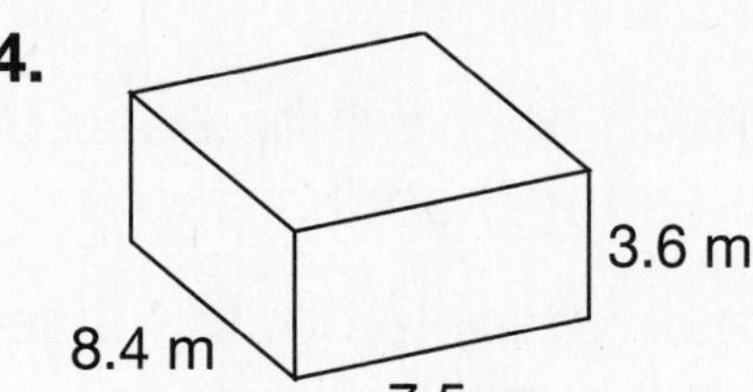

____

(Lessons 10 and 11) Complete.

5. 64 fl oz = __________ c

6. $6\frac{1}{2}$ gal = __________ pt

7. 10 tbsp = __________ fl oz

8. 48 fl oz = __________ qt

9. 0.5 L = __________ mL

10. 893 mL = __________ L

(Lesson 12) Complete.

11.

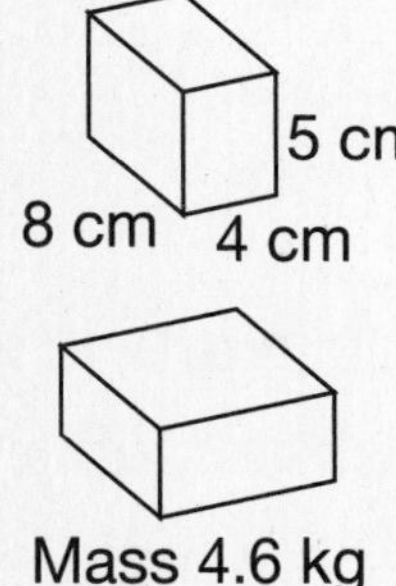

Mass 4.6 kg

Volume (cm^3)	Amount of Liquid (L)	Amount of Liquid (mL)	Mass of Liquid (kg)	Mass of Liquid (g)

(Mixed Review) Find each product.

12. $\frac{6}{9} \times \frac{5}{6} =$ __________

13. $\frac{8}{10} \times \frac{3}{4} =$ __________

Name ______________________________

Practice
Chapters 1–11

Cumulative Review

(Chapter 1 Lesson 4) Find the range, mode, and median for each set of data.

1. 6, 16, 21, 6, 17

range __________

mode __________

median __________

2. 1.5, 10, 9.8, 6.2, 5.7, 3, 4.5

range __________

mode __________

median __________

(Chapter 2 Lesson 18) Find each difference.

3. $\begin{array}{r} \$6.20 \\ -\ 2.49 \\ \hline \end{array}$

4. $\begin{array}{r} \$34.00 \\ -\ 5.75 \\ \hline \end{array}$

5. $\begin{array}{r} \$4.02 \\ -\ 0.53 \\ \hline \end{array}$

6. $\begin{array}{r} 3.41 \\ -\ 1.88 \\ \hline \end{array}$

(Chapter 9 Lesson 3) Use rounding, benchmarks, or compatible numbers to estimate each product.

7. $\frac{3}{4} \times 81$ __________

8. $3\frac{2}{7} \times 10$ __________

9. $1\frac{2}{3} \times 8$ __________

10. $\frac{5}{9} \times 22$ __________

(Chapter 10 Lessons 11 and 13) Find each area.

11. 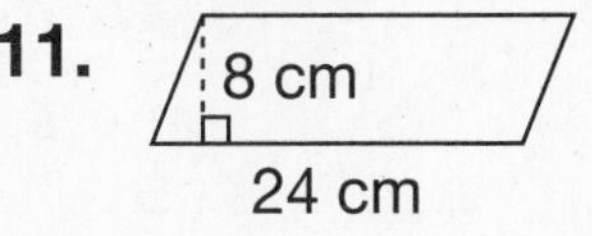

____

12. 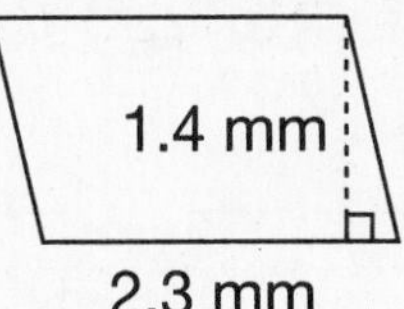

____

13. 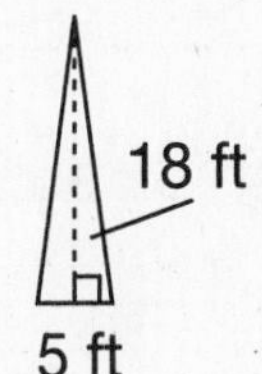

____

(Chapter 11 Lesson 7) Complete.

14. 385 kg = __________ g

15. 68 g = __________ kg

16. 19.3 kg = __________ g

17. 6,472 g = __________ kg

(Chapter 11 Lesson 8) Find each change in temperature.

18. 27°C to 8°C __________

19. 18°F to −7°F __________

20. −5°C to 19°C __________

21. 82°F to 45°F __________

Name ______________________

Practice 12-1

Ratios

Write each ratio in three ways. Simplify.

1. cats to kittens ________ ________ ________

2. puppies to dogs ________ ________ ________

3. rabbits to bunnies ________ ________ ________

4. chicks to chickens ________ ________ ________

5. large fish to small fish ________ ________ ________

6. ducklings to ducks ________ ________ ________

7. Which shows the ratio 1:2? ________ 1:3? ________

A. frogs to tadpoles **B.** tadpoles to frogs **C.** frogs to tadpoles

Name ______________________________

Practice 12-2

Patterns in Ratio Tables

Complete.

1.

7	14			35
8		24		40

2.

3	6		12	
5			20	25

3.

5	10	15		
	12		24	30

4.

	8	12		20
10		30	40	

5.

	4		8	10
9	18	27		

6.

7		21	28	
		33		55

7. In a game, each player gets 3 letter cubes. Complete the ratio table that shows how many letter cubes for 2, 3, 4, 5, or 6 players.

Number of Players		3		5	6
Number of Cubes	6				

8. A table of equal ratios includes $\frac{10}{35}$.

   a. Name another ratio in the table. ______________________

   b. Write a proportion for these ratios.

   ____

9. A table of equal ratios includes $\frac{12}{18}$.

   a. Name another ratio in the table. ______________________

   b. Write a proportion for these ratios.

   ____

Name ______________________

Practice 12-3

Exploring Equal Ratios

Complete.

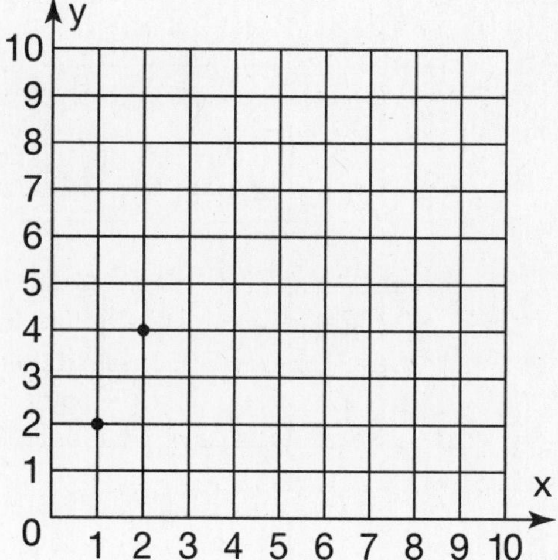

1. This graph shows two ordered pairs of equal ratios. Name the ratio it shows.

____

2. Plot another ratio on the graph that is equal to the others. Name the ratio.

____

Use grid paper. Plot the ordered pairs from each ratio table on the graph.

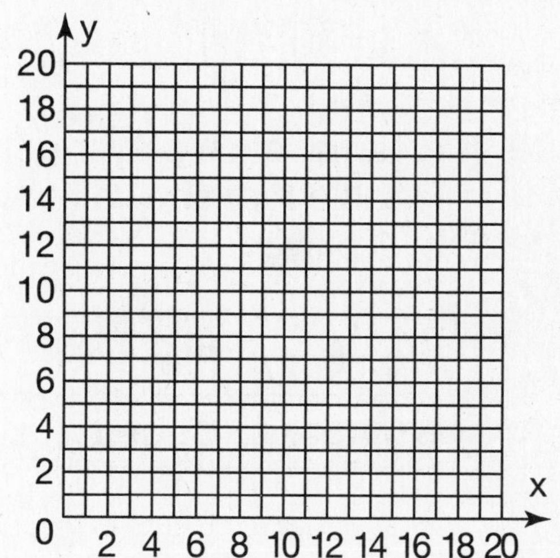

3.

4	8	12	16	20
3	6	9	12	15

4.

1	2	3	4	5
3	6	9	12	15

Plot a set of equal ratios on each graph.

5.

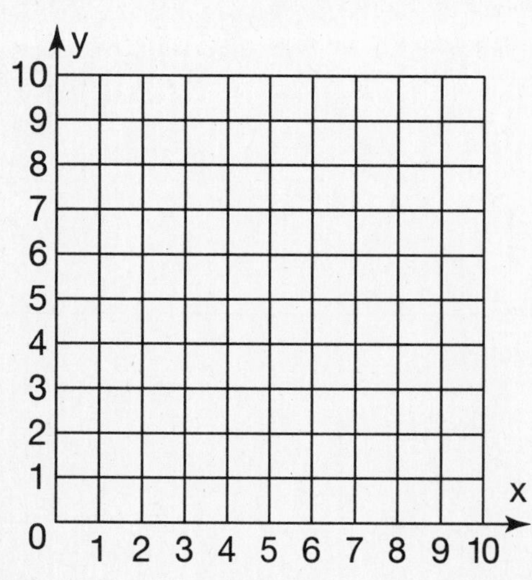

6.

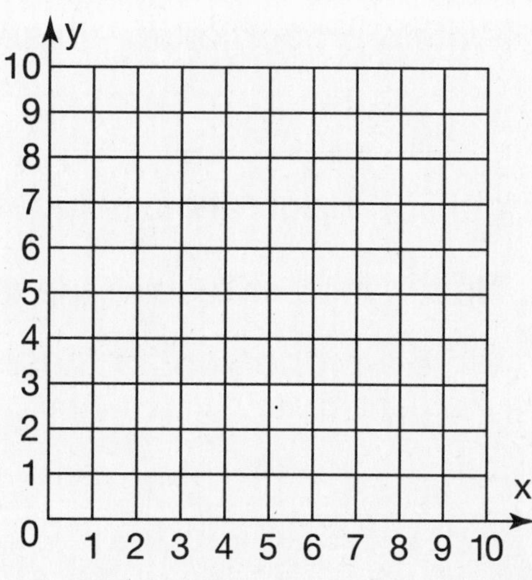

Name ____________________

Practice
12-4

Decision Making

Solve each problem.

1. A scale drawing of a car used the ratio of 1 in. to 12 in. In the drawing, the diameter of the front wheel measured 2 in. What was the diameter of the wheel on the car? ____________

2. The scale used by a map-maker was 1 cm to 15 km. If the distance between 2 cities is 60 km, how far apart will they be on the map? ____________

3. The Empire State Building is 1,250 ft tall. A toy model is built to a scale of 1 in. to 50 ft. How tall is the model?

   ____

4. A scale drawing of a garden is 4 in. by 5 in. The real garden is 20 ft by 25 ft. What does 1 in. represent in the drawing?

   ____

5. David is making a scale model of the moon, and he wants to use a beach ball. The diameter of the moon is 2,160 mi. The diameter of the beach ball is 3 ft.

   a. On David's model, how many miles could be represented by 1 ft? ____________

   b. How many miles could be represented by 1 in.?

   ____

6. A picture of a whale uses the scale 1 cm to 3 m. If the whale is actually 12 m long, how long is it in the drawing?

   ____

7. A billboard artist drew a glass of milk 18 ft tall. The real glass of milk she copied was 6 in. tall.

   a. At the same scale, how tall will she have to draw an apple that is 3 in. tall? ____________

   b. How long should she draw a banana that is 8 in. long?

   ____

Name ______________________________

Practice
Chapter 12
Section A

Review and Practice

Vocabulary Complete each sentence with a word from the list.

proportion   scale   equal ratios

1. A ______________ is a statement that two ratios are equal.

2. Ratios that give the same comparison are called ______________ .

3. A ______________ is a ratio that shows the relationship between a scale drawing and the actual object.

(Lesson 1) Write each ratio in three ways. Simplify.

4. pencils to erasers

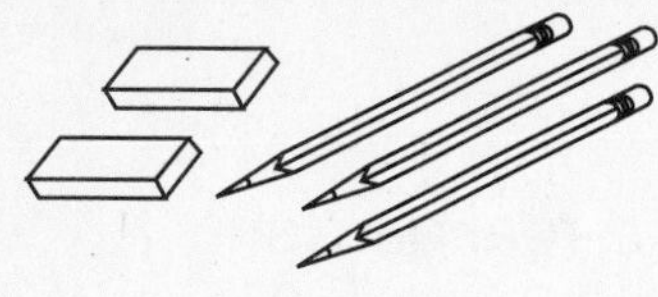

__________ __________

____

5. rectangles to triangles

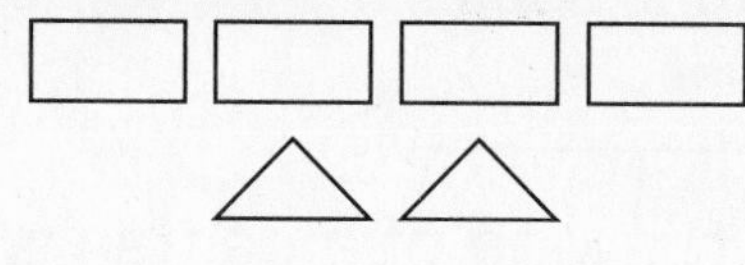

__________ __________

____

(Lesson 2) Complete.

6. For an essay test, the teacher gave 4 sheets of paper to each student. Complete a ratio table to show how many sheets would be given out in all if there were 1, 2, 3, 4, or 5 students needing paper.

Students	1				
Paper	4				

(Lesson 3) Plot the ordered pairs from the ratio table on the graph.

7.

3	6	9	12
1	2	3	4

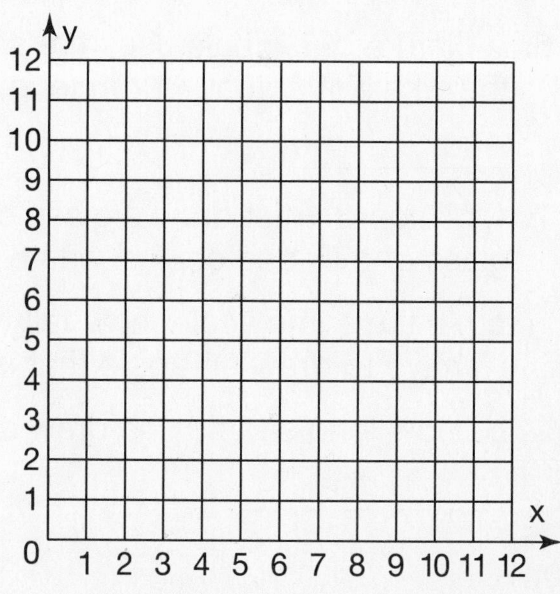

(Mixed Review) Write two equivalent fractions for each fraction.

8. $\frac{3}{10}$ = __________ = __________

9. $\frac{16}{20}$ = __________ = __________

Name ______________________________

Practice 12-5

Exploring Percent Patterns

1. Use the table to help you complete these sentences.

a. Equivalents of tenths are multiples of ______ %.

b. Equivalents of fifths are multiples of ______ %.

c. Equivalents of halves are multiples of ______ %.

Halves	Fifths	Tenths	Percents
		$\frac{1}{10}$	10%
	$\frac{1}{5}$	$\frac{2}{10}$	20%
		$\frac{3}{10}$	30%
	$\frac{2}{5}$	$\frac{4}{10}$	40%
$\frac{1}{2}$		$\frac{5}{10}$	50%

Complete each pattern. You may use a calculator to help.

2. $\frac{1}{8}$ = ________ %

$\frac{2}{8}$ = ________ %

$\frac{3}{8}$ = ________ %

$\frac{4}{8}$ = ________ %

3. $\frac{1}{4}$ = ________ %

$\frac{2}{4}$ = ________ %

$\frac{3}{4}$ = ________ %

$\frac{4}{4}$ = ________ %

4. $\frac{1}{6}$ = ________ %

$\frac{2}{6}$ = ________ %

$\frac{3}{6}$ = ________ %

$\frac{4}{6}$ = ________ %

5. $\frac{1}{3}$ = ________ %

$\frac{2}{3}$ = ________ %

$\frac{3}{3}$ = ________ %

6. Explain how knowing $\frac{1}{2}$ = 50% can help you to find the percent equivalent of $\frac{2}{4}$.

____

Name ______________________

Practice
12-6

Estimating Percent of a Number

Estimate.

1. 76% of 80 ______

2. 61% of 20 ______

3. 30% of 32 ______

4. $16\frac{2}{3}$% of 54 ______

5. 22% of 40 ______

6. 49% of 200 ______

7. 64% of 60 ______

8. 12.5% of 41 ______

9. 27% of 99 ______

10. 19% of 40 ______

11. 75% of 82 ______

12. 71% of 110 ______

13. 42% of 105 ______

14. 12.5% of 161 ______

15. 67% of 20 ______

16. 32% of 152 ______

16. Explain how finding 25% of 160 can help you estimate 73% of 160.

______

______

17. Explain how finding $\frac{1}{6}$ of 18 can help you find $16\frac{2}{3}$% of 17.

______

______

18. Amanda says she can use the benchmark $\frac{1}{4}$ to estimate the sale price of a hat that is 75% off. Explain how she can do this.

______

Name ______________________

Practice
12-7

Finding Percent of a Number

Choose a method. Find the percent of each.

1. 4% of 7.25 = ________

2. 10% of 8 = ________

3. 80% of $8.20 = ________

4. 45% of 800= ________

5. 25% of 500 = ________

6. 85% of 40 = ________

7. 75% of 24 = ________

8. 30% of $89 = ________

9. 8% of 64 = ________

10. 12% of 450 = ________

11. 65% of 720 = ________

12. 50% of 126 = ________

13. 5% of 800 = ________

14. 15% of 200 = ________

15. 23% of 400 = ________

16. 6% of 10 = ________

17. 95% of 575 = ________

18. 53% of 120 = ________

19. 48% of 82 = ________

20. 25% of 280 = ________

21. 80% of 650 = ________

22. 30% of 400 = ________

23. Since 30% of 60 = 18, 60% of 60 = ________

Explain. ______________________

24. Since 80% of 45 = 36, 40% of 90 = ________

Explain. ______________________

____

25. If a percent of a number equals the number, what percent of the number was taken? ________

Name ___________________________

Review and Practice

Vocabulary

1. Give 5 examples of common percent benchmarks.

____

(Lesson 5) Complete each pattern. You may use a calculator to help.

2. $\frac{6}{25}$ = ________ %
$\frac{7}{25}$ = ________ %
$\frac{8}{25}$ = ________ %
$\frac{9}{25}$ = ________ %

3. $\frac{9}{20}$ = ________ %
$\frac{10}{20}$ = ________ %
$\frac{11}{20}$ = ________ %
$\frac{12}{20}$ = ________ %

(Lesson 6) Estimate.

4. $33\frac{1}{3}$% of 70 ____________

5. 18% of 51 ____________

6. 11% of 99 ____________

7. 25% of 844 ____________

(Lesson 7) Find the percent of each.

8. 3% of 4.5 = ________

9. 12% of 14 = ________

10. 48% of $50,000 = ________

11. 1% of $3.45= ________

12. 90% of 83 = ________

13. 7% of 24.8 = ________

14. 15% of $25.15 = ________

15. 100% of 21 = ________

16. 42% of 103 = ________

17. 99% of 23 = ________

(Mixed Review) Multiply or divide.

18. 256×3.41

19. 509×4.87

20. 360×13.9

21. $35\overline{)469}$

22. $83\overline{)8{,}597}$

23. $21\overline{)\$2.31}$

Name ___________________________

Practice 12-8

Exploring Fairness

Complete the table. Tell if the probability of the outcomes is equally likely or not. If the outcomes are not equal, tell which outcome is more likely. Then decide if the situation is fair or unfair.

	Situation	Probability of Outcome	Fairness
1.	Spin the spinner. Outcomes: 1, 3, 5, or 7		
2.	Choose a coin. Outcomes: dime, quarter, or nickel		
3.	Draw a card. Outcomes: A or B		
4.	Draw a card. Outcomes: odd or even		

5. What are the possible outcomes of two spins of the spinner in **1**?

____

____

6. Two cubes are painted red on 3 sides and blue on 3 sides. Tina and Charlene toss the cubes. Tina earns one point when both cubes land with one color up. Charlene earns one point if the cubes land with both colors up. Is this a fair game? Explain.

____

____

7. Sam and Randy have a bag of marbles. There are 20 red marbles and 25 blue marbles. In turn, they reach into the bag without looking and take out 2 marbles. Sam earns one point if both marbles are the same color. Randy earns one point if the marbles are different colors. Is this a fair game? Explain.

____

Name ______________________________

Practice
12-9

Exploring Predicting from Samples

A bowl contains black beans, red beans, and white beans. The list shows the results of three samples.

Sample 1	11	black
	10	red
	4	white
Sample 2	8	black
	12	red
	5	white
Sample 3	15	black
	10	red

1. a. How many beans are there all together in the 3 samples? __________

   b. How many black beans were in the samples? __________

   c. How many red beans were in the samples? __________

   d. How many white beans were in the samples? __________

2. Predict the most common color bean. __________

3. Predict the least common color bean. __________

4. If sample 2 were the only sample, what color bean would you predict to be the most common? __________

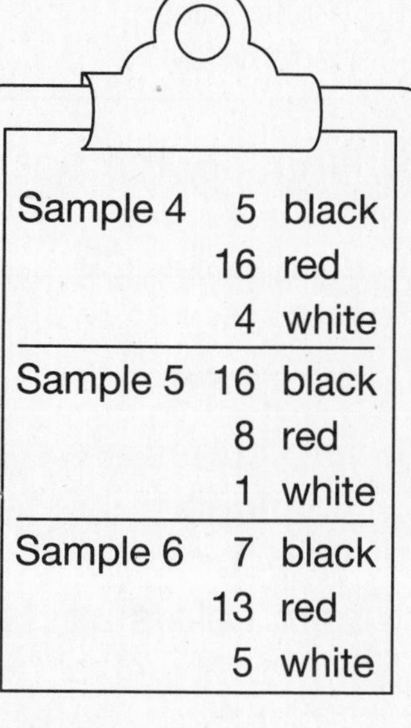

Sample 4 5 black
16 red
4 white
Sample 5 16 black
8 red
1 white
Sample 6 7 black
13 red
5 white

Three more samples (4, 5, 6) were taken.

5. In samples 4–6:

   a. What was the most common color bean? __________

   b. What was the least common color bean? __________

6. In samples 1–6 how many beans were:

   a. black __________ b. white __________ c. red __________

7. Describe the number of each color bean you think is in the bowl.

____

____

Name ____________________

Practice
12-10

Exploring Predicting from Experiments

Write the numbers 1, 3, 5, 7, and 9 twice, each on separate slips of paper. Put the slips of paper in a bag and use them to answer **1–7**.

1. Experiment to find how many different sums will occur by selecting 2 slips of paper. __________

2. Which do you think is more likely to occur; a sum of 10 or a sum of 4? Explain.

____

____

3. Is the chance of getting an odd number sum certain, likely, equally likely as unlikely, or impossible? Explain.

____

4. Which 4 sums are least likely to occur? __________

5. Name one sum that will never occur.

____

6. What do you think is more likely to occur when you take 2 slips of paper: getting 2 different numbers or 2 matching numbers? Explain.

____

____

7. Which do you think is more likely to occur; getting a sum less than 10 or a sum greater than or equal to 10? Explain.

____

____

Name ______________________________

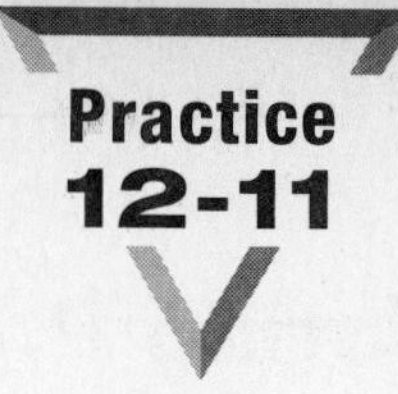

Analyzing Strategies: Make an Organized List

1. James won 4 trophies for sports. He won 1 each for soccer, football, basketball, and tennis. How many different ways can he arrange his trophies in a straight line on his bedroom shelf?

   a. Call the sports S, F, B, and T. List all the combinations if S is the first trophy on the shelf.

   ____

   b. If F is first: ______________________________

   c. If B is first: ______________________________

   d. If T is first: ______________________________

   e. How many different ways can the trophies be arranged? __________

2. The next year, James wins another trophy for hockey. How many different ways can he arrange the 5 trophies?

   ____

3. The football team will choose 2 colors for their uniforms. They can choose white, red, blue, or gold. A red and white uniform is the same as a white and red uniform. How many color combinations can they choose?

   ____

4. The basketball team travels 26 miles from school to their game. They have been traveling for 20 minutes. When they travel 5 miles farther, they will be halfway there. How far have they traveled?

   ____

Name ____________________

Practice
12-12

Expressing Probabilities as Fractions

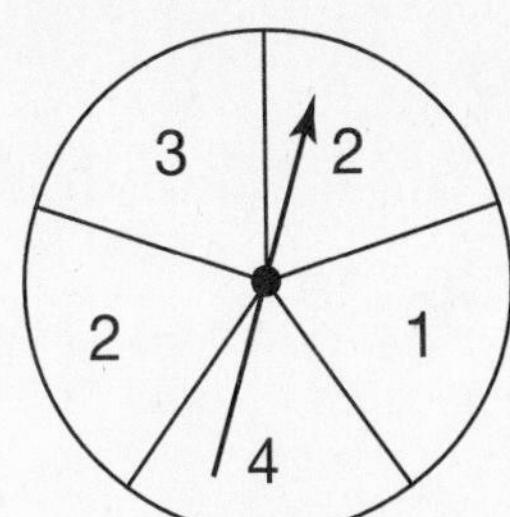

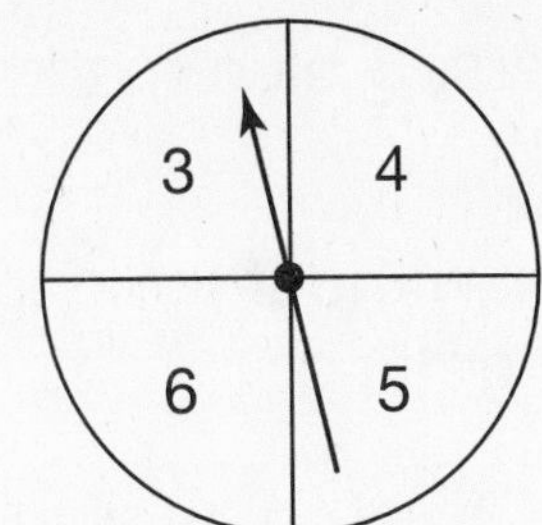

A quiz show contestant spins each spinner once and adds the numbers together. If the sum is 6 or 8, the contestant wins $100. If the sum is 4 or 10, the contestant wins $1,000.

Make tree diagrams to show the possible sums. Give the probability of each sum as a fraction. Simplify.

1. 7 __________ **2.** 4 __________ **3.** 5 __________

4. 6 __________ **5.** 8 __________ **6.** 9 __________

7. 10 __________ **8.** 6 or 8 __________ **9.** 4 or 10 __________

10. What is the probability of getting a sum of 2? __________

11. What is the probability of gettting a sum of 4, 5, 6, 7, 8, 9, or 10? __________

12. Does the contestant have a greater chance of winning $100 or $1,000? __________

13. There are 3 red, 5 green, and 4 yellow marbles in a bag. Without looking, you choose one. Give the probability of choosing a marble of each color. Express as a fraction. Simplify.

a. red __________ **b.** green __________ **c.** yellow __________

Name ______________________________

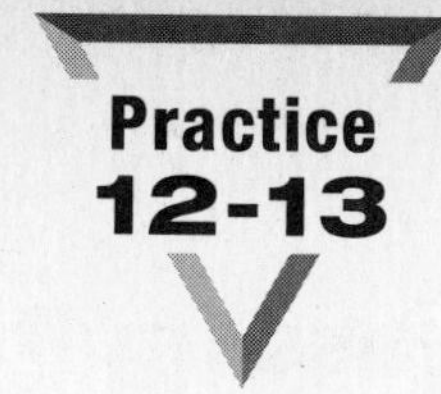

Exploring Expected and Experimental Results

A bag contains 5 red markers, 3 blue markers, and 2 green markers.

1. If you select one marker without looking, what is the expected probability of getting:

a. a red marker? __________ **b.** a blue marker? __________

c. a green marker? __________ **d.** a purple marker? __________

2. Suppose you select a marker, record its color, and put it back in the bag. If you repeat this 50 times, how many times would you expect to select:

a. a red marker? __________ **b.** a blue marker? __________

c. a green marker? __________ **d.** a pink marker? __________

Use the spinner to answer **3–6**. Decide whether each result is likely or unlikely.

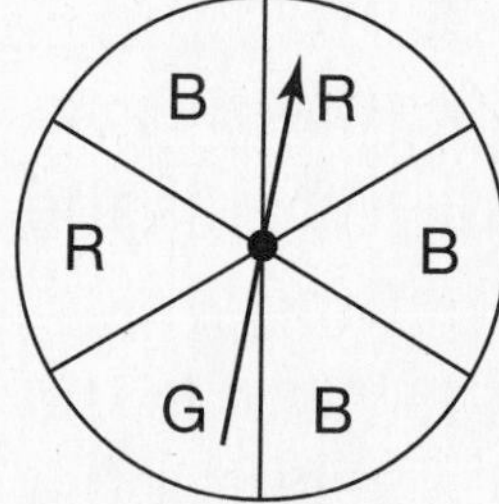

3. Outcome: R

Trial: 36 spins

Result: Get R, 14 times

____

4. Outcome: B

Trial: 300 spins

Result: Get B, 98 times

____

5. Outcome: G

Trial: 120 spins

Result: Get G, 95 times

____

6. Outcome: R or G

Trial: 200 spins

Result: Get R or G 95 times

____

7. A 1–6 number cube is tossed 200 times. About how many times would a number greater than 3 be expected?

____

Name ______________________

Practice
Chapter 12
Section C

Review and Practice

Vocabulary Write a definition for each.

1. outcome ______________________

2. probability ______________________

____

(Lesson 8) Use the spinner to answer **3** and **4**. Write if each game is fair or unfair.

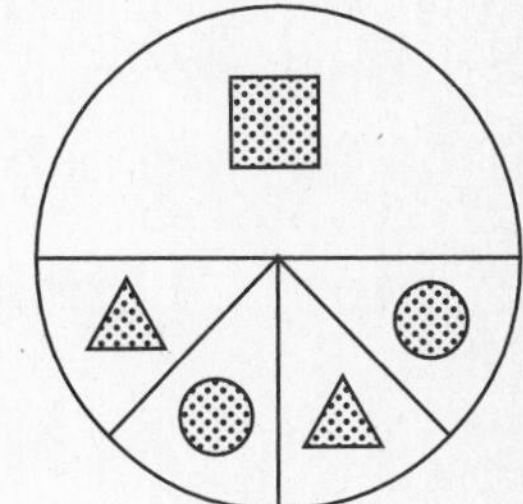

3. Player 1 gets 1 point if the spinner lands on a square. Player 2 gets 1 point if the spinner lands on a circle or a triangle. ________

4. Player 1 gets 1 point if the spinner lands on a square. Player 2 gets 1 point if the spinner lands on a triangle. ________

(Lesson 9) A bag contains different numbers of the letters A, B, C, and D. Use the sample results to answer **5** and **6**.

Sample 1

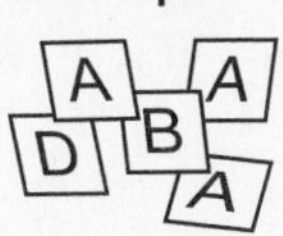

Sample 2

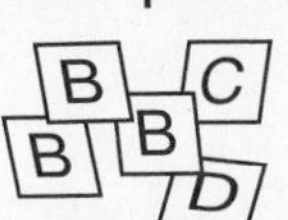

Sample 3

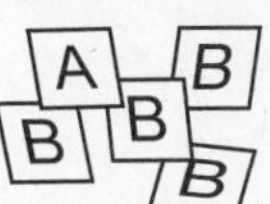

5. Predict the most common letter in the bag. ________

6. If Sample 1 were the only sample, what would you predict for the most common letter? ________

(Lessons 10, 11, and 13) Give all the outcomes for the experiment. Write whether they are equally likely or not.

7. Choose one number from the bag.

(Lesson 12) The numbers 1, 2, 7, 9, 12, and 13 are in a bag. Give the probability of each outcome as a fraction.

8. of pulling out an even number ________

9. of pulling out an odd number ________

(Mixed Review) Find each sum or difference.

10. 4.7 + 13.19 = ________ **11.** 51.8 – 27.36 = ________

Name ____________________

Cumulative Review

(Chapter 8 Lesson 13) Solve. Use any strategy.

1. Aaron gave half of his change to a friend. He then lost 5 cents. He had 50 cents left. How much money did he begin with? ____________

2. Tamara has a total of 12 sheets of construction paper. She has only red and green. She has 4 fewer green sheets than red. How many red sheets does she have? ________

(Chapter 9 Lesson 5) Find each product. Simplify.

3. $\frac{3}{4} \times \frac{4}{5} =$ ________ **4.** $\frac{5}{7} \times \frac{7}{9} =$ ________

5. $\frac{5}{6} \times \frac{6}{10} =$ ________ **6.** $\frac{5}{8} \times \frac{3}{5} =$ ________

(Chapter 11 Lesson 4) Find the surface area of each figure.

7.

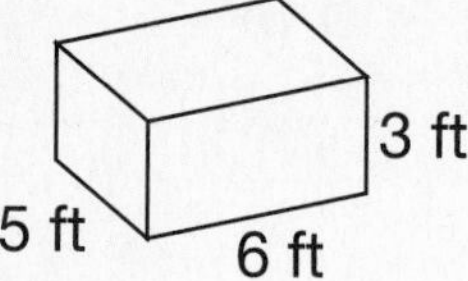

____

8.

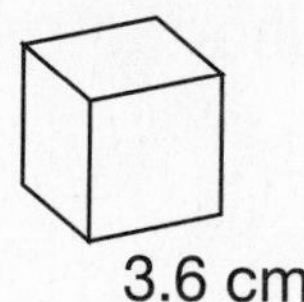

____

(Chapter 11 Lesson 11) Complete.

9. 0.9 L = ________ mL **10.** 560 mL = ________ L

(Chapter 12 Lesson 1) Write each ratio in three ways. Simplify.

11.

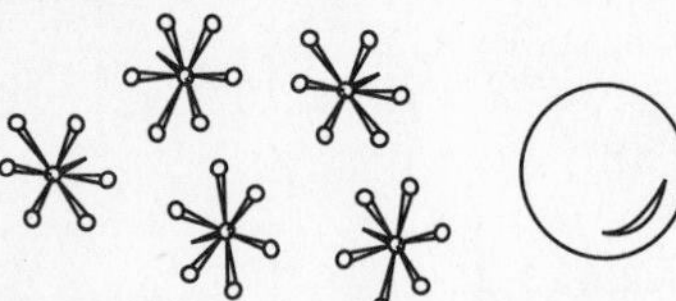

________ ________ ________

12.

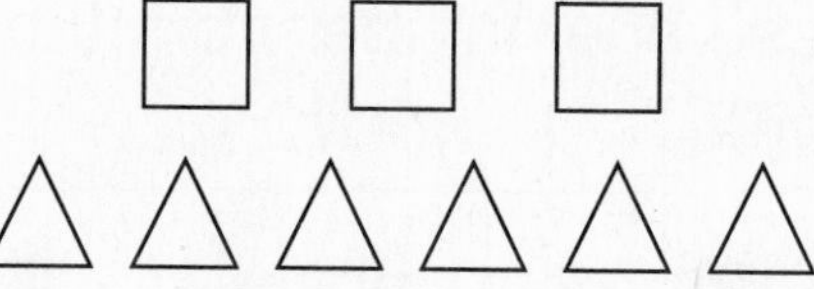

________ ________ ________

(Chapter 12 Lesson 7) Find the percent of each number.

13. 15% of \$28 = ________ **14.** 50% of 213 = ________

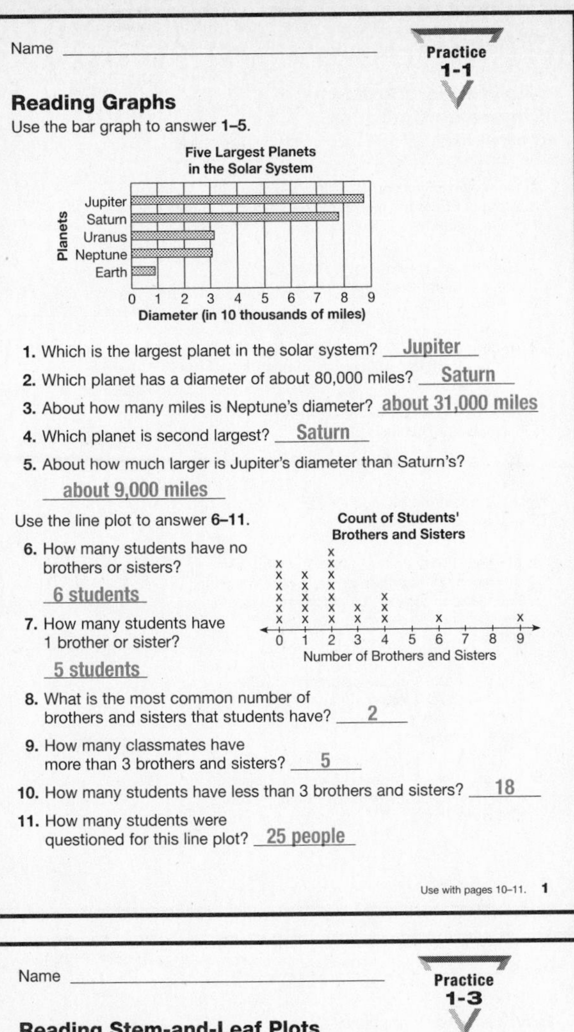

Name ______________________

Practice 1-1

Reading Graphs

Use the bar graph to answer **1–5**.

Five Largest Planets in the Solar System

1. Which is the largest planet in the solar system? <u>Jupiter</u>
2. Which planet has a diameter of about 80,000 miles? <u>Saturn</u>
3. About how many miles is Neptune's diameter? <u>about 31,000 miles</u>
4. Which planet is second largest? <u>Saturn</u>
5. About how much larger is Jupiter's diameter than Saturn's? <u>about 9,000 miles</u>

Use the line plot to answer **6–11**.

Count of Students' Brothers and Sisters

6. How many students have no brothers or sisters? <u>6 students</u>
7. How many students have 1 brother or sister? <u>5 students</u>
8. What is the most common number of brothers and sisters that students have? <u>2</u>
9. How many classmates have more than 3 brothers and sisters? <u>5</u>
10. How many students have less than 3 brothers and sisters? <u>18</u>
11. How many students were questioned for this line plot? <u>25 people</u>

Use with pages 10–11. **1**

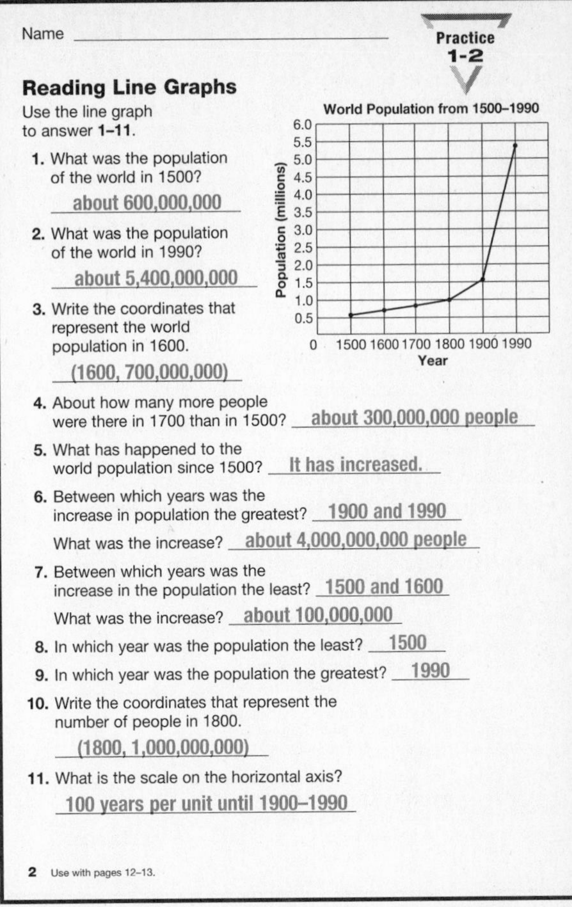

Name ______________________

Practice 1-2

Reading Line Graphs

Use the line graph to answer **1–11**.

World Population from 1500–1990

1. What was the population of the world in 1500? <u>about 600,000,000</u>
2. What was the population of the world in 1990? <u>about 5,400,000,000</u>
3. Write the coordinates that represent the world population in 1600. <u>(1600, 700,000,000)</u>
4. About how many more people were there in 1700 than in 1500? <u>about 300,000,000 people</u>
5. What has happened to the world population since 1500? <u>It has increased.</u>
6. Between which years was the increase in population the greatest? <u>1900 and 1990</u>

   What was the increase? <u>about 4,000,000,000 people</u>
7. Between which years was the increase in the population the least? <u>1500 and 1600</u>

   What was the increase? <u>about 100,000,000</u>
8. In which year was the population the least? <u>1500</u>
9. In which year was the population the greatest? <u>1990</u>
10. Write the coordinates that represent the number of people in 1800. <u>(1800, 1,000,000,000)</u>
11. What is the scale on the horizontal axis? <u>100 years per unit until 1900–1990</u>

2 Use with pages 12–13.

Name ______________________

Practice 1-3

Reading Stem-and-Leaf Plots

Every year, the best soccer teams in the state play in a state tournament. This plot shows the number of times the top ten teams have played in this tournament.

Use the plot to answer **1–4**.

Stem	Leaf
2	6 4 1
1	4 0
0	8 6 6 5

1. In what order are the stems arranged from top to bottom? <u>greatest to least</u>
2. How many teams have played 20 times or more? <u>3 teams</u>
3. Middletown has played in the state tournament the second greatest number of times. How many times have they played? <u>24</u>
4. River City and Yorktown have each played in the state tournament the same number of times. How many times have they played in the tournament? <u>6</u>

Mr. Morgan's class took part in a read-a-thon. This plot shows how many books his students read.

Stem	Leaf
2	4 3 1 2 0
1	9 4 3 7 4 0 0
0	8 9 3 9 9 8 5

Use the plot to answer **5-9**.

5. Emma read the most books. How many did she read? <u>24 books</u>
6. How many students participated in the read-a-thon? <u>19 students</u>
7. Did most students read more than 15 books? Explain. <u>No, only 7 students read more than 15 books.</u>
8. How many students read more than 20 books? <u>4 students</u>
9. What was the least number of books read? <u>3 books</u>

Use with pages 14–15. **3**

Name ______________________

Practice 1-4

Range, Mode, and Median

This line plot shows the number of hours spent doing homework for a week.

Hours Spent Doing Homework

0 1 2 3 4 5 6 7 8 9 10 11

Hours

Use the line and plot to answer **1** and **2**.

1. For the above data, give the
   a. range <u>8 hours</u> b. mode <u>8 hours, 5 hours</u>
   c. median <u>7 hours</u>
2. Did about half the students do homework for less than 6 hours? Explain. <u>No, because the median is 7 hours. About half the students did homework for less than 7 hours.</u>

Use the stem-and-leaf plot to answer **3–4**.

Points Scored by the Dallas Cowboys (1995)

Stem	Leaf
3	5 1 4 4 4 4 7
2	3 3 3 8 0 4 1
1	7 7

3. Give the: a. range <u>20 points</u>
   b. mode <u>34 points</u>
   c. median <u>26 points</u>
4. Did the Dallas Cowboys score more than 26 points in about half of the games they played in 1995? Explain. <u>yes, because the median is 26 points</u>

Use the line plot to answer **5–6**.

Price of Inline Skates

\$80 \$110 \$150 \$200

5. Give the:
   a. range <u>\$120</u> b. mode <u>\$110</u> c. median <u>\$110</u>
6. Is it true that most of the inline skates cost less than \$100? Explain. <u>No, because the median is \$110.</u>

4 Use with pages 16–17.

Name ______________________

Practice 1-5

Introduction to the Problem Solving Guide

How many BMX and mountain bikes were sold?

You can use the bar graph to learn how many BMX and mountain bikes were sold.

Use the graph to answer **1–5**.

Metro Bicycle Shop Weekly Sales

Bicycles Sold: 0 2 4 6 8 10 12 14 16 18 20 22

Types of Bicycles: Mountain BMX Road Tandem Children's

1. What information do you need to answer the question?
   The number of BMX and mountain bikes sold.
2. What operation would you use to solve the problem? addition
3. Give the answer. 17 + 22 = 39; 39 bikes

Choose the number sentence you would use to solve the problem.

4. How many more mountain bikes were sold than road bikes? B
   A. 22 + 6 = 28 **B.** 22 − 6 = 16
5. What is the total number of road and tandem bikes sold? A
   A. 6 + 1 = 7 **B.** 6 − 1 = 5

Use any strategy to solve each problem.

6. Roger bought a mountain bike for $130. He used $85 of his own money, and his father paid the rest. How much did his father pay? $45
7. One family bought 3 children's bicycles. Each cost the same amount. If their total bill was $225, what was the cost of each bicycle? $75
8. For 4 days, the bicycle shop sold the same number of bicycles each day. They sold a total of 52 bicycles in all. How many did they sell on the first day? 13 bicycles

Name ______________________

Practice 1-6

Analyze Word Problems: Choose an Operation

Choose the operation for each problem. Then solve each problem.

Jeffrey mows lawns and trims bushes during the spring. He charges $8 for each lawn mowed and $4 for each row of bushes he trims.

1. How much more money does Jeffrey make if he mows 1 lawn than if he trims 1 row of bushes? subtraction, $4
2. **a.** Jeffrey earned $20 for the bushes he trimmed. How many rows of bushes did he trim? division, 5
   b. How much money did he make mowing 5 lawns? multiplication, $40
   c. How much did he earn in all? addition, $60

Write the operation needed for each problem. Then solve each problem.

3. Martina delivers newspapers to 60 houses on her route. She had so many customers, she decided to give 12 customers to her brother. To how many houses does Martina deliver now? subtraction, 48
4. Louisa charges each customer the same amount to rake leaves. In one week, 3 of her customers paid her $18.75. How much did each customer pay? division, $6.25
5. Steven drinks 3 glasses of water a day. How many glasses of water does he drink in a week? multiplication, 21

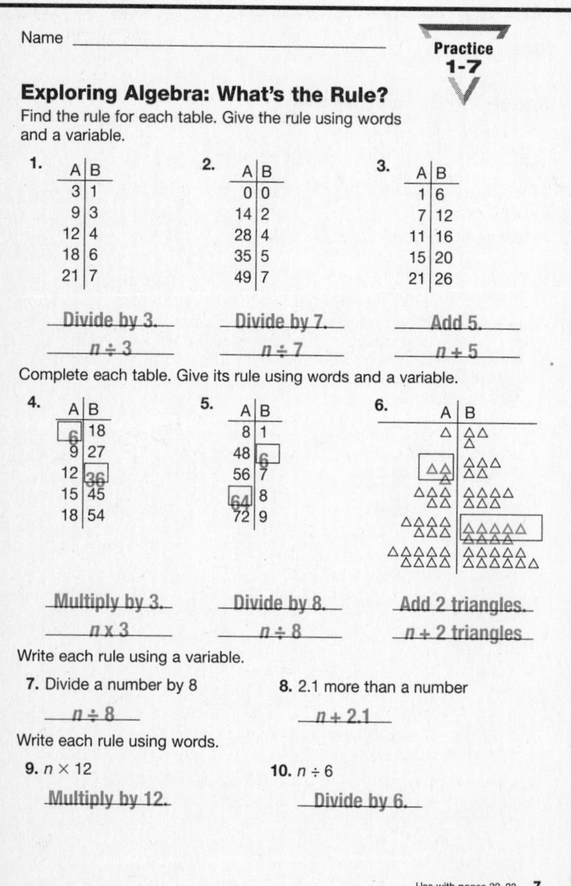

Name ______________________

Practice 1-7

Exploring Algebra: What's the Rule?

Find the rule for each table. Give the rule using words and a variable.

1.

A	B
3	1
9	3
12	4
18	6
21	7

Divide by 3. $n \div 3$

2.

A	B
0	0
14	2
28	4
35	5
49	7

Divide by 7. $n \div 7$

3.

A	B
1	6
7	12
11	16
15	20
21	26

Add 5. $n + 5$

Complete each table. Give its rule using words and a variable.

4.

A	B
6	18
9	27
12	36
15	45
18	54

Multiply by 3. $n \times 3$

5.

A	B
8	1
48	6
56	7
64	8
72	9

Divide by 8. $n \div 8$

6.

A	B
△	△△△
△△△	△△△△△
△△△△△	△△△△△△△
△△△△△△△	△△△△△△△△△
△△△△△△△△△	△△△△△△△△△△△

Add 2 triangles. n + 2 triangles

Write each rule using a variable.

7. Divide a number by 8 $n \div 8$
8. 2.1 more than a number $n + 2.1$

Write each rule using words.

9. $n \times 12$ Multiply by 12.
10. $n \div 6$ Divide by 6.

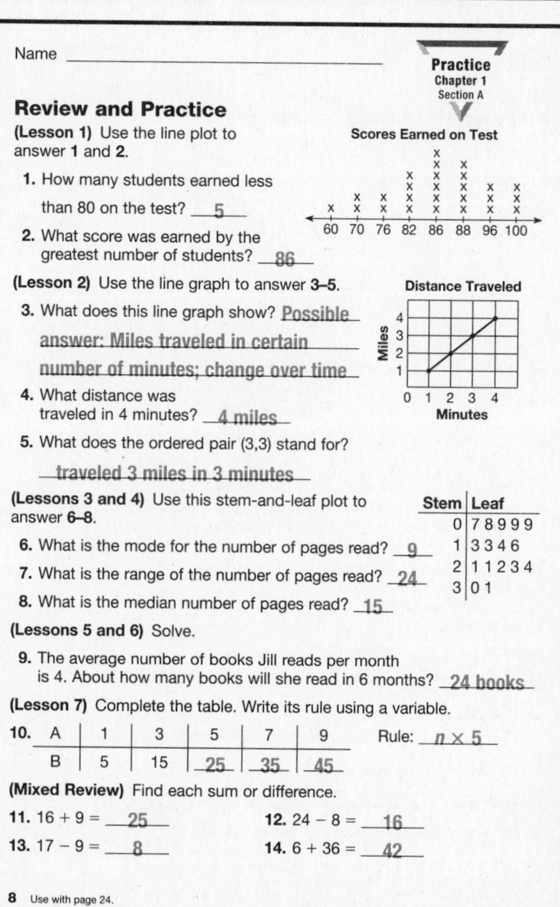

Name ______________________

Practice Chapter 1 Section A

Review and Practice

(Lesson 1) Use the line plot to answer **1** and **2**.

1. How many students earned less than 80 on the test? 5
2. What score was earned by the greatest number of students? 86

(Lesson 2) Use the line graph to answer **3–5**.

3. What does this line graph show? Possible answer: Miles traveled in certain number of minutes; change over time
4. What distance was traveled in 4 minutes? 4 miles
5. What does the ordered pair (3,3) stand for? traveled 3 miles in 3 minutes

(Lessons 3 and 4) Use this stem-and-leaf plot to answer **6–8**.

Stem	Leaf
0	7 8 9 9 9
1	3 3 4 6
2	1 1 2 3 4
3	0 1

6. What is the mode for the number of pages read? 9
7. What is the range of the number of pages read? 24
8. What is the median number of pages read? 15

(Lessons 5 and 6) Solve.

9. The average number of books Jill reads per month is 4. About how many books will she read in 6 months? 24 books

(Lesson 7) Complete the table. Write its rule using a variable.

10.

A	1	3	5	7	9
B	5	15	25	35	45

Rule: $n \times 5$

(Mixed Review) Find each sum or difference.

11. 16 + 9 = 25
12. 24 − 8 = 16
13. 17 − 9 = 8
14. 6 + 36 = 42

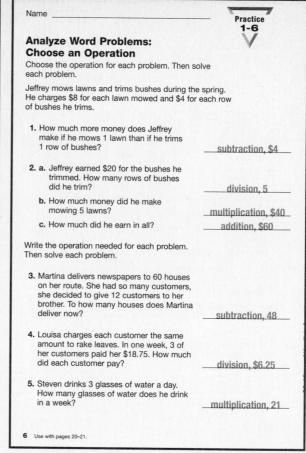

Name ______________________

Practice 1-8

Scales and Bar Graphs

Use the graphs to answer **1–5**.

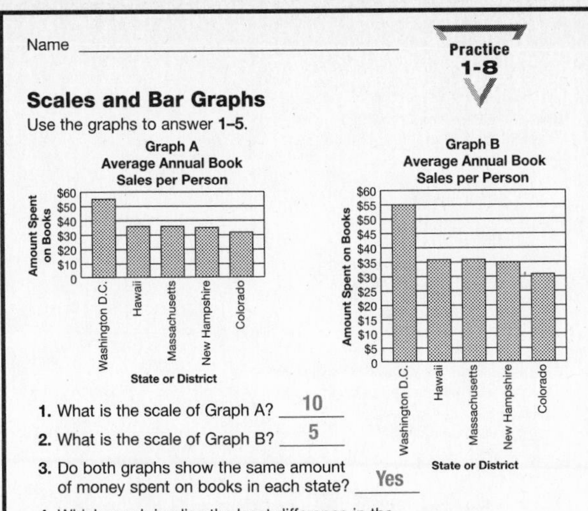

1. What is the scale of Graph A? 10
2. What is the scale of Graph B? 5
3. Do both graphs show the same amount of money spent on books in each state? Yes
4. Which graph implies the least difference in the amount of money spent on books in each state? Graph A
5. Which graph is easier to read? Explain. Possible answer: Graph B; the smaller scale makes comparisons easier.
6. Choose a scale and make a bar graph of the data in the table.

Check students' graphs.

Patton Middle School Students' Favorite Colors	
Color	Number of Students
blue	14
red	29
hot pink	25
green	12
yellow	36

7. What scale did you choose? Why?
Possible answers: 1, so the graph could be read easily; 2, so the graph would fit in the space

Name ______________________

Practice 1-9

Exploring Making Line Graphs

1. Line graphs are used to show changes or trends in data.
2. Use this table to make a line graph.

New York City Bus Riders	
Hour	Number of Riders (thousands)
12 P.M.	125
2 P.M.	115
4 P.M.	140
6 P.M.	185
8 P.M.	145

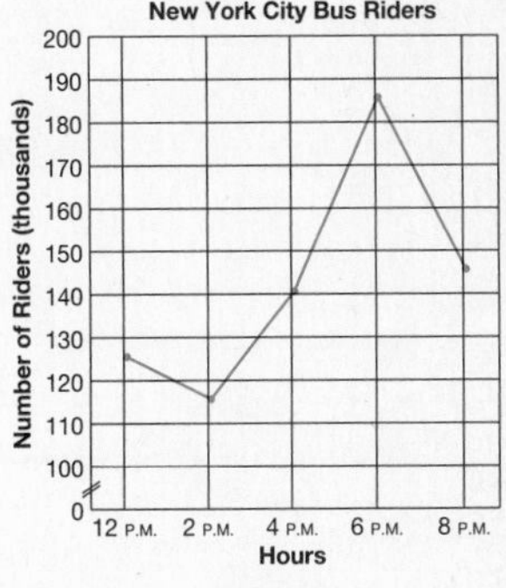

3. Use the graph to determine about how many riders there would be at 3 P.M. Possible answer: Between 115 and 140 thousand people; about 128,000 people
4. a. Between which times shown on the graph did the number of riders decrease? between 12 P.M. and 2 P.M., and between 6 P.M. and 8 P.M.

   b. Why do you think fewer people traveled at these times?
   Possible answer: Fewer people ride during the lunch hour and after rush hour.

Name ______________________

Practice 1-10

Exploring Making Stem-and-Leaf Plots

1. Make a stem-and-leaf plot for the temperature data.

Daily Highs for the Month of July in degrees Farenheit											
88	74	78	86	90	91	94	92	85	87	83	79
81	90	87	84	83	79	84	85	90	83	78	83

Stem	Leaf
7	4 8 8 9 9
8	1 3 3 3 3 4 4 5 5 6 7 7 8
9	0 0 0 1 2 4

2. Most of the temperatures fell between 80 and 90 degrees.

Use the table to answer **3–8**.

National Ice Hockey Final 1995–1996 Standings			
Atlantic Division	Wins	Pacific Division	Wins
Washington	39	Colorado	47
New Jersey	37	Vancouver	32
Philadelphia	45	Anaheim	35
New York	22	Calgary	34
Tampa Bay	38	Los Angeles	24
Florida	41	Edmonton	30
New York	41	San Jose	20

3. Make a stem-and-leaf plot for the Atlantic Division wins.

Stem	Leaf
4	1 1 5
3	7 8 9
2	2

4. Make a stem-and-leaf plot for the Pacific Division wins.

Stem	Leaf
4	7
3	0 2 4 5
2	0 4

5. Which division had more teams win 40–49 games? Atlantic
6. Which division had only one team win less than 30 games? Atlantic
7. The median number of games won by the:
   Atlantic Division: 39 Pacific Division: 32.
8. Describe the shapes of stem-and-leaf plots for the divisions.
   Possible answer: Have the same number of stems; however, Atlantic has more leaves in the 40–50 range.

Name ______________________

Practice 1-11

Analyze Strategies: Use Logical Reasoning

Use logical reasoning to solve each problem.

1. A family of four—mother, father, son, and daughter—sits down to have dinner together. Father and son sit across from one another, while the daughter sits to her father's right. Where does each person sit?

Mother

Father 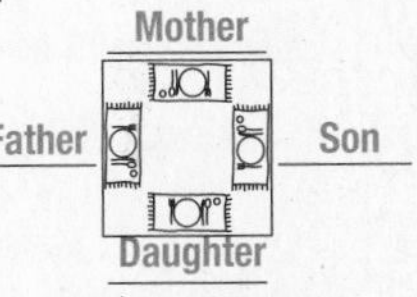 Son

Daughter

2. At a fast food restaurant, Peter and Patricia can choose from burgers, hot dogs, chicken, and fish. Peter and Patricia both eat two entrees, but neither eats the same one. Patricia is allergic to fish. Neither Peter nor Patricia will eat a burger and chicken together. What entrees did each choose?
   Possible answers: Peter eats chicken and fish; Peter eats burger and fish; Patricia eats a burger and hot dog; Patricia eats chicken and hot dog.

Use any strategy to solve each problem.

3. Here is some information about campers' favorite card games. No one liked to play *Old Maid*. *Go Fish* was liked slightly better than *Snap*, but not as well liked as *500 Rummy*. *War* got one more vote than *Old Maid*. *Concentration* was more favored than *Go Fish*, but just a little less liked than *500 Rummy*. List the order of the campers' favorite games.
   500 Rummy; Concentration; Go Fish; Snap; War; Old Maid
4. A road cleanup crew needs 2 volunteers for every 15 miles of road.If there are 60 miles of roads to be cleaned, how many volunteers are needed? 8 volunteers
5. A cook wants to use $150 to buy hams and turkeys. The hams cost $45 and turkeys cost $35. How many hams and turkeys can the cook buy?
   3 turkeys, 1 ham

Name ______________________

Practice
Chapter 1
Section B

Review and Practice

(Lesson 8) Choose a scale and make a bar graph of the data in the table.

1.

Technology in the Home	
Technology	Number of Students
Television	25
Telephone	21
VCR	15
Computer	5

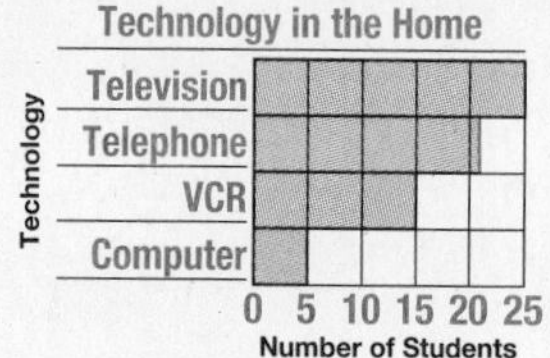

(Lesson 9) Make a line graph. Use the data in the table.

2.

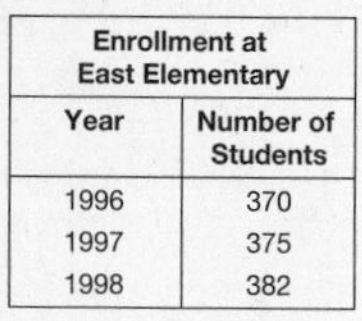

Enrollment at East Elementary	
Year	Number of Students
1996	370
1997	375
1998	382

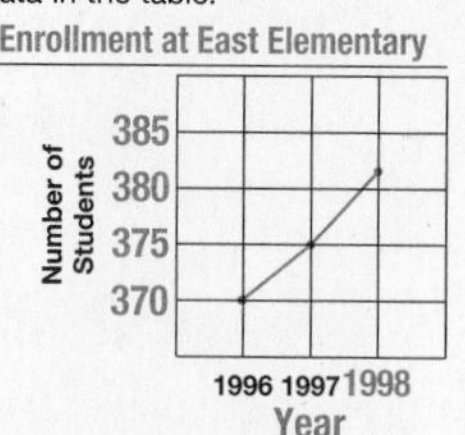

(Lesson 10) Make a stem-and-leaf plot for the data given.

3.

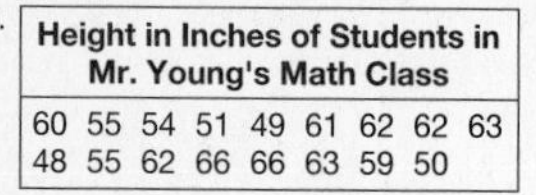

Height in Inches of Students in Mr. Young's Math Class							
60	55	54	51	49	61	62	62	63
48	55	62	66	66	63	59	50

Height of Students

6	0 1 2 2 3 2 6 6 3
5	5 4 1 5 9 0
4	9 8

(Mixed Review) Find each product or quotient.

4. $5 \times 7 =$ 35
5. $56 \div 8 =$ 7
6. $7 \times 9 =$ 63
7. $32 \div 4 =$ 8
8. $25 \div 5 =$ 5
9. $6 \times 7 =$ 42
10. $18 \div 3 =$ 6
11. $4 \times 7 =$ 28
12. $81 \div 9 =$ 9

Name ______________________

Practice
Chapter 1

Cumulative Review

(Chapter 1 Lessons 2 and 9) Use the data to complete the line graph and answer the question.

1.

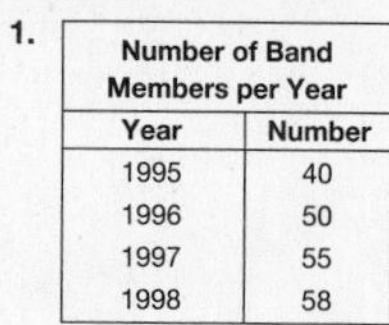

Number of Band Members per Year	
Year	Number
1995	40
1996	50
1997	55
1998	58

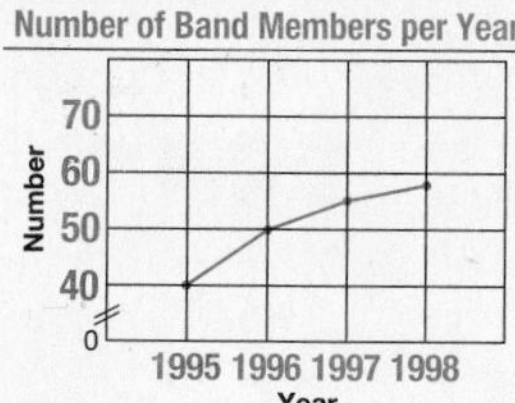

2. What can you predict about the number of band members there will be in the future?
Possible answer: Membership will increase.

(Chapter 1 Lesson 4) Find the range, mode, and median for each set of data.

3. 23, 34, 45, 43, 56, 24, 62   39, none, 43
4. 8, 9, 8, 6, 8, 6, 4, 9, 3, 6   6, 6, 8, 7

(Chapter 1 Lesson 8) Use the data to complete the bar graph.

5.

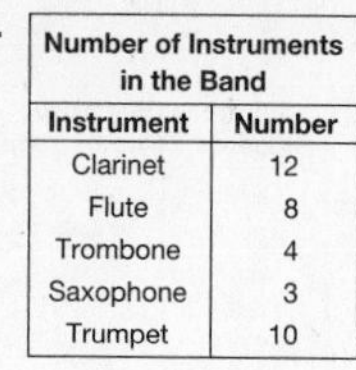

Number of Instruments in the Band	
Instrument	Number
Clarinet	12
Flute	8
Trombone	4
Saxophone	3
Trumpet	10

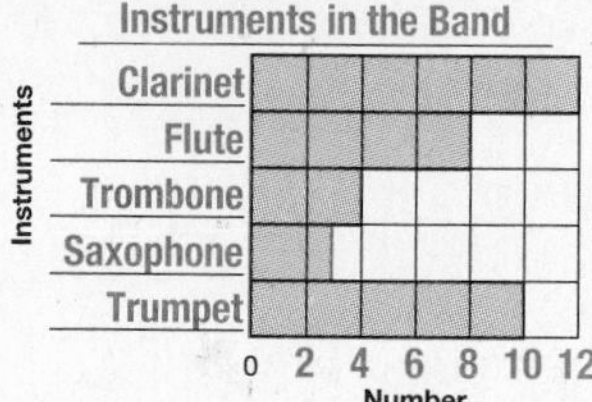

(Facts Review) Add, subtract, multiply or divide.

6. $2 \times 6 =$ 12
7. $45 \div 9 =$ 5
8. $3 \times 12 =$ 36
9. $4 + 7 =$ 11
10. $17 - 9 =$ 8
11. $15 + 8 =$ 23

Name ______________________

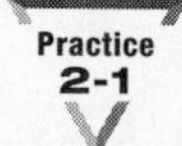

Exploring a Million

Use a calculator to answer **1–2.**

1 hour = 60 minutes   1 day = 24 hours   1 week = 7 days

1. If your heart beats 70 times every minute, how many times does it beat:
   a. in one hour? 4,200
   b. in 3 hours? 12,600
   c. in one day? 100,800
   d. in one week? 705,600
2. How long would it take for your heart to beat 1,000,000 times? about 10 days

Use patterns to solve **3–7.**

3. Suppose you have sheets of grid paper that are 5×5. Would you need more or less of these sheets than the 10×10 sheets to show one million squares? Explain.
Possible answer: More; these sheets only have 25 squares instead of 100 squares.
4. A roll of pennies holds 100 pennies. How many pennies are in:
   a. 3 rolls? 300 pennies
   b. 10 rolls? 1,000 pennies
   c. 100 rolls? 10,000 pennies
   d. 1,000 rolls? 100,000 pennies
5. How many rolls of pennies makes one million pennies? 10,000 rolls
6. 500 pennies are worth $5. How much are each of these groups of pennies worth in dollars?
   a. 800 pennies = $ 8
   b. 1,000 pennies = $ 10
   c. 5,000 pennies = $ 50
   d. 25,000 pennies = $ 250
7. How much is one million pennies worth in dollars? $10,000

Name ______________________

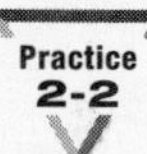

Place Value Through Millions

Write each number in word form.

1. 2,430,156 two million, four hundred thirty thousand, one hundred fifty-six
2. 83,705,019 eighty-three million, seven hundred five thousand, nineteen
3. 614,720,308 six hundred fourteen million, seven hundred twenty thousand, three hundred eight

Write each number in standard form.

4. fifty-three million, two hundred sixteen thousand, eight hundred four   53,216,804
5. four hundred sixty-four million, five hundred two thousand, forty-three   464,502,043
6. seven million, seventy-six thousand, two hundred eighty-nine   7,076,289
7. $80{,}000{,}000 + 9{,}000{,}000 + 400{,}000 + 7{,}000 + 200 + 60 + 5$ 89,407,265
8. $100{,}000{,}000 + 10{,}000{,}000 + 7{,}000{,}000 + 300{,}000 + 50{,}000 + 600 + 50$ 117,350,650
9. Look at these numbers.
   3,500   30,500   3,000,500
   a. How are the three numbers alike? Possible answers: They use the same digits: 0, 3, and 5. Five has the same place value in each number.
   b. How are the three numbers different? Possible answers: The 3 is in different place-value positions; each has a different number of zeros.

Name ______________________

Practice 2-3

Exploring Place-Value Relationships

Complete the following pattern.

1. $100 = 10 \times$ 10 $= 10^{\boxed{2}}$
2. $1{,}000 =$ 10 $\times$ 10 $\times$ 10 $= 10^{\boxed{3}}$
3. $10{,}000 =$ $10 \times 10 \times 10 \times 10$ $= 10^{\boxed{4}}$
4. $100{,}000 =$ $10 \times 10 \times 10 \times 10 \times 10$ $=$ 10^5
5. $1{,}000{,}000 =$ $10 \times 10 \times 10 \times 10 \times 10 \times 10$ $=$ 10^6
6. How many 10s make 100? 10
7. How many 100s make 100,000? 1,000
8. How many 1,000s make 100,000? 100
9. How many 10,000s make 1 million? 100
10. How many 100s make 1 million? 10,000

Write each number using exponents.

11. 10,000 10^4
12. 10 10^1
13. 1,000 10^3
14. 1,000,000 10^6
15. 100,000 10^5
16. 100 10^2

Complete.

17. $10^{\boxed{7}} = 10{,}000{,}000$
18. $10^{\boxed{8}} = 100{,}000{,}000$
19. $\boxed{10}^2 = 100$
20. $10^{\boxed{4}} = 10{,}000$
21. How does the number on the right of the equals sign help you to find the exponents in **17–20**?
    You can count the zeros.

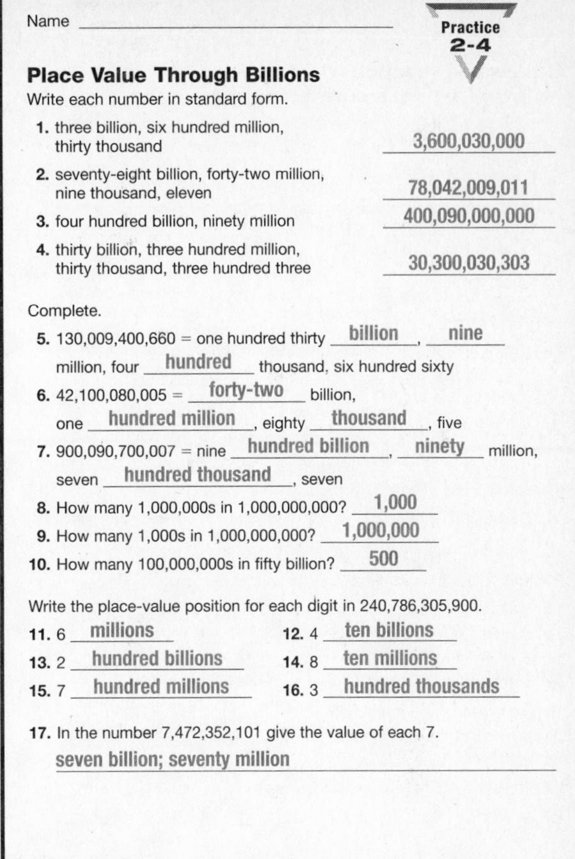

Name ______________________

Practice 2-4

Place Value Through Billions

Write each number in standard form.

1. three billion, six hundred million, thirty thousand — 3,600,030,000
2. seventy-eight billion, forty-two million, nine thousand, eleven — 78,042,009,011
3. four hundred billion, ninety million — 400,090,000,000
4. thirty billion, three hundred million, thirty thousand, three hundred three — 30,300,030,303

Complete.

5. 130,009,400,660 = one hundred thirty billion, nine million, four hundred thousand, six hundred sixty
6. 42,100,080,005 = forty-two billion, one hundred million, eighty thousand, five
7. 900,090,700,007 = nine hundred billion, ninety million, seven hundred thousand, seven
8. How many 1,000,000s in 1,000,000,000? 1,000
9. How many 1,000s in 1,000,000,000? 1,000,000
10. How many 100,000,000s in fifty billion? 500

Write the place-value position for each digit in 240,786,305,900.

11. 6 millions
12. 4 ten billions
13. 2 hundred billions
14. 8 ten millions
15. 7 hundred millions
16. 3 hundred thousands
17. In the number 7,472,352,101 give the value of each 7.
    seven billion; seventy million

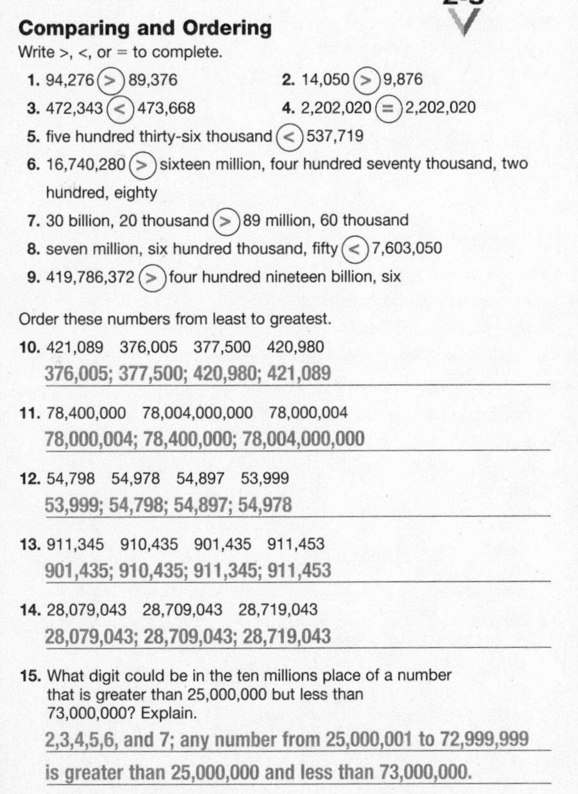

Name ______________________

Practice 2-5

Comparing and Ordering

Write >, <, or = to complete.

1. 94,276 (>) 89,376
2. 14,050 (>) 9,876
3. 472,343 (<) 473,668
4. 2,202,020 (=) 2,202,020
5. five hundred thirty-six thousand (<) 537,719
6. 16,740,280 (>) sixteen million, four hundred seventy thousand, two hundred, eighty
7. 30 billion, 20 thousand (>) 89 million, 60 thousand
8. seven million, six hundred thousand, fifty (<) 7,603,050
9. 419,786,372 (>) four hundred nineteen billion, six

Order these numbers from least to greatest.

10. 421,089 376,005 377,500 420,980
    376,005; 377,500; 420,980; 421,089
11. 78,400,000 78,004,000,000 78,000,004
    78,000,004; 78,400,000; 78,004,000,000
12. 54,798 54,978 54,897 53,999
    53,999; 54,798; 54,897; 54,978
13. 911,345 910,435 901,435 911,453
    901,435; 910,435; 911,345; 911,453
14. 28,079,043 28,709,043 28,719,043
    28,079,043; 28,709,043; 28,719,043
15. What digit could be in the ten millions place of a number that is greater than 25,000,000 but less than 73,000,000? Explain.
    2,3,4,5,6, and 7; any number from 25,000,001 to 72,999,999 is greater than 25,000,000 and less than 73,000,000.

Name ______________________

Practice 2-6

Rounding Greater Numbers

18,000,000 ——— 19,000,000

1. Use the number line to help you round 18,521,425 to the nearest million. 19,000,000

Round to the nearest hundred thousand.

2. 872,768 900,000
3. 8,243,956 8,200,000
4. 2,035,467 2,000,000
5. 43,974,012 44,000,000

Round to the nearest million.

6. 8,643,231 9,000,000
7. 75,499,999 75,000,000
8. 987,645,312 988,000,000
9. 489,753,274 490,000,000

Round to the nearest ten million.

10. 78,634,021 80,000,000
11. 7,630,998,432 7,630,000,000
12. 646,000,000 650,000,000
13. 801,009,999 800,000,000
14. If 789,364,768 rounds to 789,400,000, to which place did you round?
    hundred thousand place
15. What is the greatest number that rounds to 65,000,000 when rounded to the million place? 65,499,999

Use the table to answer **16** and **17**.

City	Population in 1990
Austin, Texas	846,227
Louisville, Kentucky	948,829
Memphis, Tennessee	1,007,306
Las Vegas, Nevada	852,737

16. Which city has a population closest to 1,000,000 people?
    Memphis
17. Which two cities would have the same population if rounded to the nearest 10,000?
    Austin, Texas and Las Vegas, Nevada

Name ______________________

Practice
Chapter 2
Section A

Review and Practice

Vocabulary Write whether each is true or false.

1. A period is one of the symbols: 0, 1, 2, 3, 4, 5, 6, 7, 8, 9. false
2. A number line shows numbers in order. true
3. A digit is a group of three numbers. false

(Lesson 1) What is the value in dollars of the money in each stack?

4. one hundred $10 bills $1,000
5. ten $100 bills $1,000

(Lesson 3) Complete.

6. 10 × 5,000 = 50,000
7. 100 × 800 = 80,000
8. 10^{5} = 100,000

(Lessons 2 and 4) In the number 79,402,356,108 write the value of:

9. 4 400,000,000
10. 7 70,000,000,000
11. 9 9,000,000,000
12. 2 2,000,000

13. Write one hundred fifty million, two hundred fifty-seven thousand, nine hundred forty-five in standard form. 150,257,945

(Lesson 5) Write >, <, or = to complete.

14. 235,641 (>) 93,584
15. 90,006 (=) ninety thousand six
16. 899,002 (<) six hundred million
17. 89,903 (>) 89,099

(Lesson 6) Use the table to answer **18** and **19**.

18. Write the letter for the breed that has registered about:
    a. 70,000 dogs E
    b. 100,000 dogs B
19. To the nearest thousand, how many Labrador retrievers are registered? 125,000

Top 5 American Kennel Club Registrations

Breed	Registrations
A. Labrador Retrievers	124,899
B. Rottweilers	104,160
C. German Shepherds	79,936
D. Cocker Spaniels	75,882
E. Golden Retrievers	68,125

(Mixed Review) Find each product or quotient.

20. 36 ÷ 9 = 4
21. 7 × 7 = 49
22. 48 ÷ 6 = 8

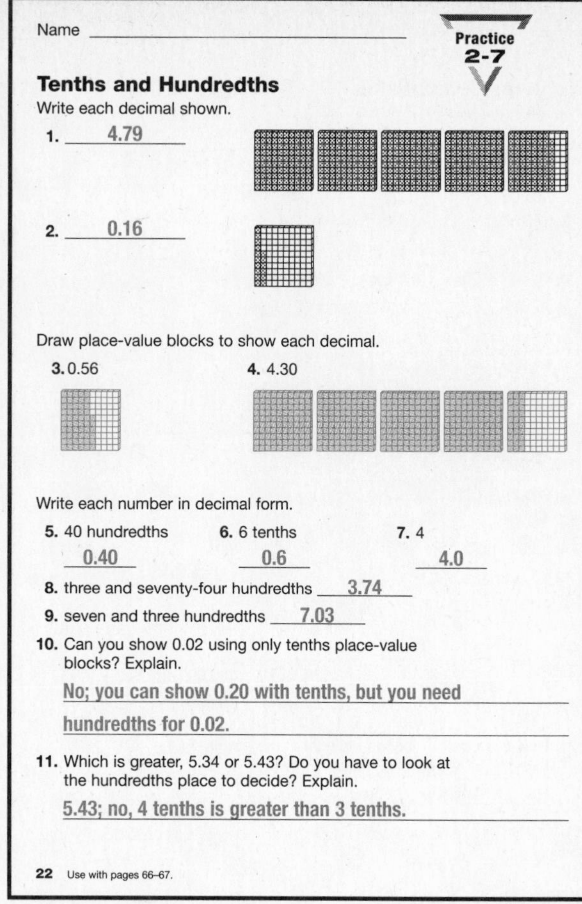

Name ______________________

Practice
2-7

Tenths and Hundredths

Write each decimal shown.

1. 4.79
2. 0.16

Draw place-value blocks to show each decimal.

3. 0.56
4. 4.30

Write each number in decimal form.

5. 40 hundredths 0.40
6. 6 tenths 0.6
7. 4 4.0
8. three and seventy-four hundredths 3.74
9. seven and three hundredths 7.03
10. Can you show 0.02 using only tenths place-value blocks? Explain.
    No; you can show 0.20 with tenths, but you need hundredths for 0.02.
11. Which is greater, 5.34 or 5.43? Do you have to look at the hundredths place to decide? Explain.
    5.43; no, 4 tenths is greater than 3 tenths.

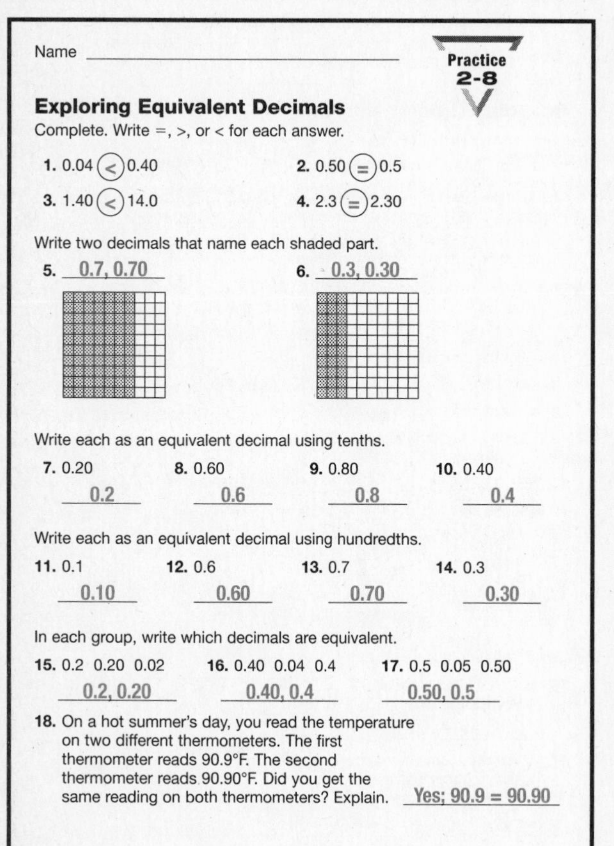

Name ______________________

Practice
2-8

Exploring Equivalent Decimals

Complete. Write =, >, or < for each answer.

1. 0.04 (<) 0.40
2. 0.50 (=) 0.5
3. 1.40 (<) 14.0
4. 2.3 (=) 2.30

Write two decimals that name each shaded part.

5. 0.7, 0.70
6. 0.3, 0.30

Write each as an equivalent decimal using tenths.

7. 0.20 0.2
8. 0.60 0.6
9. 0.80 0.8
10. 0.40 0.4

Write each as an equivalent decimal using hundredths.

11. 0.1 0.10
12. 0.6 0.60
13. 0.7 0.70
14. 0.3 0.30

In each group, write which decimals are equivalent.

15. 0.2 0.20 0.02 0.2, 0.20
16. 0.40 0.04 0.4 0.40, 0.4
17. 0.5 0.05 0.50 0.50, 0.5

18. On a hot summer's day, you read the temperature on two different thermometers. The first thermometer reads 90.9°F. The second thermometer reads 90.90°F. Did you get the same reading on both thermometers? Explain. Yes; 90.9 = 90.90

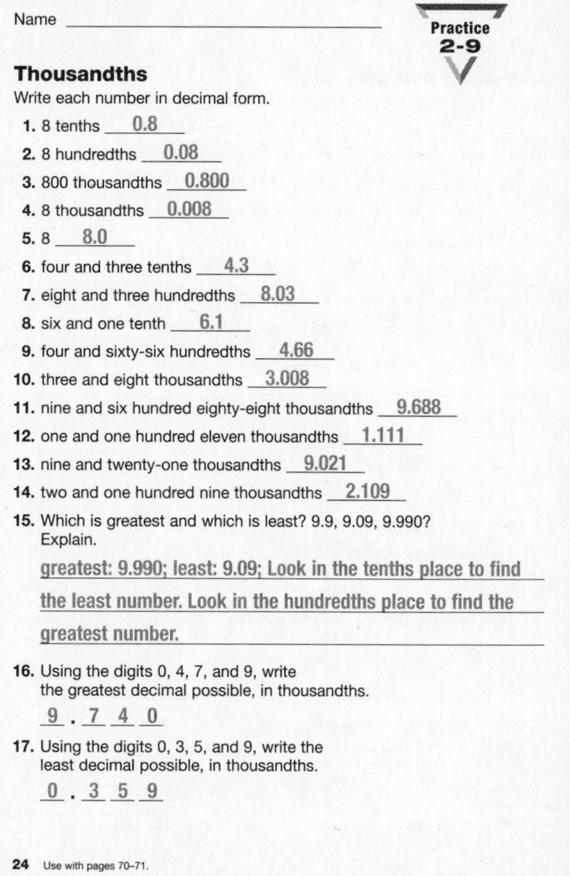

Name ______________________

Practice
2-9

Thousandths

Write each number in decimal form.

1. 8 tenths 0.8
2. 8 hundredths 0.08
3. 800 thousandths 0.800
4. 8 thousandths 0.008
5. 8 8.0
6. four and three tenths 4.3
7. eight and three hundredths 8.03
8. six and one tenth 6.1
9. four and sixty-six hundredths 4.66
10. three and eight thousandths 3.008
11. nine and six hundred eighty-eight thousandths 9.688
12. one and one hundred eleven thousandths 1.111
13. nine and twenty-one thousandths 9.021
14. two and one hundred nine thousandths 2.109
15. Which is greatest and which is least? 9.9, 9.09, 9.990? Explain.
    greatest: 9.990; least: 9.09; Look in the tenths place to find the least number. Look in the hundredths place to find the greatest number.
16. Using the digits 0, 4, 7, and 9, write the greatest decimal possible, in thousandths.
    9 . 7 4 0
17. Using the digits 0, 3, 5, and 9, write the least decimal possible, in thousandths.
    0 . 3 5 9

Name ______________________

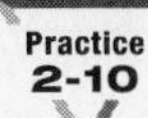

Practice 2-10

Decimals on the Number Line

Complete the number line.

1.
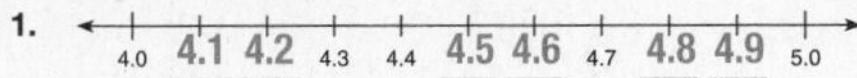

Name the number shown by each letter.

2.
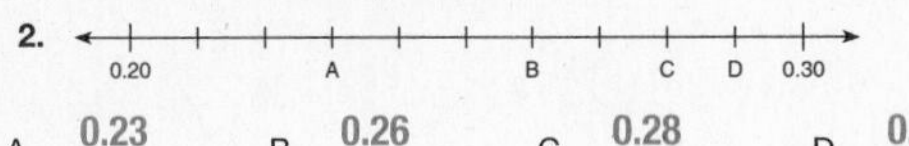

A 0.23 B 0.26 C 0.28 D 0.29

Use the number line shown to answer **3** and **4**. Name two numbers:

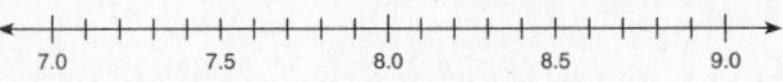

3. Between 7.5 and 8.0 Possible answers: 7.6, 7.7, 7.8, 7.9
4. Between 8.0 and 8.5 Possible answers: 8.1, 8.2, 8.3, 8.4

Use the number line shown to answer **5–7**.

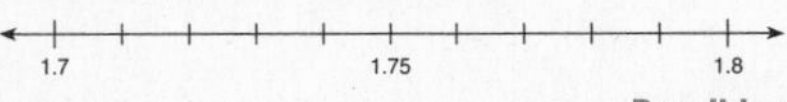

5. Name three numbers between 1.7 and 1.8. Possible answers: 1.71, 1.72, 1.73, 1.74, 1.75, 1.76, 1.77, 1.78, 1.79
6. Is 1.799 between 1.7 and 1.8? Explain your thinking. Yes, because 0.799 is less than 0.8 and greater than 0.7
7. Is 1.07 the half-way point between 1.7 and 1.8? Tell how you know. No, because 1.07 is less than 1.7 and 1.8

Name ______________________

Practice 2-11

Exploring Comparing and Ordering Decimals

1. Compare 3.277 and 3.274.
   a. Starting at the left, look for the first place where the digits are different. What place is it? thousandths
   b. Which number is greater? 3.277
2. Order 3.277, 3.274, and 3.27 from greatest to least by comparing numbers two at a time. Use > or < to compare.
   a. 3.277 (>) 3.274
   b. 3.274 (>) 3.27
   c. The order from greatest to least is 3.277, 3.274, 3.27
3. Order 0.4, 0.04, 4.00, and 0.44 from least to greatest by comparing numbers two at a time. Use < or > to compare.
   a. 0.04 (<) 0.4
   b. 0.04 (<) 0.44
   c. 0.44 (<) 4.00
   d. The order from least to greatest is 0.04, 0.4, 0.44, 4.00

Write >, <, or = to complete.

4. 0.2 (>) 0.03	5. 0.4 (<) 0.54	6. 0.89 (<) 2.1
7. 0.7 (<) 79	8. 0.4 (<) 0.44	9. 0.2 (=) 0.20
10. 2.6 (>) 2.36	11. 3.9 (>) 3.09	12. 0.1 (<) 0.16
13. 0.3 (<) 0.34	14. 4.1 (<) 4.19	15. 2.1 (=) 2.10
16. 0.3 (>) 0.03	17. 0.5 (<) 0.56	18. 8.7 (>) 8.07
19. 7.3 (<) 7.33	20. 3.39 (<) 33.9	21. 5.1 (>) 5.09

Name ______________________

Practice 2-12

Rounding Decimals

Round each number to the place of the underlined digit.

1. 73.49 — 73	2. 2.009 — 2.0	3. 36.415 — 36.42	4. 4.708 — 5
5. 0.82 — 0.8	6. 0.887 — 0.89	7. 9.77 — 10	8. 2.207 — 2.2
9. 7.757 — 7.76	10. 46.960 — 47.0	11. 42.59 — 43	12. 9.65 — 10
13. 0.68 — 0.7	14. 34.225 — 34.23	15. 4.05 — 4.1	16. 4.56 — 5
17. 19.01 — 19	18. 0.087 — 0.09	19. 4.050 — 4.05	20. 6.957 — 7
21. 0.3 — 0	22. 0.824 — 0.8	23. 3.989 — 4	24. 6.064 — 6.1
25. 48.05 — 48.1	26. 3.25 — 3	27. 0.857 — 0.9	28. 0.055 — 0.06
29. 7.019 — 7.0	30. 11.297 — 11.3	31. 3.54 — 3.5	32. 0.9 — 1.0

33. Name two decimals with digits in the hundredths place that could be rounded to the tenths place as 0.4. Possible answers: 0.44, 0.43, 0.42, 0.41, 0.40, 0.39, 0.38, 0.37, 0.36, 0.35
34. Name two decimals with digits in the tenths place that could be rounded to the ones place as 1. Possible answers: 0.5, 0.6, 0.7, 0.8, 0.9, 1.0, 1.1, 1.2, 1.3, 1.4

Name ______________________

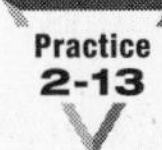

Practice 2-13

Analyze Strategies: Draw a Picture

Draw a picture to solve.

1. Jessica, Sarah, Annie, Tiffany, and Megan decide to go to an early movie that will cost them each $4. Jessica and Tiffany want to split a container of popcorn that costs $2. Megan and Annie want to share nachos that cost $4. Sarah wants to buy the souvenir movie poster for $3. Everyone brings $6.
   a. Will everyone have enough money for the movie and the items they want to buy? No; Sarah needs another dollar.
   b. Who will spend the most money? Sarah
   c. How much money will Jessica have left? $1
2. Sam is 12 years old. Garrett is younger than Sam but older than David and Mark. David is 9 and Mark is 10. What is Garrett's age? 11
3. The school is having a skating party. The students decide to do a line dance. They form three lines. The longest line is 60 students. One of the other lines has half as many students but is twice as long as the third line. How many students are in each of the other two lines? 30, 15
4. Danny, Philip, Jennifer, and Emily are having a bike race. Jennifer only finishes ahead of Philip, who comes in last. Emily finishes behind Danny. What was the order of the finish from first to last? Danny, Emily, Jennifer, Philip
5. Jean is younger than Dan but older than Rob. Sue is the oldest of the four. Who is the youngest? Rob

Name ______________________

Practice
Chapter 2
Section B

Review and Practice

(Lessons 7 and 9) Write each number in decimal form.

1. 29 hundredths 0.29
2. 7 hundredths 0.07
3. 16 thousandths 0.016
4. 7 tenths 0.7
5. eight and forty hundredths 8.40
6. nine and two hundred three thousandths 9.203

(Lesson 8) In each group circle equivalent decimals.

7. (0.4) 0.04 (0.40) **8.** 0.02 (0.20) (0.2)

(Lesson 10) Name the number shown by each letter.

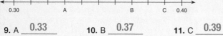

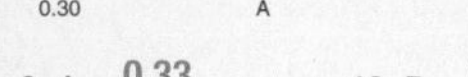

9. A 0.33 **10.** B 0.37 **11.** C 0.39

(Lesson 11) Write >, <, or = to complete.

12. 0.71 (>) 0.231 **13.** 0.6 (=) 0.600 **14.** 2.38 (>) 1.8

15. 6.07 (=) 6.070 **16.** 0.29 (<) 0.3 **17.** 5.8 (<) 6.7

(Lesson 12) Round each number to the place of the underlined digit.

18. 0.6̲51 0.7 **19.** 5̲.63 6

20. Carolyn owes Michael 72¢. She only has dimes. What is the nearest amount she can give him? 70¢

(Mixed Review) Write >, <, or =.

21. 6 + 9 + 3 (<) 9 + 4 + 6 **22.** 18 − 5 (=) 17 − 4

23. 9 × 3 (<) 15 + 13 **24.** 5 + 0 (>) 0 × 8

Name ______________________

Practice
2-14

Estimating Sums and Differences

Estimate each sum or difference.

1. 232 − 75 = 100–150
2. $9.67 + 3.44 = $12.00–$14.00
3. 718 + 457 = 1,100–1,300
4. $6.98 − 4.87 = $2.00–$3.00
5. 728 + 96 + 293 = 9,000–1,100
6. 382 + 249 + 777 = 1,200–1,400
7. $11.93 + 2.55 = $11.00–$15.00
8. 599 + 607 = 1,100–1,200
9. 431 − 65 = 300–400
10. $5.68 + 7.55 = $12.00–$14.00
11. 737 + 216 = 900–1,000
12. $4.76 − 2.99 = $1.00–$2.00
13. 525 + 37 + 168 = 600–700
14. 345 + 268 + 188 = 600–800
15. $9.99 − 4.89 = $4.00–$5.00
16. 699 + 103 = 700–800
17. 906 − 367 = 500–600
18. $6.59 − 3.80 = $2.00–$3.00
19. 608 − 398 = 200–300
20. $6.78 − 2.80 = $3.00–$4.00

Estimate. Write >, <, or = to complete.

21. 67 + 49 (<) 130 **22.** $16.75 − $7.00 (<) $23.00

23. 48 + 34 + 95 (>) 170 **24.** 444 + 856 (=) $1,300

25. If you decrease both addends when rounding to add, what can you say about your estimated sum?
The actual sum is greater than the estimated sum.

Name ______________________

Practice
2-15

Adding and Subtracting Whole Numbers

Find each sum or difference. Then estimate to check your answer.

1. 686 + 208 = 894
2. 506 − 331 = 175
3. 748 + 992 = 1,740
4. 252 + 3,889 = 4,141
5. 376 + 49 = 425
6. 776 − 634 = 142
7. 600 − 277 = 323
8. 308 − 87 = 221
9. 47 + 599 + 23 + 55 = 724
10. 548 + 329 + 101 + 88 = 1,066

11. 372 + 65 + 133 + 435 = 1,005

12. 446 + 9,675 + 11,007 + 329 + 32 = 21,489

13. Subtract 8,435 from 9,074. 639

14. Find the sum of 4,882, 12,443, 3,229, and 356. 20,910

15. Find 7,999 + 4,999 mentally. Explain why it is easier to do this sum mentally than by writing it out.
12,998, because you can add 1 to both numbers, then subtract 2.

16. Find 3,000 − 1,002 mentally. Explain your reasoning.
1,998; because you can subtract 1,000 from 3,000 and then subtract 2 from the difference.

17. Find 399 + 598 + 701 mentally. 1,698

Name ______________________

Practice
2-16

Exploring Adding and Subtracting Decimals

Use place-value blocks to add or subtract.

1. 0.34 + 0.59 = 0.93

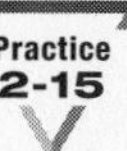

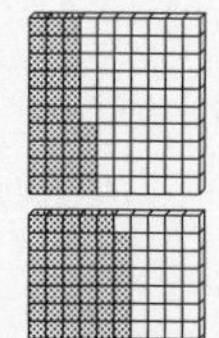

2. 0.67 − 0.59 = 0.08

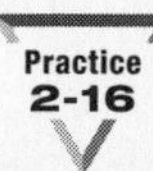

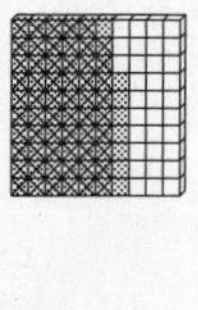

Use place-value blocks or drawings to find each sum or difference.

3. 4.32 + 5.87 = 10.19
4. 5.41 − 1.74 = 3.67
5. 5.29 + 8.47 = 13.76
6. 4.1 − 3.7 = 0.4
7. 3.8 + 5.6 = 9.4
8. 6.8 + 2.6 = 9.4
9. 9.53 − 4.79 = 4.74
10. 15.7 + 0.6 = 16.3
11. 6.2 + 9.5 = 15.7
12. 8.35 − 0.79 = 7.56

13. 4.23 + 5.74 + 6.8 = 16.77 **14.** 5.9 − 2.8 = 3.1

Complete. Use place-value blocks or drawings to help you.

15. 4.87 − 3.64 = 1.23 **16.** 2.35 + 6.05 = 8.40

17. Explain how you can show 4.37 using dollars, dimes, and pennies.
4 dollars for ones, 3 dimes for tenths, and 7 pennies for hundredths

Name ____________________

Practice 2-17

Adding Decimals

Find each sum.

1. 6.23 + 8.94 = 15.17
2. 4.03 + 5.67 = 9.70
3. 4.05 + 0.96 = 5.01
4. 5.20 + 0.36 = 5.56
5. 6.31 + 7.41 = 13.72
6. 4.24 + 0.56 + 3.65 = 8.45
7. $3.49 + 0.87 + 2.26 = $6.62
8. 0.84 + 2.76 + 0.12 = 3.72
9. 4.59 + 2.77 + 6.0 = 13.36
10. 3.9 + 1.1 + 8.0 = 13.0
11. $5.29 + 0.44 = $5.73
12. 6.5 + 0.47 = 6.97
13. 0.67 + 3.2 + 1.25 = 5.12
14. 2.0 + 3.69 + 2.77 = 8.46
15. 43.0 + 2.60 = 45.6

16. 3.5 + 4.5 + 3 = 11

17. 0.86 + 0.5 = 1.36

18. 4.6 + 6.7 + 2 = 13.3

19. 0.73 + 0.48 = 1.21

20. Find the sum of 4.99 and 3.45. 8.44

21. Find the sum of 3.9 + 3.09 + 30.9. 37.89

22. Explain why you cannot write 9.2 as 9.02.

Because 9.2 is 9 and 2 tenths and 9.02 is 9 and 2 hundredths. The 2 is not in the same place in 9.2 and 9.02.

Name ____________________

Practice 2-18

Subtracting Decimals

Find each difference.

1. $7.99 − 4.99 = $3.00
2. 13.0 − 2.47 = 10.53
3. 35.50 − 0.87 = 34.63
4. 8.9 − 0.54 = 8.36
5. 3.33 − 2.67 = 0.66
6. 14.89 − 6.55 = 8.34
7. $4.00 − 3.49 = $0.51
8. 8.9 − 7.0 = 1.9
9. 5.0 − 0.6 = 4.4
10. 2.08 − 0.99 = 1.09
11. $4.44 − 2.99 = $1.45
12. 4.0 − 0.67 = 3.33
13. 8.45 − 4.96 = 3.49
14. 3.98 − 0.79 = 3.19
15. 14.2 − 13.27 = 0.93
16. 6.5 − 0.76 = 5.74
17. 4.7 − 4.07 = 0.63
18. $9.99 − 3.68 = $6.31
19. 9.09 − 5.99 = 3.10
20. $1.00 − 0.79 = $0.21

21. 8 − 4.65 = 3.35

22. 14.6 − 8.76 = 5.84

23. Find the difference of 7 and 3.64. 3.36

24. If you have zeros in the tenths and hundredths place in the first number and fives in the tenths and hundredths place of the second number, how do you subtract?

Regroup 1 one as 10 tenths. Then regroup 1 tenth as 10 hundredths.

Complete.

25. 4.7 − 4.1 = 0.6

26. 4.43 − 1.75 = 2.68

Name ____________________

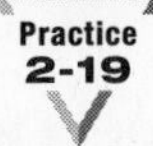

Practice 2-19

Analyze Word Problems: Choose an Operation

Write the letter of the number sentence you would use.

1. The deluxe soccer gear set costs $55. The regular soccer set costs $27. What is the difference in costs between the two sets?
   - **A.** $27 + $55 = $82
   - **B.** $55 − $27 = $28
   - **C.** $27 + $82 + $55 = $164

   B

Write the number sentence or sentences you would use. Then solve each problem.

2. The special chess set is $14 less than the deluxe chess set, which costs $68. How much is the special chess set?

   $68 − $14 = $54; the special chess set costs $54.

3. Brandon planned on using $80 to buy the deluxe chess set. He wanted to use his leftover money to buy a book on chess strategy which costs $10.99. How much money will Brandon have left?

   Brandon will have $1.01 left; $80.00 − $68.00 = $12.00; $12.00 − $10.99 = $1.01.

4. Brianna had $34 in babysitting money plus $12 allowance. She would also like to buy the deluxe chess set. How much more money will she need?

   Brianna needs $22; $34 + $12 = $46; $68 − $46 = $22.

5. Steven and his sister Jenna want to buy a gift for their parents that costs $54. Steven has $15 and Jenna has $24. Do they have enough money to buy the gift? If not, how much more money do they need?

   No. They need $15 more; $15 + $24 = $39; $54 − $39 = $15.

Name ____________________

Practice Chapter 2 Section C

Review and Practice

(Lessons 14 and 15) Find each sum or difference. Estimate to check.

1. 544 − 397 = 147
2. 878 + 663 = 1,541
3. 502 − 47 = 455
4. $12.16 + 5.08 = $17.24
5. $62.90 − 23.17 = $39.73
6. $34.07 + 25.27 = $59.34
7. 5,002 − 357 = 4,645
8. 16,892 + 5,308 = 22,200
9. 24,000 − 13,571 = 10,429

(Lessons 16 and 17) Find each sum.

10. 42.26 + 5.08 = 47.34
11. $62.90 + 16.88 + 35.02 = $114.80
12. 9.7 + 3.72 + 1.08 = 14.50
13. 5.2 + 0.3 + 28.17 = 33.67

(Lessons 16 and 18) Find each difference.

14. 7.03 − 3.47 = 3.56
15. $16.75 − 13.57 = $3.18
16. 3.81 − 0.5 = 3.31
17. 9 − 1.61 = 7.39

(Lesson 19) Choose any strategy to solve the problem.

18. Amy had $15 to buy a CD for $12.95. The tax on the purchase was $0.65. How much money did Amy have left?

    Possible answer: $15 − ($12.95 + 0.65) = $1.40

(Mixed Review) Multiply.

19. 400 × 2 = 800

20. 3 × 300 = 900

21. 200 × 9 = 1,800

22. 4 × 600 = 2,400

Name ______________________

Practice
Chapters 1–2

Cumulative Review

(Chapter 1 Lesson 2) Use the data from the graph to answer each question.

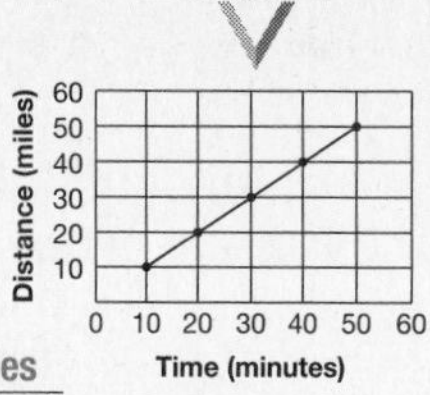

1. How many miles were traveled in 20 minutes? **20 miles**
2. How many miles would you expect to travel in 60 minutes? **60 miles**

(Chapter 1 Lesson 4) Find the range, median, and mode for each set of numbers.

3. 10, 12, 12, 9, 3 **range: 9**, **median: 10**, **mode: 12**
4. 29, 25, 20, 20, 15, 22 **range: 14**, **median: 21**, **mode: 20**

(Chapter 1 Lesson 6) Write a number sentence and use it to solve the problem.

5. Seth estimates he will need 45 minutes to do his homework. He needs 15 minutes to do spelling. The rest of the time he will do his math homework. How many minutes will Seth spend doing math homework?
45 − 15 = *n*, 30 minutes

(Chapter 2 Lesson 4) Write each number in standard form.

6. three billion, four hundred thirty-six million **3,436,000,000**
7. ten billion, five million, six hundred twenty-one thousand, two hundred thirteen **10,005,621,213**

(Chapter 2 Lesson 12) Round each number to the place of the underlined digit.

8. 45.<u>5</u>1 **45.5** 9. 0.0<u>0</u>9 **0.01** 10. <u>3</u>.93 **4**

(Chapter 2 Lesson 15) Add or subtract.

11. 369 − 197 = **172** 12. 371 + 263 = **634** 13. 901 − 38 = **863** 14. 66,092 + 13,505 = **79,597**

Name ______________________

Practice
3-1

Exploring Multiplication Patterns and Properties

Match each property with an example.

1. Commutative property **a** a. 6 × (3 × 5) = 6 × (5 × 3)
2. Associative property **b** b. 4 × (8 × 10) = (4 × 8) × 10

Find each product. Use mental math.

3. 20 × 80 = **1,600** 4. 6 × 80 = **480**
5. 40 × 40 = **1,600** 6. 17 × 20 = **340**
7. 12 × (5 × 10) = **600** 8. (80 × 3) × 20 = **4,800**
9. 100 × (3 × 90) = **27,000** 10. 6 × (60 × 3) = **1,080**

Complete.

11. 40 × **40** = 1,600 12. 30 × **30** = 900
13. 50 × **600** = 30,000 14. **40** × 80 = 3,200
15. 60 × **700** = 42,000 16. **10,000** × 70 = 700,000

Complete. For each product the factors are the same.

17. **70** × **70** = 4,900 18. **500** × **500** = 250,000
19. **40** × **40** = 1,600 20. **300** × **300** = 90,000

Find each product. Use mental math and multiplication properties.

21. (22 × 25) × 4 = **2,200** 22. 2 × (47 × 5) = **470**
23. (2 × 36) × 5 = **360** 24. (60 × 900) × 100 = **5,400,000**

25. How many $10 bills are equal to three $20 bills? **6**
26. How many zeros are in the product of 4 × 25 × 200? Explain.
4; 2 zeros from the product of 4 × 25 and two from the 200
27. Which is greater, the product of 50 × 200 × 3 or 5 × 20 × 300? Explain.
Neither, they are equal; there are 3 zeros in each set of factors and 1 zero in the fact 5 × 2 = 10.

Name ______________________

Practice
3-2

Estimating Products

Estimate each product.

1. 9 × 34 **270** 2. 53 × 6 **300**
3. 8 × 47 **400** 4. 66 × 4 **280**
5. 11 × 48 **500** 6. 37 × 29 **1,200**
7. 72 × 31 **2,100** 8. 58 × 32 **1,800**
9. 19 × 41 **800** 10. 27 × 433 **12,000**
11. 742 × 68 **49,000** 12. 77 × 518 **40,000**

13. 98 × 21 = **2,000** 14. 71 × 63 = **4,200** 15. 649 × 42 = **24,000** 16. 262 × 68 = **21,000**

17. 309 × 47 = **15,000** 18. 487 × 31 = **15,000** 19. 49 × 49 = **2,500** 20. 135 × 77 = **8,000**

21. Estimate the product of 416 and 72. **28,000**
22. The product of what two numbers is about 400?
Possible answers: 21 and 19; 11 and 37
23. The product of 42 and what number is about 1,200?
Possible answers: 25 to 34
24. The product of what two numbers is about 42,000?
Possible answers: 63 × 721; 583 × 68
25. The product of 345 and what number is 21,000?
Possible answers: 65 to 74

Name ______________________

Practice
3-3

Multiplying Whole Numbers

Estimate Find each product. Estimate to check.

1. 66 × 29 = **1,914** 2. 95 × 56 = **5,320** 3. 73 × 45 = **3,285** 4. 83 × 77 = **6,391** 5. 115 × 39 = **4,485**

6. 324 × 8 = **2,592** 7. 289 × 5 = **1,445**

8. 294 × 9 = **2,646** 9. 326 × 6 = **1,956** 10. 565 × 24 = **13,560** 11. 683 × 37 = **25,271** 12. 333 × 99 = **32,967**

13. 24 × 309 = **7,416** 14. 41 × 37 = **1,517**

15. 375 × 9 = **3,375** 16. 544 × 6 = **3,264** 17. 663 × 24 = **15,912** 18. 792 × 36 = **28,512** 19. 436 × 87 = **37,932**

20. Find the product of 84 and 93. **7,812**
21. Multiply 409 and 37. **15,133**
22. What is the greatest number of times you would regroup when multiplying a 3-digit factor by a 2-digit factor? Give an example.
6 times: ones to tens, tens to hundreds, hundreds to thousands, tens to hundreds, hundreds to thousands, thousands to ten-thousands; Examples will vary.
23. Which is greater, 456 × 65 or 465 × 56?
456 × 65

Name ______________________

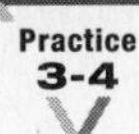
Practice 3-4

Distributive Property

Find each product.

1. 32 × 9 = 288
2. 304 × 8 = 2,432
3. 5 × 801 = 4,005
4. 698 × 3 = 2,094
5. 6 × 703 = 4,218
6. 2 × 599 = 1,198
7. 801 × 9 = 7,209
8. 597 × 7 = 4,179
9. 29 × 4 = 116
10. 42 × 8 = 336
11. 697 × 3 = 2,091
12. 40 × 89 = 3,560
13. 79 × 12 = 948
14. 298 × 11 = 3,278
15. Multiply 347 and 28. 9,716
16. Find the product of 80 and 14. 1,120
17. Would you use the distributive property to find 810 × 9? Explain.
    yes, (800 × 9) + (10 × 9) = 7,200 + 90 = 7,290
18. Use the distributive property and multiplication patterns to find 62 × 5 × 10.
    (60 × 5) + (2 × 5) × 10 = (300 + 10) × 10 =
    310 × 10 = 3,100

Name ______________________

Practice 3-5

Choosing a Calculation Method

Choose a method. Find each product.

1. 63 × 99 = 6,237
2. 800 × 20 = 16,000
3. 242 × 87 = 21,054
4. 110 × 9 = 990
5. 199 × 33 = 6,567
6. 47 × 42 = 1,974
7. 490 × 400 = 196,000
8. 76 × 67 = 5,092
9. 346 × 56 = 19,376
10. 290 × 200 = 58,000
11. 705 × 120 = 84,600
12. 83 × 15 = 1,245
13. Find the product of 483 and 264. 127,512
14. Multiply 204 and 8. 1,632
15. Jan and her friend each solve 483 multiplied by 276. Jan's answer is 85,988. Her friend's answer is 133,308. Which answer is reasonable? Explain.
    her friend's answer; 500 × 300 = 150,000
16. Estimate the product of 52 and 328. Is it closer to 15,000 or 20,000? Explain.
    Closer to 15,000; 300 is closer to 328 than 400.

Name ______________________

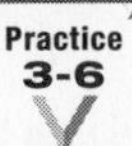
Practice 3-6

Exploring Patterns with Multiples

This chart shows some multiples of 4 and 5.

4	4	8	12	20	24	28	32	36	40	44
5	5	10	15	20	25	30	35	40	45	50

1. Shade the common multiples of 4 and 5. Which is the least common multiple? 20

Find the LCM for each pair or set of numbers.

2. 3 and 4 12
3. 5 and 9 45
4. 2 and 8 8
5. 6 and 8 24
6. 2 and 3 6
7. 7 and 10 70
8. 10 and 20 20
9. 3 and 9 9
10. 9 and 10 90
11. 5 and 6 30
12. 4 and 8 8
13. 2 and 7 14
14. 2, 4, and 6 12
15. 3, 5, and 7 105
16. 2, 4, and 8 8
17. 2, 5, and 10 10
18. 3, 6, and 9 18
19. 2, 3, and 7 42
20. 3, 4, and 7 84
21. 2, 3, and 9 18
22. Use your calculator to find the LCM for 35 and 25. Enter ON/AC + 25 = = and so on. List the multiples. Do the same for 35. What is the first multiple that is a multiple for both 25 and 35?
    175
23. Make a list of the multiples of 30. Do you need to make a list of multiples of 7 to find the LCM of 30 and 7? Explain.
    No, you can check each multiple in your list of multiples of 30 to see if one is a multiple of 7.
24. What if you want to find the greatest common multiple of 7, 9, and 0? Could you do this? Explain.
    Yes, the greatest common multiple is 0, since the only multiple of 0 is 0.

Name ______________________

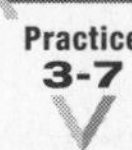
Practice 3-7

Decision Making

A local movie theater sells tickets for $6.00 each and a box of popcorn for $2.00. But if you pay $36.00 for a movie pass, you can see 8 movies in 8 weeks, and get 1 free box of popcorn with each movie. Would you choose to buy the movie pass or not?

What are you asked to do? Decide whether to get a movie pass or not.

How much would you have to pay for a ticket and a box of popcorn at the regular price? $6.00 + $2.00 = $8.00

How much would each movie and a box of popcorn cost if you got the movie pass? $36.00 ÷ 8 = $4.50

About how often would you have to see a movie to go 8 times in 8 weeks? Once a week

1. Would it make sense to get the pass if you only go to the movies once or twice in 8 weeks? Explain.
   No, because you would pay $36.00 for just 1 or 2 movies
2. Would it make sense to get the pass if you to go the movies 8 times in 8 weeks? Explain.
   Yes, because you would pay $4.50 for each movie and popcorn which would normally cost $8.00

Suppose the same movie theater offered a $12.00 movie pass that allowed you to see 3 movies in the next year.

3. How much would each movie cost? $4.00
4. How much money would you save if you bought the pass and saw 3 movies that year? $6.00
5. How much money would you lose if you only saw 1 movie that year? $6.00
6. Would you buy this movie pass? Explain.
   Possible answer: Yes, I usually see at least 3 movies a year.

Name ______________________

Practice Chapter 3 Section A

Review and Practice

Vocabulary Fill in each blank with a word from the word bank.

commutative	distributive	least common multiple	multiple

1. 5 × (3 + 4) = (5 × 3) + (5 × 4) is an example of the distributive property.
2. 5 × 3 = 3 × 5 is an example of the commutative property.
3. 16 is a multiple of 2.
4. 48 is the least common multiple of 16 and 24.

(Lesson 1) Find each product. Use mental math and multiplication properties.

5. 50 × 3 = 150
6. 40 × 70 = 2,800
7. 60 × (3 × 30) = 5,400
8. 80 × 25 × 4 = 8,000

(Lesson 2) Estimate each product.

9. 65 × 27 1,200–2,100
10. 38 × 72 2,100–3,200
11. 81 × 19 800–1,800
12. 52 × 94 4,500–6,000

(Lessons 3–5) Find each product.

13. 584 × 7 = 4,088
14. 98 × 13 = 1,274
15. 92 × 45 = 4,140
16. 705 × 4 = 2,820
17. 600 × 80 = 48,000
18. 362 × 42 = 15,204
19. 375 × 43 = 16,125
20. 481 × 93 = 44,733

(Lesson 6) Find the LCM for each set of numbers.

21. 6 and 32 96
22. 3, 6, and 7 42

(Mixed Review) Solve.

23. 8 ÷ 4 × 6 − 10 = 2
24. 4 × 4 ÷ 8 + 3 = 5

Name ______________________

Practice 3-8

Exploring Decimal Patterns

Draw arrows to show the number of places to move the decimal. Then write the product.

1. 2.38 × 10 23.8
2. 2.38 × 100 238
3. 2.380 × 1,000 2,380
4. 0.356 × 10 3.56
5. 0.356 × 100 35.6
6. 0.356 × 1,000 356

Find each product.

7. 4.7 × 10 = 47
   4.7 × 100 = 470
   4.7 × 1,000 = 4,700
8. 0.96 × 10 = 9.6
   0.96 × 100 = 96
   0.96 × 1,000 = 960
9. 0.06 × 10 = 0.6
   0.06 × 100 = 6
   0.06 × 1,000 = 60
10. 8.437 × 10 = 84.37
    8.437 × 100 = 843.7
    8.437 × 1,000 = 8,437

Place the decimal point in the product. Write extra zeros if necessary.

11. 1.63 × 10 = 1 6 3 16.3
12. 3.72 × 100 = 3 7 2 372
13. 0.035 × 1,000 = 3 5 35
14. 0.0068 × 1,000 = 6 8 6.8
15. 1.063 × 100 = 1 0 6 3 106.3
16. 7.04 × 1,000 = 7 0 4 7,040

Find each product. Use mental math.

17. 100 × 2.93 = 293
18. 1,000 × 3.049 = 3,049
19. 5.47 × 10 = 54.7
20. 8.05 × 1,000 = 8,050
21. 100 × 0.635 = 63.5
22. 10 × 0.514 = 5.14

23. **Money** 10 members of the science club each paid $2.50 for a field trip. How much did they pay all together? $25

Name ______________________

Practice 3-9

Estimating Decimal Products

Estimate each product. Explain what you did.

1. 5.2 × 6 30; 5 × 6
2. 7.8 × 5 40; 8 × 5
3. 9.1 × 3 27; 9 × 3
4. 1.7 × 8 16; 2 × 8
5. 39.7 × 9 360; 40 × 9
6. 25.1 × 4 100; 25 × 4
7. 4.19 × 8 32; 4 × 8
8. 88.9 × 2 180; 90 × 2
9. 72.3 × 49 3,500; 70 × 50
10. 728.1 × 28 21,000; 700 × 30
11. 6.6 × 97 700; 7 × 100
12. 32 × 511.9 15,000; 30 × 500

Is each product greater than 250? Write yes or no. Explain.

13. 25.3 × 8 no; 30 × 8 = 240
14. 9 × 29.97 yes; 9 × 30 = 270
15. 10 × 22.19 no; 10 × 22 = 220
16. 52.37 × 5 yes; 50 × 5 = 250
17. 47.3 × 6 yes; 50 × 6 = 300
18. 11 × 22.3 no; 10 × 22 = 220

Is each product greater than 2,500? Write yes or no. Explain.

19. 927.4 × 2 no; 900 × 2 = 1,800
20. 24.1 × 99 no; 20 × 100 = 2,000
21. 111 × 27.43 yes; 100 × 30 = 3,000
22. 19.86 × 198 yes; 20 × 200 = 4,000
23. 24.4 × 100 no; 24 × 100 = 2,400
24. 51.2 × 51.2 yes; 50 × 50 = 2,500
25. Estimate the product of 51.07 and 9.87. 5,000
26. Estimate the product of 98.57 and 303. 30,000
27. Estimate the product of 68.9 and 74.2. 4,900

Name ______________________

Practice 3-10

Multiplying Whole Numbers and Decimals

Find each product.

1. 3.14 × 7 = 21.98
2. 6.05 × 8 = 48.40
3. 15.45 × 6 = 92.70
4. 4.51 × 13 = 58.63
5. 29.4 × 76 = 2,234.4
6. 89.03 × 39 = 3,472.17
7. $15.75 × 6 = $94.50
8. $33.99 × 4 = $135.96
9. $12.45 × 13 = $161.85
10. $21.95 × 11 = $241.45
11. $3.95 × 24 = $94.80
12. $74.63 × 8 = $597.04
13. 18 × 347.6 = 6,256.8
14. 93 × 72.6 = 6,751.8
15. 9 × $26.37 = $237.33
16. 6 × $147.50 = $885.00

Choose the number that is closest to the actual product.

17. $3.25 × 11 C — A. $300 B. $50 C. $30
18. $6.80 × 39 B — A. $28 B. $280 C. $180
19. $4.75 × 22 B — A. $1,000 B. $100 C. $80
20. 2.008 × 100 C — A. 20 B. 2,000 C. 200

21. What is the product of 7.09 and 16? 113.44
22. What is the product of $1.85 and 34? $62.90
23. Bill says the product of 6 and 3.79 is 227.4. Is he correct? Explain.
    No, he placed the decimal in the wrong place. There are two decimal places so the product is 22.74.
24. Circle each multiplication sentence whose product is a whole number.

3 × 45.7	(12.2 × 5)	(6 × 8.5)	7.6 × 4
23.5 × 45	6.15 × 4	(5 × 32.8)	(4 × 7.25)

Name ______________________

Practice 3-11

Analyzing Word Problems: Multiple-Step Problems

Solve each problem.

1. Sandwiches at the diner are $3.75, a salad costs $1.19, and a glass of juice costs $0.99. A family went to the diner and ordered 3 sandwiches, 2 salads, and 3 glasses of juice.
   a. How much will the family pay for the 3 sandwiches? $11.25
   b. How much will the family pay for the 2 salads? $2.38
   c. How much will the family pay for the 3 glasses of juice? $2.97
   d. How much is the total bill? $16.60

Solve each problem. Chose any strategy.

2. The hobby shop sells many different varieties of kites. Box kites are $6.69, diamonds are $5.95, and dragon kites are $11.98.
   a. Mr. Sanders bought 2 box kites and 2 diamond kites for his 4 children. How much did he spend? $25.28
   b. Ms. Byars bought 3 box kites and 2 dragon kites for her 5 children. How much did she spend? $44.03
3. A video store charges $2.50 for new movies and $1.50 for children's movies. If a family rents 2 new movies and 3 children's movies, how much will they pay? $9.50
4. At a state fair, the Lanier family had 120 jars of their homemade jelly to sell. Large jars were $4.50 each and small jars were $2.50 each.
   a. How much would you pay if you bought 3 large jars and 4 small ones? $23.50
   b. By the end of the day, the Laniers sold 40 large jars of jelly. They made $330 in all. How much did they make selling small jars of jelly? $150
   c. How many small jars of jelly did they sell? 60 jars
   d. How many jars did the Laniers have leftover? 20 jars

Name ______________________

Practice Chapter 3 Section B

Review and Practice

Vocabulary Underline the word that correctly to completes the sentence.

1. 4 and 25 are (compatible, decimal) numbers for multiplication.
2. The product of 0.23 and 10 is a (compatible, decimal) number.

(Lesson 8) Find each product.

3. 6.04 × 10 = 60.4
4. 1.85 × 100 = 185
5. 0.92 × 100 = 92
6. 0.0065 × 1,000 = 6.5
7. 1.98 × 10 = 19.8
8. 0.0236 × 1,000 = 23.6

(Lesson 9) Estimate each product.

9. 16 × 8.46 160
10. 6.12 × 82 480
11. 307 × 9.5 2,700–3,000
12. 4.78 × 30 150
13. 25 × 0.12 2–3
14. 1.11 × 73 73

(Lesson 10) Use estimation to place the decimal point in each product.

15. 6.15 × 98 = 6 0 2 7 602.7
16. 9.82 × 35 = 3 4 3 7 343.7
17. 52.7 × 23 = 1 2 1 2 1 1212.1
18. 11.1 × 49 = 5 4 3 9 543.9
19. $1.23 × 9 = $1 1 0 7 $11.07
20. $6.88 × 707 = $4 8 6 4 1 6 $4864.16

(Lesson 11) Solve each problem.

21. A granola bar sells for $0.55. An eight-pack of the same bars costs $4.00. How much could you save on a purchase of an eight-pack? $0.40
22. A candle maker can make 3 candles from 6 pounds of wax. How many pounds of wax would be needed to make 15 of the same candles? 30 pounds

(Mixed Review) Multiply or divide.

23. 3 × 8 = 24
24. 45 ÷ 9 = 5
25. 42 ÷ 7 = 6
26. 5 × 7 = 35
27. 8 × 9 = 72
28. 36 ÷ 6 = 6

Name ______________________

Practice 3-12

Exploring Decimal Multiplication

1. Use the 10 × 10 grid to show 0.7 of 0.9.

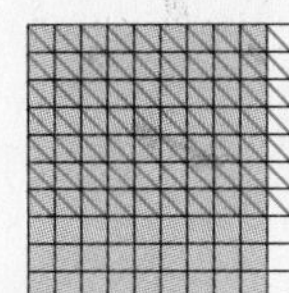

   a. Use yellow to shade 0.7 on the grid as 7 rows.
   b. Use blue to shade 0.9 on the grid as 9 columns.
   c. Count the green squares. 0.7 of 0.9 is 0.63.

Find each product. You can use 10 × 10 grids to help.

2. 0.4 of 0.5 0.20
3. 0.3 of 0.7 0.21
4. 0.4 of 0.7 0.28
5. 0.9 of 0.2 0.18
6. 0.8 of 0.5 0.40
7. 0.8 of 0.9 0.72
8. 0.8 of 0.6 0.48
9. 0.3 of 0.6 0.18
10. 0.6 of 0.6 0.36
11. 0.4 of 0.6 0.24
12. 0.6 of 0.3 0.18
13. 0.8 of 0.7 0.56
14. 0.5 of 0.6 0.30
15. 0.3 of 0.9 0.27
16. 0.4 of 0.1 0.04
17. 0.9 of 0.9 0.81
18. Find the product of 0.7 and 0.7. 0.49
19. The product is 0.64. One of the factors is 0.8. What is the other factor? 0.8
20. Write two numbers whose product is 0.35. 0.5, 0.7
21. Write two numbers whose product is 0.49. 0.7, 0.7
22. A can of dog food weighs 0.6 lb. Arthur's dog gets 0.5 can of food for dinner. How much does the dog's dinner weigh? 0.3 lb

Name ______________________

Practice 3-13

Multiplying Decimals by Decimals

Find each product. Round to the nearest cent when necessary.

1. 3.45 × 0.4 = 1.38
2. $7.10 × 42 = $298.20
3. 1.45 × 4.5 = 6.525
4. $43.38 × 1.65 = $71.577; $71.58
5. 3.81 × 4.121 = 15.70101
6. 6.09 × 5.4 = 32.886
7. 0.091 × 74.4 = 6.7704
8. 4.799 × 5 = 23.995
9. 231 × 0.301 = 69.531
10. $17.32 × 0.04 = $0.6928; $0.69
11. 3.5 × 3.5 = 12.25
12. $12.30 × 4 = $49.20
13. Find the product of 49.3 and 0.22. 10.846
14. Find the product of $8.43 and 24.5. Round to the nearest cent. $206.535; $206.54
15. The product of 4,005 × 6,004 is 24,046,020. What is the product of 4.005 and 6.004? 24.04602
16. Without doing the multiplication, tell how many decimal places are in the product of 4.97 and 3.456. 5
17. Without doing the multiplication, tell how many decimal places are in the product of 72.35 and 14.12. 3 or 4

Name ______________________

Practice 3-14

Finding High and Low Estimates

Between which two numbers will each product be found?

1. 8.6 × 8.762 C
   A. 8 and 9 B. 16 and 48 C. 64 and 81
2. 7.9 × 5.23 C
   A. 7 and 5 B. 57 and 75 C. 35 and 48
3. 9.6 × 0.74 B
   A. 9 and 16 B. 0 and 10 C. 9 and 63

Estimate low and high. Then find each product.

4. 5.4 × 6 = 32.4
   Estimate: 30–36
5. 41.3 × 7 = 289.1
   Estimate: 280–350
6. 9.3 × 4 = 37.2
   Estimate: 36–40
7. 7.8 × 3 = 23.4
   Estimate 21–24

8. 14.4 × 6.2 = 89.28 Estimate: 84–105
9. 4.9 × 8.1 = 39.69 Estimate: 32–45
10. 6.9 × 3.2 = 22.08 Estimate: 18–28
11. 7.9 × 8.3 = 65.57 Estimate 56–72

12. Estimate low and high. Then find the product of 89.4 and 4.8.
    320–450; 429.12
13. What 2 decimal factors when multiplied result in a product between 15 and 24? Possible answer: 3.9 × 5.26
14. How can you use estimation to know that the product of 4.5 and 6.89 is more than 24?
    because a low estimate is 24

Name ______________________

Practice 3-15

Decimals and Zeros

Find each product. Write zeros where needed.

1. 0.2 × 0.3 = 0.06
2. 7.2 × 0.0007 = 0.00504
3. 1.25 × 0.05 = 0.0625
4. 0.004 × 0.08 = 0.00032
5. 3.4 × 0.0006 = 0.00204
6. 0.04 × 0.04 = 0.0016
7. 5.05 × 4.02 = 20.301
8. 0.08 × 10.05 = 0.804
9. 0.008 × 0.004 = 0.000032
10. 0.07 × 0.006 = 0.00042
11. 8.9 × 0.003 = 0.0267
12. 2.1 × 0.08 = 0.168
13. 12 × 0.005 = 0.06
14. 0.045 × 0.004 = 0.00018
15. 7.005 × 0.06 = 0.4203
16. 5.05 × 5.04 = 25.452
17. 12.4 × 0.004 = 0.0496
18. 18.4 × 0.0002 = 0.00368
19. 9.3 × 0.0044 = 0.04092
20. 76 × 0.0003 = 0.0228
21. Find the product of 0.25 and 3.9. 0.975
22. Find the product of 6.2 and 0.4. 2.48
23. Is the product of 0.006 and 1.5 greater or less than 1.5? Explain.
    Less than; multiplying by a number less than 1 gives a product less than the other factor.

Name ______________________

Practice 3-16

Analyzing Strategies: Guess and Check

Use the Guess and Check strategy to solve each problem.

Two owners compared the weights of their dogs. Together, the two dogs weigh 36 lb. The spaniel weighs 6 lb more than the poodle.

1. What is a reasonable first guess for the weight of the poodle?
   Possible answer: 12–18 lb
2. The two dogs together weigh 36 lb. Is it possible for the spaniel to weigh 24 lb? Explain.
   No, because there is only 6 lb difference between the dogs
3. How much did each dog weigh?
   21 lb for the spaniel; 15 lb for the poodle

Use Guess and Check or any strategy to help solve each problem.

4. Together, Fred and Frank have been working 25 years. Frank has worked 7 years longer than Fred. How many years has each been working?
   Fred: 9 years; Frank: 16 years
5. The cross country team is planning a 30 km relay. Each team member will run either 4 or 6 km. The same number of team members will run each distance. How many team members will run each distance?
   3 team members; (3 × 4) + (3 × 6) = 30
6. At the hardware store, doorbells cost $12, while doorknobs cost $8. Greg's Refinishing Company spent $120 on 12 items. How many of each item did they buy?
   6 doorbells, and 6 doorknobs; (6 × 12) + (6 × 8) = 120
7. Lawrence has $10. He gets a $6 a week allowance for doing household chores. How many weeks will it take him to save for a video game that costs $52?
   7 weeks; $10 + $42 = $52

Name ______________________

Practice Chapter 3 Section C

Review and Practice

(Lesson 12) Place a decimal in each product.

1. 0.4 × 0.7 = 028 0.28
2. 0.08 × 5 = 040 0.40
3. 0.2 × 0.9 = 018 0.18
3. 0.15 × 9 = 0135 01.35

(Lesson 13) Find each product. Round to the nearest cent when necessary.

5. 14.4 × 6.2 = 89.28
6. 4.9 × 8.1 = 39.69
7. $6.90 × 3.2 = $22.08
8. 7.9 × 8.3 = 65.57

(Lesson 14) Between which two numbers will each product be found?

9. 3.91 × 0.95 B A. 1 and 3 B. 3 and 4 C. 4 and 5
10. 6.6 × 9.2 A A. 54 and 70 B. 40 and 54 C. 6 and 9
11. 9.43 × 7.99 C A. 7 and 9 B. 56 and 63 C. 63 and 80

(Lesson 15) Find each product. Insert zeros where necessary.

12. 3.009 × 0.0028 = 0.0084252
13. 8.59 × 1.01 = 8.6759
14. 0.00038 × 0.05 = 0.000019

(Lesson 16) Solve.

15. Sandro's skateboard cost $8 more than Kim's. Together their skateboards cost $80. How much did each pay for their skateboards?
    Sandro spent $44; Kim spent $36.

(Mixed Review) Add or subtract.

16. 73.5 + 3.5 = 77.0
17. 36.81 + 3.5 = 40.31
18. 122.89 − 32.98 = 89.91
19. $23.00 − 5.99 = $17.01

Name ______________________

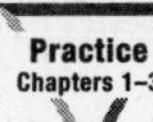

Practice
Chapters 1–3

Cumulative Review

(Chapter 1 Lesson 10) Use the data to answer 1 and 2.

Number of Sit-ups in Gym Class									
23	24	15	16	23	30	30	14	22	33
13	19	20	30	32	30	20	10	22	23

1. Make a stem-and-leaf plot for the number of sit-ups in gym class.

1	0 3 4 5 6 9
2	0 0 2 2 3 3 3 4
3	0 0 0 0 2 3

2. What is the median, range, and mode of the number of sit-ups? 22.5, 23, 30

Order of numbers in leaves may vary.

(Chapter 2 Lesson 9) Write each number in decimal form.

3. 8 thousandths 0.008
4. 40 hundredths 0.40
5. three hundred one thousandths 0.301

(Chapter 2 Lesson 18) Subtract.

6. $\$3.69 - 1.97 = \$1.72$
7. $9.71 - 2.03 = 7.68$
8. $6.01 - 3 = 3.01$
9. $8 - 1.35 = 6.65$

(Chapter 3 Lesson 3) Find each product.

10. $267 \times 5 = 1{,}335$
11. $612 \times 6 = 3{,}672$
12. $501 \times 3 = 1{,}503$
13. $736 \times 8 = 5{,}888$

(Chapter 3 Lesson 6) Find the LCM for each set of numbers.

14. 3 and 7 21
15. 5, 6, and 10 30

(Chapter 3 Lesson 15) Find each product. Insert zeros where necessary.

16. $2.019 \times 0.005 = 0.010095$
17. $1.567 \times 0.016 = 0.025072$
18. $0.000043 \times 0.03 = 0.00000129$

Use with page 163. 57

Name ______________________

Practice
4-1

Reviewing the Meaning of Division

Find each quotient.

1. 56 ÷ 7 = 8
2. 42 ÷ 6 = 7
3. 24 ÷ 4 = 6
4. 32 ÷ 8 = 4
5. 30 ÷ 5 = 6
6. 54 ÷ 6 = 9
7. 36 ÷ 6 = 6
8. 21 ÷ 3 = 7
9. 35 ÷ 7 = 5
10. 72 ÷ 9 = 8
11. 36 ÷ 4 = 9
12. 15 ÷ 5 = 3
13. 12 ÷ 3 = 4
14. 64 ÷ 8 = 8
15. 49 ÷ 7 = 7

16. Identify each number in the equations 7 × 4 = 28 and 28 ÷ 7 = 4 as a factor, a product, a divisor, a dividend, or a quotient.

7 → factor × 4 → factor = 28 → product

28 → dividend ÷ 7 → divisor = 4 → quotient

17. If you know that 6 × 3 = 18, you also know that 3 × 6 = 18. Solve for *n*
    a. 18 ÷ 6 = *n* $n = 3$
    b. 18 ÷ 3 = *n* $n = 6$

18. Laura's uncle would not tell his age. Instead he gave some clues: "When you divide my age by 5, the quotient is less than 10. I am younger than 55 but older than 35." What is his age? 40

58 Use with pages 168–169.

Name ______________________

Practice
4-2

Exploring Patterns to Divide

Complete the patterns.

1. 36 ÷ 4 = 9
   360 ÷ 4 = 90
   3,600 ÷ 4 = 900
   36,000 ÷ 4 = 9,000
2. 42 ÷ 7 = 6
   420 ÷ 7 = 60
   4,200 ÷ 7 = 600
   42,000 ÷ 7 = 6,000
3. 64 ÷ 8 = 8
   640 ÷ 8 = 80
   6,400 ÷ 8 = 800
   64,000 ÷ 8 = 8,000
4. 20 ÷ 5 = 4
   200 ÷ 5 = 40
   2,000 ÷ 5 = 400
   20,000 ÷ 5 = 4,000

Use patterns and basic facts to divide mentally.

5. 27 ÷ 9 = 3
6. 270 ÷ 9 = 30
7. 3,600 ÷ 6 = 600
8. 12,000 ÷ 2 = 6,000
9. 350 ÷ 5 = 70
10. 1,500 ÷ 3 = 500
11. 49,000 ÷ 7 = 7,000
12. 7,200 ÷ 8 = 900

Complete.

13. 1,800 ÷ [3] = 600
14. [480] ÷ 6 = 80
15. 21,000 ÷ [7] = 3,000
16. 400 ÷ [5] = 80
17. [1,600] ÷ 4 = 400
18. 24,000 ÷ [3] = 8,000

Use with pages 170–171. 59

Name ______________________

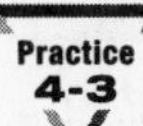

Practice
4-3

Estimating Quotients

Estimate each quotient.

1. 635 ÷ 9 70
2. 233 ÷ 6 40
3. 371 ÷ 6 60
4. 517 ÷ 7 70
5. 386 ÷ 5 80
6. 145 ÷ 8 20
7. 163 ÷ 3 50
8. 801 ÷ 9 90
9. 117 ÷ 2 60
10. 468 ÷ 9 50
11. 554 ÷ 7 80
12. 354 ÷ 4 90
13. Estimate the quotient of 203 ÷ 6. 30
14. Estimate the quotient of 391 ÷ 8. 50
15. Estimate the quotient of 264 ÷ 3. 90
16. You know that 481 ÷ 7 is about 70. Is the exact quotient greater than or less than the estimate? Find estimates for 4,810 ÷ 7, 48,100 ÷ 7, and 48 ÷ 7. less than; 700; 7,000; 7
17. You know that 332 ÷ 4 is about 80. Find estimates for 33 ÷ 4 and 33,200 ÷ 4. 8; 8,000
18. You know that 351 ÷ 6 is about 60. Find estimates for 3,510 ÷ 6 and 35,100 ÷ 6. 600; 6,000

60 Use with pages 172–173.

Name ______________________

Practice
Chapter 4
Section A

Review and Practice

Vocabulary Use the example to answer each question.

$$3\overline{)28}\text{ = 9 R1}$$

1. Which number is the quotient? 9
2. Which number is the dividend? 28
3. Which number is the divisor? 3
4. Which number is the remainder? 1

(Lesson 1) Find each quotient. Use mental math.

5. 24 ÷ 3 = 8
6. 25 ÷ 5 = 5
7. 36 ÷ 9 = 4
8. 56 ÷ 8 = 7
9. Whitney poured 36 ounces of juice in 6 glasses. How many ounces of juice are in each glass? 6 ounces

(Lesson 2) Find each quotient. Use mental math.

10. 4,500 ÷ 9 = 500
11. 40,000 ÷ 5 = 8,000
12. 1,200 ÷ 2 = 600
13. 540 ÷ 6 = 90

Complete.

14. 14,000 ÷ 2 = 7,000
15. 240 ÷ 8 = 30

(Lesson 3) Estimate each quotient by substituting compatible numbers.

16. 163 ÷ 2 80
17. 459 ÷ 9 50
18. 761 ÷ 8 90–100
19. 358 ÷ 4 90

(Mixed Review) Add or subtract.

20. 6,512 + 739 = 7,251
21. 3,003 − 1,439 = 1,564
22. 117 − 99 = 18
23. 997 + 53 = 1,050

Name ______________________

Practice
4-4

Exploring Dividing

Complete. You may use play money to help.

1. 7)$9.28 = $[1].3[2] R[4]
 −7
 [2]2
 −[2][1]
 1[8]
 −14
 [4]

2. 3)$8.93 = $[2].9[7] R[2]
 −[6]
 29
 −[2][7]
 [2]3
 −21
 [2]

3. 4)$9.53 $2.38 R1
4. 6)$8.75 $1.45 R5
5. 2)$3.72 $1.86
6. 7)$7.94 $1.13 R3
7. 3)$4.36 $1.45 R1
8. 3)$9.34 $3.11 R1
9. 5)$8.97 $1.79 R2
10. 4)$6.41 $1.60 R1

Name ______________________

Practice
4-5

Dividing by 1-Digit Divisors

Divide.

1. 96 ÷ 4 24
2. 622 ÷ 5 124 R2
3. 473 ÷ 2 236 R1
4. 547 ÷ 3 182 R1
5. 2)483 241 R1
6. 7)247 35 R2
7. 3)881 293 R2
8. 8)964 120 R4
9. 2)726 363
10. 4)973 243 R1
11. 5)362 72 R2
12. 4)739 184 R3
13. Estimate the quotient for 735 ÷ 3. What number is in the hundreds place in the quotient? 2
14. When dividing a 3-digit number by a 1-digit number, for what divisors can you get a remainder of 8? Explain. 9; the remainder must be less than the divisor.

Name ______________________

Practice
4-6

Analyze Word Problems: Interpret Remainders

Solve. Use the picture to answer **1–3**.

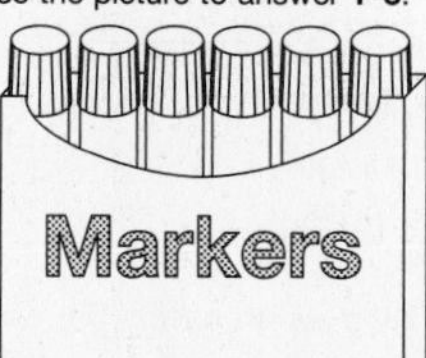

1. If you need markers for a class of 28 students, how many full boxes will you use? 4 full boxes
2. How many more markers will you need after using the full boxes? 4 markers
3. If you opened enough boxes to supply the entire class with markers, how many boxes would you open? 5 boxes
4. In the store room, folders are stored in packages of 8. What is the least number of packages needed for a class of 35 students? 5 packages
5. The cafeteria workers keep small milk cartons in the refrigerator in stacks of 6. If each worker carries no more than one stack, what is the least number of cafeteria workers needed to carry small milk cartons for a class of 32? 6 workers
6. In the cafeteria's refrigerator, cups of yogurt are kept in stacks of 9. If each worker carries no more than one stack, what is the least number of workers needed to carry cups of yogurt for a class of 42? 5 workers
7. In the teachers' lunchroom, teachers sit at tables for 6. There are 22 teachers eating lunch. How many tables must be set up? 4 tables

Name ____________________

Practice 4-7

Deciding Where to Place the First Digit

Divide. Check your answer.

1. 7)381 **54 R3**
2. 5)208 **41 R3**
3. 6)682 **113 R4**
4. 8)329 **41 R1**
5. 4)173 **43 R1**
6. 8)484 **60 R4**
7. 5)571 **114 R1**
8. 4)925 **231 R1**
9. 6)674 **112 R2**

10. 317 ÷ 4 = **79 R1**
11. 815 ÷ 7 = **116 R3**
12. 997 ÷ 3 = **332 R1**
13. 411 ÷ 9 = **45 R6**
14. 859 ÷ 4 = **214 R3**
15. 371 ÷ 7 = **53**
16. Divide 723 by 5. **144 R3**
17. Find 673 divided by 4. **168 R1**
18. The divisor is 6 and the dividend is 752. Divide. **125 R2**
19. The divisor is 9 and the dividend is 255. Divide. **28 R3**

Use with pages 182–185. 65

Name ____________________

Practice 4-8

Zeros in the Quotient

Divide. Multiply to check.

1. 6)242 **40 R2**
2. 3)90 **30**
3. 7)213 **30 R3**
4. 9)918 **102**
5. 5)2,004 **400 R4**
6. 3)627 **209**
7. 4)8,012 **2,003**
8. 6)2,460 **410**
9. 5)3,015 **603**
10. 7)709 **101 R2**
11. 8)2,408 **301**
12. 6)1,892 **315 R2**
13. 5)2,205 **441**
14. 3)1,229 **409 R2**
15. 9)6,311 **701 R2**

Use mental math to find each quotient.

16. 360 ÷ 6 = **60**
17. 5,600 ÷ 8 = **700**
18. 42,000 ÷ 7 = **6,000**
19. 180 ÷ 3 = **60**
20. 48,000 ÷ 8 = **6,000**
21. 15,000 ÷ 5 = **3,000**
22. Divide 965 by 9. **107 R2**
23. Are there any zeros in the quotient of 495 ÷ 4? How can you tell without finding the quotient?
No; the hundreds, tens, and ones can each be divided by 4.

66 Use with pages 186–187.

Name ____________________

Practice 4-9

Exploring Mean

Complete each sentence using a word from the word bank.

56 64 72 72 81 83 97

mean
median
mode

1. The **mode** is 72 because it is the number that appears most.
2. To find the **mean**, add all the numbers and divide by 7.
3. The **median** is 72 because it is the middle number.

Find the mean, median, and mode for each set of data.

4. 115, 124, 130, 122, 124
123, **124**, **124**
5. $5.26, $5.50, $4.87, $4.04, $6.21, $5.26,
$5.19, **$5.26**, **$5.26**
6. $7.08, $7.78, $8.07, $8.70, $8.87
$8.10, **$8.07**, **no mode**
7. Find the mean, median, and mode for the set of data in the bar graph.
$4.20; $4.25; $4.75

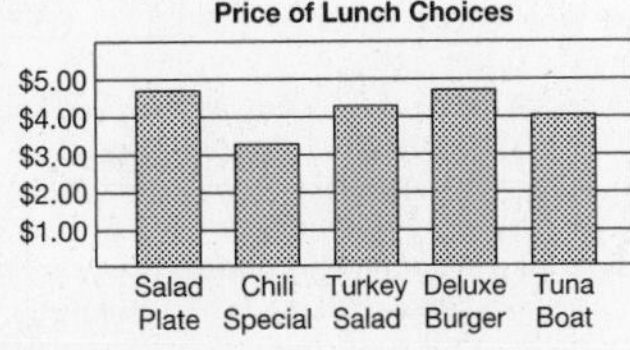

8. Can the median of a set of numbers ever be the greatest number in the set of data? Explain.
Yes, if it is repeated so that it is also the middle number. Five is the median of 1, 2, 5, 5, 5.
9. Suppose you wanted to find the mean, median, and mode of 55, 56, 57, 58, 59. How could you find them mentally?
Since there are 5 consecutive numbers in the sequence, the middle number is the median and the mean. There is no mode.

Use with pages 190–191. 67

Name ____________________

Practice Chapter 4 Section B

Review and Practice

Vocabulary Fill in each blank with a word from the word bank.

mean	median	mode

1. The **median** is the middle number of an ordered set of numbers.
2. The **mean** is the average of a set of numbers.
3. The **mode** is the most common value in a set of data.

(Lessons 4, 5, 7, and 8) Divide. Multiply to check your answer.

4. $15.50 ÷ 5 = **$3.10**
5. $9.68 ÷ 8 = **$1.21**
6. 6)2,406 **401**
7. 7)287 **41**
8. 3)762 **254**
9. 4)4,191 **1,047 R3**
10. 8)417 **52 R1**
11. 9)3,687 **409 R6**

12. A box holds 7 candles. Each of the 29 students in science class needs 1 candle.
    a. How many boxes are needed? **5 boxes**
    b. How many candles will be left over? **6 candles**

(Lesson 9) Find the mean, median, and mode for each set of data.

13. 15, 17, 15, 11, 12 — **14**, **15**, **15**
14. 5, 8, 8, 10, 11, 6 — **8**, **8**, **8**
15. $27, $36, $51, $42, $36, $48 — **$40**, **$39**, **$36**

(Mixed Review) Add.

16. 7 + 5 + 2 + 8 = **22**
17. 1 + 8 + 2 + 9 = **20**

68 Use with page 192.

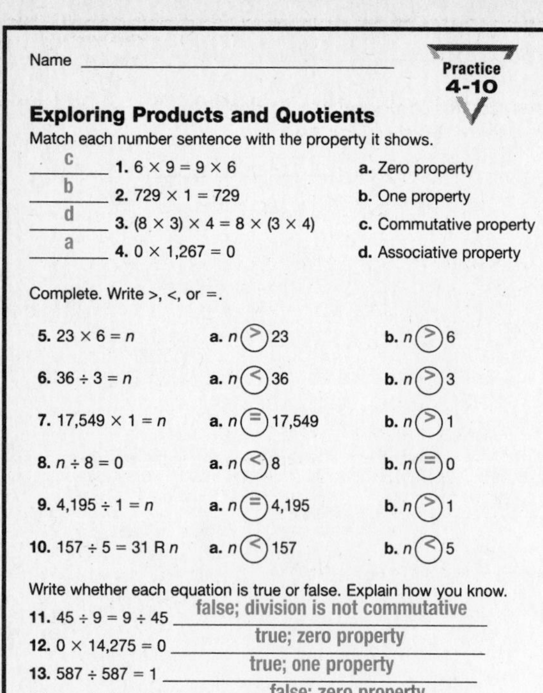

Name ______________________

Practice 4-10

Exploring Products and Quotients

Match each number sentence with the property it shows.

c 1. 6 × 9 = 9 × 6 — a. Zero property

b 2. 729 × 1 = 729 — b. One property

d 3. (8 × 3) × 4 = 8 × (3 × 4) — c. Commutative property

a 4. 0 × 1,267 = 0 — d. Associative property

Complete. Write >, <, or =.

	a.	b.
5. 23 × 6 = *n*	*n* (>) 23	*n* (>) 6
6. 36 ÷ 3 = *n*	*n* (<) 36	*n* (>) 3
7. 17,549 × 1 = *n*	*n* (=) 17,549	*n* (>) 1
8. *n* ÷ 8 = 0	*n* (<) 8	*n* (=) 0
9. 4,195 ÷ 1 = *n*	*n* (=) 4,195	*n* (>) 1
10. 157 ÷ 5 = 31 R *n*	*n* (<) 157	*n* (<) 5

Write whether each equation is true or false. Explain how you know.

11. 45 ÷ 9 = 9 ÷ 45 false; division is not commutative
12. 0 × 14,275 = 0 true; zero property
13. 587 ÷ 587 = 1 true; one property
14. 0 ÷ 4,113 = 4,113 false; zero property
15. 81 ÷ 9 = 9 ÷ 81 false; division is not commutative
16. 24 × 3 = 3 × 24 true; multiplication is commutative
17. Peter said he divided 7 into a number and got zero. What is the number? Explain how you know.
    0; zero property

Use with pages 194–195. 69

Name ______________________

Practice 4-11

Dividing Money

Find each quotient. Multiply to check.

$6.00 1. 7)$42.00	$1.01 2. 4)$4.04	$4.44 3. 3)$13.32
$5.03 4. 5)$25.15	$5.72 5. 6)$34.32	$10.27 6. 7)$71.89
$60.70 7. 3)$182.10	$65.07 8. 5)$325.35	$58.68 9. 8)$469.44

Use a calculator to divide. Write each answer to the nearest cent.

10. $5.11 ÷ 4 = $1.28	11. $12.77 ÷ 5 = $2.55
$128.30 12. 7)$898.13	$9.18 13. 8)$73.45
$335.68 14. 6)$2,014.10	$248.44 15. 3)$745.31

16. For $42.01 ÷ 2, $297.66 ÷ 6, and $8.43 ÷ 8, are any of the quotients less than a dollar? How can you tell?
    No; none of the divisors are greater than the whole dollar amounts of the dividends.

70 Use with pages 196–199.

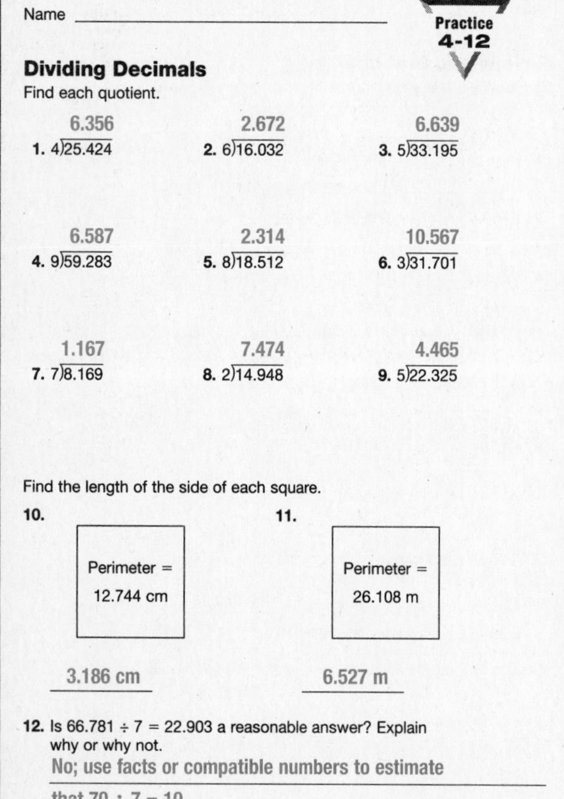

Name ______________________

Practice 4-12

Dividing Decimals

Find each quotient.

6.356 1. 4)25.424	2.672 2. 6)16.032	6.639 3. 5)33.195
6.587 4. 9)59.283	2.314 5. 8)18.512	10.567 6. 3)31.701
1.167 7. 7)8.169	7.474 8. 2)14.948	4.465 9. 5)22.325

Find the length of the side of each square.

10. Perimeter = 12.744 cm — 3.186 cm

11. Perimeter = 26.108 m — 6.527 m

12. Is 66.781 ÷ 7 = 22.903 a reasonable answer? Explain why or why not.
    No; use facts or compatible numbers to estimate that 70 ÷ 7 = 10.

Use with pages 200–201. 71

Name ______________________

Practice 4-13

Factors and Divisibility

Find the factors for each number.

1. 25 1, 5, 25	2. 12 1, 2, 3, 4, 6, 12
3. 21 1, 3, 7, 21	4. 40 1, 2, 4, 5, 8, 10, 20, 40
5. 36 1, 2, 3, 4, 6, 9, 12, 18, 36	6. 45 1, 3, 5, 9, 15, 45
7. 49 1, 7, 49	8. 33 1, 3, 11, 33
9. 30 1, 2, 3, 5, 6, 10, 15, 30	10. 56 1, 2, 4, 7, 8, 14, 28, 56

11. What are the factors of 65? 1, 5, 13, 65
12. What are the factors of 28? 1, 2, 4, 7, 14, 28
13. What are the factors of 32? 1, 2, 4, 8, 16, 32
14. What are the factors of 27? 1, 3, 9, 27
15. Is 3 a factor of 261? Explain how you know.
    yes; because the digits add up to 9, which is divisible by 3
16. Is 10 a factor of 325? Explain how you know.
    no; because 325 does not end in 0
17. Is 6 a factor of 492? Explain how you know.
    Yes; 492 is divisible by 2 because it is an even number. 492 is divisible by 3 because the digits add up to 15, which is divisible by 3. 492 is divisible by 6 because it is divisible by 2 and 3.

72 Use with pages 202–203.

Name ______________________

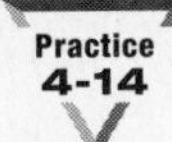

Exploring Prime and Composite Numbers

Complete each sentence using a word from the word bank.

composite number factors factor tree prime number products

1. A ___prime number___ has exactly two different factors.
2. 21 is an example of a ___composite number___.
3. You can use a ___factor tree___ to show the factors of a composite number.
4. A composite number has more than two ___factors___.

Write whether each number is prime or composite.

5. 38 ___composite___ 6. 19 ___prime___ 7. 83 ___prime___

Use factor trees to find the prime factors of each number.

8. 12 9. 32 10. 30

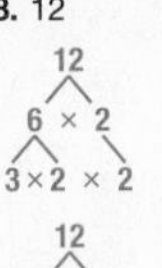

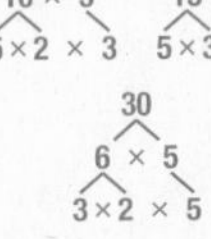

Write the missing factors.

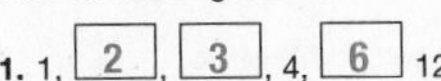

11. 1, [2], [3], 4, [6] 12 12. 1, [7], 49

13. Can a whole number ending in 8 be prime? Explain. ___No, a whole number ending in 8 has a factor of 2, so it is composite.___

Name ______________________

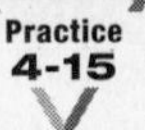

Analyze Strategies: Work Backward

Work backward to solve each problem.

1. On Sundays, Bernie's Bagel shop gets very busy. Two hours after they opened, Bernie's sold one third of their bagels. During the next hour, they sold another 50 bagels. During the rest of the day, half of the remaining bagels were bought. At closing, there were only 25 bagels left.
   a. How many bagels were left at closing? ___25 bagels___
   b. What operation undoes dividing the number of bagels in half? ___multiplying by 2___
   c. What operation undoes subtracting 50? ___adding 50___
   d. How many bagels were in the store when it opened on Sunday? ___150 bagels___

Use any strategy to solve each problem.

2. Arlene keeps track of her weekly expenses. At the end of a week, she had $2.35 left. She had bought 2 bottles of juice for $0.80 each and one package of markers for $4.55. How much did Arlene have at the beginning of the week?

   ___$8.50___

3. The tag on the shirt shows that the price has been lowered twice. What was the original price of the shirt?

   ___$48.00___

4. Louis had homework in 2 subjects. He finished his homework at 6:00 P.M. He spent 30 minutes doing his science homework. He spent twice that amount of time doing his reading homework. At what time did Louis start his homework?

   ___4:30 P.M.___

Name ______________________

Practice
Chapter 4
Section C

Review and Practice

Vocabulary Write true or false for each statement.

1. A whole number greater than 1 that has more than two different factors is a composite number. ___true___
2. Any number that divides another number with a remainder of 2 is called a factor. ___false, remainder of 0___

(Lesson 10) Complete.

3. ___0___ ÷ 678 = 0 4. 389 × ___1___ = 389

(Lesson 11) Find each quotient. Round to the nearest cent.

5. 3)$16.00 = $5.33 6. 7)$125.10 = $17.87 7. 4)$8.31 = $2.08

(Lesson 12) Find each quotient.

8. 2)13.162 = 6.581 9. 6)37.662 = 6.277 10. 7)8.491 = 1.213

(Lesson 13) Find all the factors for each number.

11. 8 ___1, 2, 4, 8___ 12. 18 ___1, 2, 3, 6, 9, 18___

13. 36 ___1, 2, 3, 4, 6, 9, 12, 18, 36___

(Lesson 14) Use factor trees to find the prime factors of each number.

14. 20 15. 31 16. 50

20
10 × 2
2×5 × 2

20
4 × 5
2×2 × 5

31
1 × 31

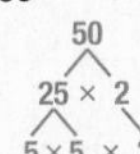

(Mixed Review) Find each sum or difference.

17. 426 + 238 = ___664___ 18. 204 − 97 = ___107___

Name ______________________

Practice
Chapters 1–4

Cumulative Review

(Chapter 2 Lesson 18) Subtract.

1. $23.12 − 8.97 = $14.15 2. 0.71 − 0.46 = 0.25 3. $5.00 − 3.99 = $1.01 4. 3 − 1.35 = 1.65

(Chapter 3 Lesson 13) Find each product.

5. 2.67 × 0.5 = 1.335 6. $6.12 × 26 = $159.12 7. 4.81 × 7.3 = 35.113 8. 8.36 × 0.58 = 4.8488

(Chapter 3 Lesson 15) Find each product. Insert zeros where necessary.

9. 1.075 × 0.003 = 0.003225 10. 1.092 × 0.006 = 0.006552 11. 2.3 × 0.00008 = 0.000184

(Chapter 4 Lessons 7, 8, and 12) Find each quotient.

12. 5)69 = 13 R4 13. 9)369 = 41 14. 7)1,456 = 208

15. 4)820 = 205 16. 8)4,809 = 601 R1 17. 3)9,245 = 3,081 R2

18. 6)19.404 = 3.234 19. 2)6.238 = 3.119 20. 9)37.926 = 4.214

Name ____________________

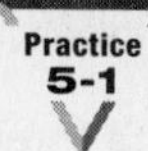

Exploring Division Patterns

You can use number sense and basic facts to divide with multiples of 10.

1. a. What basic fact would you use to find 810 ÷ 90? 81 ÷ 9 = 9
   b. 810 ÷ 90 = 9
2. a. What basic fact would you use to find 42,000 ÷ 70? 42 ÷ 7 = 6
   b. 42,000 ÷ 70 = 600

Find each quotient. Use mental math.

3. 2,400 ÷ 60 = 40
4. 2,700 ÷ 90 = 30
5. 350 ÷ 50 = 7
6. 1,800 ÷ 300 = 6
7. 32,000 ÷ 80 = 400
8. 60,000 ÷ 200 = 300
9. 4,000 ÷ 500 = 8
10. 63,000 ÷ 70 = 900
11. 1,600 ÷ 40 = 40
12. 720 ÷ 90 = 8

Complete.

13. 1,200 ÷ 30 = 40
14. 24,000 ÷ 300 = 80
15. 25,000 ÷ 500 = 50
16. 64,000 ÷ 80 = 800

For each pair, write whether the quotient is the same or different. Explain.

17. 500 ÷ 50 and 5,000 ÷ 500
    same; same basic fact and pattern in multiples of 10
18. 240 ÷ 3 and 24,000 ÷ 30
    different; same basic fact but difference in multiples of 10
19. How would you find 49,000 ÷ 7?
    Possible answer: Divide 49 by 7, then use number sense to determine how many zeros to use.

Name ____________________

Practice
5-2

Estimating Quotients: High and Low

Estimate each quotient. Give a high and low estimate.

1. 16,786 ÷ 50 — 400, 300
2. $26,521 ÷ 30 — $900, $800
3. 4,033 ÷ 60 — 70, 60
4. 6,945 ÷ 80 — 90, 80
5. 22,487 ÷ 40 — 600, 500
6. $33,132 ÷ 70 — $500, $400
7. 5,399 ÷ 80 — 70, 60
8. 13,452 ÷ 30 — 500, 400
9. 3,000 ÷ 90 — 40, 30
10. 4,465 ÷ 60 — 80, 70
11. 57,029 ÷ 70 — 900, 800
12. 1,553 ÷ 20 — 80, 70
13. $3,909 ÷ 50 — $80, $70
14. 2,517 ÷ 40 — 70, 60
15. 14,129 ÷ 30 — 500, 400
16. 57,221 ÷ 60 — 1,000; 900
17. 4,417 ÷ 50 — 90, 80
18. 26,951 ÷ 80 — 400, 300
19. How is estimating the quotient of 4,740 and 60 similar to estimating the quotient of 474,000 and 600?
    You use the same basic fact (48 ÷ 6 = 8) and multiples of 10.
20. How is estimating the quotient of 6,840 and 90 similar to estimating the quotient of 684,000 and 9,000?
    You use the same basic fact (72 ÷ 9 = 8) and multiples of 10.

Name ____________________

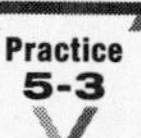

Estimating with 2-Digit Divisors

Estimate each quotient using compatible numbers.

1. 821 ÷ 18 — about 40
2. 592 ÷ 33 — about 20
3. 3,465 ÷ 49 — about 70
4. 809 ÷ 92 — about 9
5. 7,468 ÷ 82 — about 90
6. $24,424 ÷ 59 — about $400
7. 585 ÷ 58 — about 10
8. 21,000 ÷ 74 — about 300
9. $557 ÷ 83 — about $7
10. 362 ÷ 51 — about 7
11. 4,106 ÷ 55 — about 80
12. $8,123 ÷ 20 — about $400
13. 32,128 ÷ 36 — about 800
14. $1,107 ÷ 21 — about $50
15. 3,727 ÷ 45 — about 80
16. Estimate the quotient of 989 ÷ 48. Is the exact quotient greater than or less than your estimate?
    about 20; greater than; 1,000 ÷ 50 = 20
17. Estimate the quotient of 607 ÷ 22. Is the exact quotient greater than or less than your estimate?
    about 30; less than; 600 ÷ 20 = 30
18. Which quotient is greater: 4,322 ÷ 18 or 4,322 ÷ 19? 4,322 ÷ 18
19. Which quotient is greater: 1,868 ÷ 32 or 1,868 ÷ 27? 1,868 ÷ 27

Name ____________________

Practice
Chapter 5
Section A

Review and Practice

Vocabulary Write true or false for each statement.

1. Six is the quotient. false
2. 17 is the dividend. true

$6\overline{)17}$ = 2 R5

(Lesson 1) Find each quotient. Use mental math.

3. 1,800 ÷ 30 = 60
4. 24,000 ÷ 80 = 300
5. 450 ÷ 90 = 5
6. 5,600 ÷ 700 = 8
7. Are the quotients for 560 ÷ 8 and 56,000 ÷ 80 the same or different? different

(Lesson 2) Estimate each quotient. Give a high and low estimate.

8. 16,993 ÷ 20 — 900–800
9. 49,695 ÷ 90 — 600–500
10. 7,613 ÷ 80 — 100–90
11. 35,800 ÷ 60 — 600–500

(Lesson 3) Estimate each quotient by using compatible numbers.

12. 4,499 ÷ 93 50
13. 33,617 ÷ 59 500
14. $1,178 ÷ 33 $40
15. 712,540 ÷ 86 8,000
16. Which quotient is greater: 54,689 ÷ 63 or 54,689 ÷ 59?
    54,689 ÷ 59

(Mixed Review) Find each product.

17. 517 × 39 = 20,163
18. 803 × 439 = 352,517
19. 347 × 99 = 34,353
20. 997 × 62 = 61,814

Name ____________________

Practice 5-4

Dividing by 2-Digit Divisors

Complete.

1. 16)74 = 4 R 10
2. 29)205 = 7 R 2
3. 42)396 = 9 R 18
4. 33)166 = 5 R 1
5. 78)686 = 8 R 62
6. 61)377 = 6 R 11

Divide.

7. 54)175 = 3 R13
8. 96)488 = 5 R8
9. 13)117 = 9
10. 25)167 = 6 R17
11. 82)351 = 4 R23
12. 47)401 = 8 R25
13. 77)309 = 4 R1
14. 50)400 = 8
15. 69)503 = 7 R20
16. 70)150 = 2 R10
17. 36)323 = 8 R35
18. 28)175 = 6 R7
19. 174 ÷ 8 = 21 R6
20. 424 ÷ 61 = 6 R58
21. 527 ÷ 98 = 5 R37
22. 215 ÷ 35 = 6 R5
23. What is 189 divided by 44? 4 R13
24. Divide 166 by 20. 8 R6
25. Can a divisor be less than a remainder? Explain.
Possible answer: No, if the divisor is less than the remainder, then the divisor can divide the dividend at least one more time.

Use with pages 230–233. 81

Name ____________________

Practice 5-5

Dividing Greater Numbers

Divide. Check your answer.

1. 17)85 = 5
2. 36)288 = 8
3. 52)1,300 = 25
4. 68)1,090 = 16 R2
5. 75)4,575 = 61
6. 43)516 = 12
7. 29)2,233 = 77
8. 84)924 = 11
9. 37)851 = 23
10. 98 ÷ 14 = 7
11. 704 ÷ 44 = 16
12. 1,801 ÷ 56 = 32 R9
13. 2,059 ÷ 71 = 29
14. 621 ÷ 27 23
15. 376 ÷ 34 = 11 R2

Estimate. Use your number sense to choose the best answer for **16–18**.

16. 512 ÷ 30 is B
 A. less than 17 **B.** more than 17 **C.** exactly 17
17. 1,180 ÷ 60 is B
 A. less than 2 **B.** less than 20 **C.** more than 20
18. 8,999 ÷ 50 is C
 A. less than 150 **B.** more than 200 **C.** between 150 and 200
19. Divide 686 by 26. 26 R10
20. 735 divided by 49 is what number? 15
21. If your divisor is 63, what is the greatest possible remainder you could have? 62

82 Use with pages 234–237.

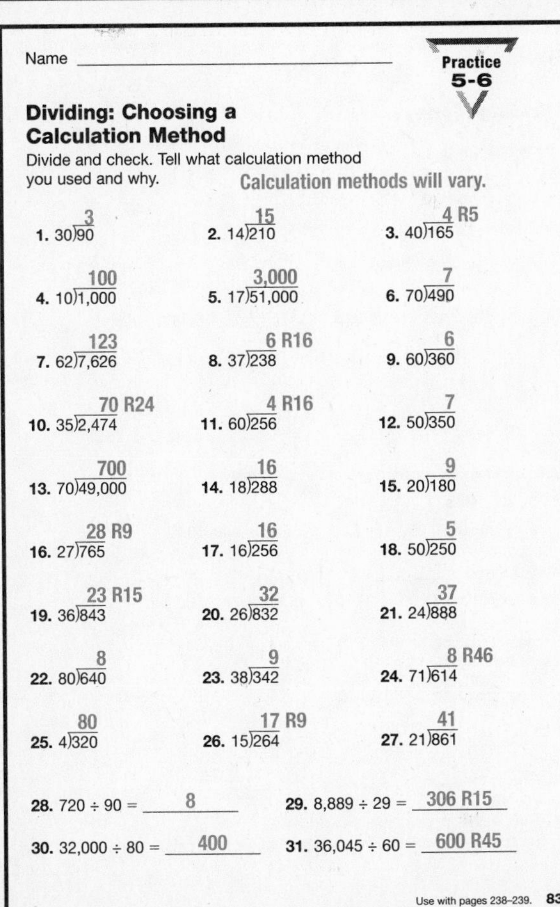

Name ____________________

Practice 5-6

Dividing: Choosing a Calculation Method

Divide and check. Tell what calculation method you used and why. Calculation methods will vary.

1. 30)90 = 3
2. 14)210 = 15
3. 40)165 = 4 R5
4. 10)1,000 = 100
5. 17)51,000 = 3,000
6. 70)490 = 7
7. 62)7,626 = 123
8. 37)238 = 6 R16
9. 60)360 = 6
10. 35)2,474 = 70 R24
11. 60)256 = 4 R16
12. 50)350 = 7
13. 70)49,000 = 700
14. 18)288 = 16
15. 20)180 = 9
16. 27)765 = 28 R9
17. 16)256 = 16
18. 50)250 = 5
19. 36)843 = 23 R15
20. 26)832 = 32
21. 24)888 = 37
22. 80)640 = 8
23. 38)342 = 9
24. 71)614 = 8 R46
25. 4)320 = 80
26. 15)264 = 17 R9
27. 21)861 = 41
28. 720 ÷ 90 = 8
29. 8,889 ÷ 29 = 306 R15
30. 32,000 ÷ 80 = 400
31. 36,045 ÷ 60 = 600 R45

Use with pages 238–239. 83

Name ____________________

Practice 5-7

Zeros in the Quotient

Divide and check.

1. 18)735 = 40 R15
2. 48)30,256 = 630 R16
3. 15)1,063 = 70 R13
4. 36)28,980 = 805
5. 22)4,565 = 207 R11
6. 82)62,324 = 760 R4
7. 25)7,642 = 305 R17
8. 63)30,902 = 490 R32
9. 46)9,649 = 209 R35
10. 92)10,120 = 110
11. 75)17,313 = 230 R63
12. 44)26,547 = 603 R15
13. 41,883 ÷ 82 = 510 R63
14. 11,780 ÷ 29 = 406 R6
15. 16,585 ÷ 54 = 307 R7
16. 9,377 ÷ 18 = 520 R17
17. 15,417 ÷ 28 = 550 R17
18. 16,192 ÷ 23 = 704

Use number sense to decide whether each answer is reasonable.

19. 56)39,312 = 702 — reasonable
20. 35)17,675 = 42 — not reasonable
21. 34)14,280 = 410 — reasonable

84 Use with pages 242–243.

Name ______________________

Practice 5-8

Exploring Algebra: Using Expressions

Decide what operation is needed; then replace the variable with a number and do the computation.

1. There are 12 space meals in a box. How many space meals are in n boxes?

Evaluate $12 \times n$.

a. For $n = 5$.
$12 \times n = 12 \times$ 5
= 60 space meals

b. For $n = 12$.
$12 \times n = 12 \times$ 12
= 144 space meals

Evaluate each expression for $n = 6$ and $n = 15$.

2. $n + 15$ 21 30
3. $5 \times n$ 30 75
4. $n \div 3$ 2 5
5. $n - 5$ 1 10
6. $207 + n$ 213 222
7. $10 \times n$ 60 150
8. $36 - n$ 30 21
9. $30 \div n$ 5 2

Complete.

10.

n	$n + 9$
6	15
15	24
23	32

11.

n	$n \div 4$
8	2
16	4
20	5

12.

n	$n - 15$
30	15
25	10
48	33

13.

n	$n \times 9$
3	27
7	63
9	81

14. If $n = 8$, what is $7 \times n$? 56

15. If $n = 64$, what is $n \div 8$? 8

16. A baker uses 3 cups of wheat flour and n cups of rye flour in the bread. Write an expression for the total number of cups used.
$3 + n$

Name ______________________

Practice 5-9

Analyzing Strategies: Use Objects/Act It Out

Use objects to solve each problem.

1. You want to design a small hotel in the shape of a cube. Each side of the hotel will be four rooms long. Use cubes to make a model.
   a. How many rooms will be on the first floor? 16
   b. How many floors high will the hotel be? 4
   c. How many rooms will be in the hotel in all? 64
   d. If you use the design, how many rooms will have no windows? 16

Use any strategy to solve each problem.

2. In the hotel you designed in the shape of a cube, each outside wall in each room has one window. How many rooms have a total of
   a. only one window? 32
   b. two windows? 16
3. You want to design a hotel with 24 rooms so that each room has a window on each of two walls.
   a. How many rooms will be on each floor? 4
   b. How many floors will the hotel have? 6
   c. How many windows are needed for the hotel? 48
4. You want to build a fence in the shape of a square around the hotel. Each side of the square has 12 posts. There are posts on each corner of the square. How many posts will be needed in all? 44
5. Mr. Munez used 4.5 gallons of paint to paint each room in the hotel. The hotel has 8 floors and each floor has 9 rooms. How many gallons of paint did Mr. Munez use to paint all of the rooms in the hotel?
   324 gallons
6. A hotel has 36 one-bed rooms, 42 two-bed rooms, and 12 suites. How many rooms are there in the hotel? 90 rooms

Name ______________________

Practice Chapter 5 Section B

Review and Practice

(Lessons 4 and 5) Divide.

1. 32)155 — 4 R27
2. 92)472 — 5 R12
3. 47)787 — 16 R35
4. 64)13,322 — 208 R10
5. 38)15,599 — 410 R19
6. 99)3,970 — 40 R10

(Lesson 6) Divide and check. Tell which method you used.

7. 30)90,600 — 3,020
method: mental math

8. 15)3,847 — 256 R7
method: paper and pencil or calculator

(Lesson 7) Divide and check.

9. $3{,}621 \div 34 =$ 106 R17
10. $45{,}127 \div 43 =$ 1,049 R20

(Lesson 9) Solve.

11. 26 fifth graders collected 500 canned goods. If some students collected one more can than the rest, how many collected 19 and how many collected 20?
6 collected 20 cans and 20 collected 19

(Mixed Review) Find each quotient.

12. $4{,}800 \div 60 =$ 80
13. $6{,}300 \div 700 =$ 9

Name ______________________

Practice 5-10

Dividing Money

Divide and check.

1. 25)$12.50 — $0.50
2. 18)$7.92 — $0.44
3. 13)$8.97 — $0.69
4. 15)$24.00 — $1.60
5. 23)$32.43 — $1.41
6. 40)$246.00 — $6.15

7. $537.60 ÷ 35 = $15.36
8. $35.25 ÷ 75 = $0.47

Use your number sense to select the best answer.

9. $2.20 ÷ 40 is b
   a. less than $0.05
   b. more than $0.05
10. $325 ÷ 50 is b
   a. more than $7.00
   b. between $6.00 and $7.00

Estimate to decide whether each quotient in **11–13** is more or less than $1.00.

11. 32)$45.00 — more
12. 32)$31.00 — less
13. 7)$8.08 — more

14. Find the quotient of $412.80 ÷ 40 = $10.32

15. If you had $325.50 to share with 25 people, how much should each person get? $13.02

Name ______________________

Practice 5-11

Decision Making

Rock & Roll Hall of Fame and Museum Cleveland, Ohio
Admission: $12.95 Adults, $9.50 Children
Hours: 10:00 A.M. to 5:30 P.M.

Features
Ground Level Artists' Careers Interactive Videos Mystery Train Cinema
Level 2 Memphis Recording Studio
Level 3 Museum Café
Level 4 Rock & Roll Cinema
Level 5 Radio Studio Past Hall of Fame Inductees
Level 6 Hall of Fame

1. You want to plan a day for you and your family at the Rock & Roll Hall of Fame. You buy 2 adult and 2 children admissions.

   How much do you spend? $44.90

Circle your choice in each of the following.

2. Your family will drive 2 hours to the museum. You want to arrive at 10:00 A.M.

   What time should you leave? 8:00 A.M.
3. You plan to spend 3 hours at the museum. At what time will you leave? 1:00 P.M.
4. On which level will you eat lunch? Level 3
5. Name 3 levels you want to visit. Answers will vary.
6. Plan a schedule. Include rest periods, gift shop, and lunch in your schedule.

Time	Activity	Time	Activity
	Leave home	Check students' schedules.	
	Arrive museum		
			Leave museum
			Arrive home

Name ______________________

Practice 5-12

Exploring Decimal Patterns in Division

Complete the table.

	÷	10	100	1,000
1.	1,346.5	134.65	13.465	1.3465
2.	596.3	59.63	5.963	0.5963
3.	876.42	87.642	8.7642	0.87642
4.	66.75	6.675	0.6675	0.06675
5.	2,002.2	200.22	20.022	2.0022

Find each quotient. Use mental math.

6. 302.6 ÷ 10 = 30.26
7. 78.61 ÷ 100 = 0.7861
8. 362 ÷ 1,000 = 0.362
9. 13.4 ÷ 100 = 0.134
10. 378 ÷ 1,000 = 0.378
11. 6.25 ÷ 100 = 0.0625
12. $925 ÷ 10 = $92.50
13. 8.49 ÷ 100 = 0.0849
14. 4.3 ÷ 1,000 = 0.0043
15. 32.25 ÷ 10 = 3.225
16. 823 ÷ 1,000 = 0.823
17. 73 ÷ 1,000 = 0.073

Use 10, 100, or 1,000 to complete each.

18. 32.7 ÷ 10 = 3.27
19. 632.7 ÷ 100 = 6.327
20. 435 ÷ 100 = 4.35
21. $85 ÷ 100 = $0.85
22. 78 ÷ 1,000 = 0.078
23. 0.26 ÷ 1,000 = 0.00026

Choose the word or number to complete **24–25.**

24. If you divide 3.67 by 1,000, 0 is in the tenths and hundredths places in the quotient.
25. Dividing 81.7 by 10 gives the same quotient as dividing 8,170 by 1,000.
26. If you were to divide 58.3 by 1,000, how many places would you move the decimal point? Explain.

    3 places to the left; 58.3 ÷ 1,000 = 0.0583

Name ______________________

Practice Chapter 5 Section C

Review and Practice

(Lesson 10) Find each quotient.

1. 30)$316.20 — $10.54
2. 17)$15.98 — $0.94
3. 54)$68.58 — $1.27
4. 22)$73.26 — $3.33
5. 86)$7.74 — $0.09
6. 40)$88.40 — $2.21

(Lesson 11) Use any strategy to solve each problem.

7. Would it be cheaper per ounce to buy a 20-ounce bottle of soda for $1.35 or a 64-ounce bottle for $5.00?

   20; $0.07 < $0.08
8. The bus for your field trip is arriving at 8:00 A.M. It is a half-hour trip to the glass factory. There are three tours available for the class. Tour A lasts 2 hours; tour B lasts 1 hour 45 minutes; and tour C lasts 75 minutes. If you must be back at school by noon which tours could your class take?

   either tour A or tours B and C

(Lesson 12) Find each quotient. Use mental math.

9. 54.16 ÷ 10 = 5.416
10. 1,245 ÷ 100 = 12.45
11. 4.1 ÷ 10 = 0.41
12. 3,745.9 ÷ 1,000 = 3.7459
13. 0.37 ÷ 100 = 0.0037
14. 0.2 ÷ 1,000 = 0.0002

(Mixed Review) Subtract.

15. 45.67 − 2.45 = 43.22
16. 39.00 − 16.8 = 22.2
17. 55 − 2.89 = 52.11
18. 7.1 − 5.8 = 1.3

Name ______________________

Practice Chapters 1–5

Cumulative Review

(Chapter 2 Lesson 19) Choose an operation then solve.

1. Rob is 60 inches tall. He has grown 7 inches in the last 5 years. How tall was he 5 years ago? subtract; 53 in.

(Chapter 3 Lesson 16) Solve.

2. At the scout shop a compass costs $5 and a flashlight costs $8. The scouts spent a total of $90 on 15 items. How many compasses and how many flashlights did they buy?

   10 compasses, 5 flashlights

(Chapter 4 Lesson 15) Solve.

3. If you add 3 to Sandro's age and divide by 3 you get 6. How old is Sandro? 15

(Chapter 4 Lesson 12) Find each quotient.

4. 3)29.202 — 9.734
5. 5)8.275 — 1.655
6. 6)67.224 — 11.204

(Chapter 5 Lessons 4 and 10) Divide.

7. 23)221 — 9 R14
8. 16)133 — 8 R5
9. 48)153 — 3 R9
10. 21)$99.96 — $4.76
11. 13)$8.97 — $0.69
12. 40)$675.20 — $16.88

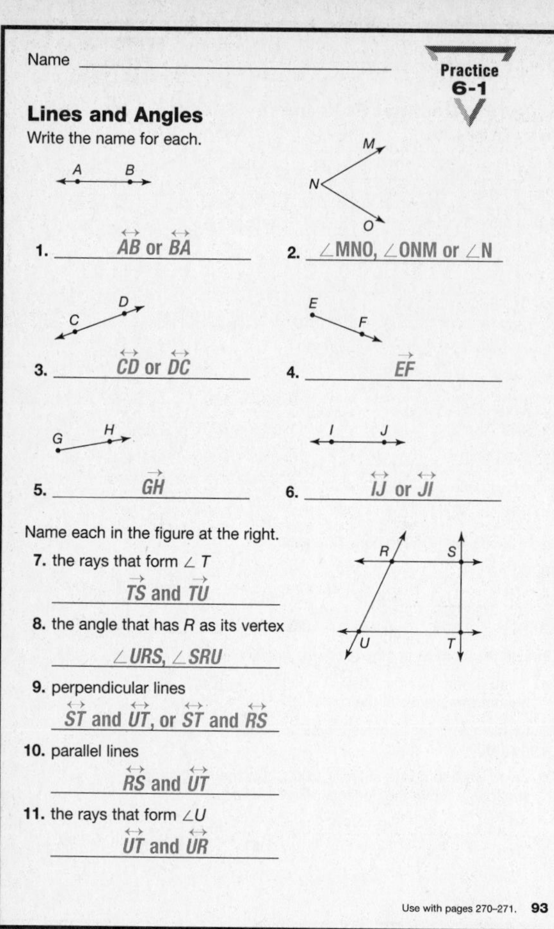

Name ______________________

Practice 6-1

Lines and Angles

Write the name for each.

1. $\overleftrightarrow{AB}$ or $\overleftrightarrow{BA}$
2. $\angle MNO$, $\angle ONM$ or $\angle N$
3. $\overleftrightarrow{CD}$ or $\overleftrightarrow{DC}$
4. $\overrightarrow{EF}$
5. $\overrightarrow{GH}$
6. $\overleftrightarrow{IJ}$ or $\overleftrightarrow{JI}$

Name each in the figure at the right.

7. the rays that form $\angle T$ — $\overrightarrow{TS}$ and $\overrightarrow{TU}$
8. the angle that has R as its vertex — $\angle URS$, $\angle SRU$
9. perpendicular lines — $\overleftrightarrow{ST}$ and $\overleftrightarrow{UT}$, or $\overleftrightarrow{ST}$ and $\overleftrightarrow{RS}$
10. parallel lines — $\overleftrightarrow{RS}$ and $\overleftrightarrow{UT}$
11. the rays that form $\angle U$ — $\overleftrightarrow{UT}$ and $\overleftrightarrow{UR}$

Use with pages 270–271. 93

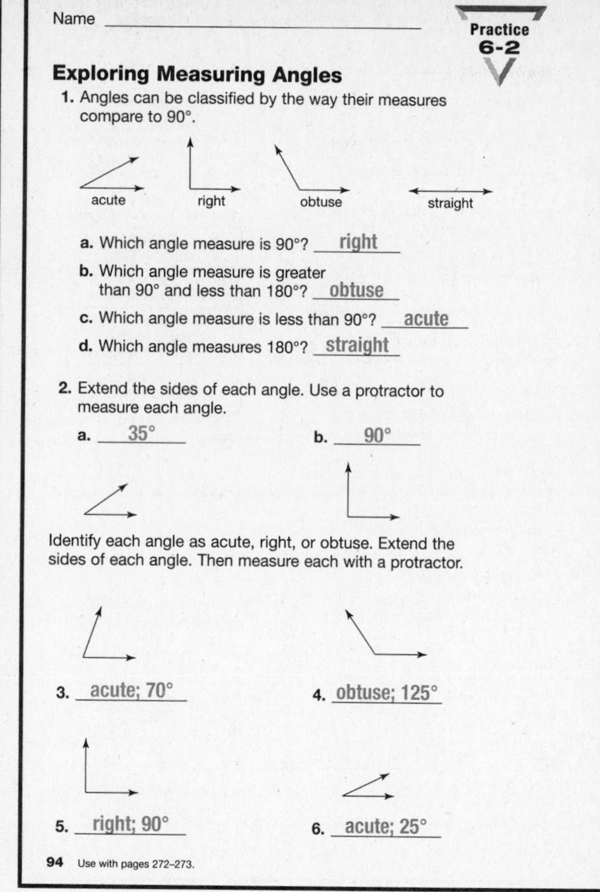

Name ______________________

Practice 6-2

Exploring Measuring Angles

1. Angles can be classified by the way their measures compare to 90°.

acute right obtuse straight

a. Which angle measure is 90°? right

b. Which angle measure is greater than 90° and less than 180°? obtuse

c. Which angle measure is less than 90°? acute

d. Which angle measures 180°? straight

2. Extend the sides of each angle. Use a protractor to measure each angle.

a. 35° b. 90°

Identify each angle as acute, right, or obtuse. Extend the sides of each angle. Then measure each with a protractor.

3. acute; 70°
4. obtuse; 125°
5. right; 90°
6. acute; 25°

94 Use with pages 272–273.

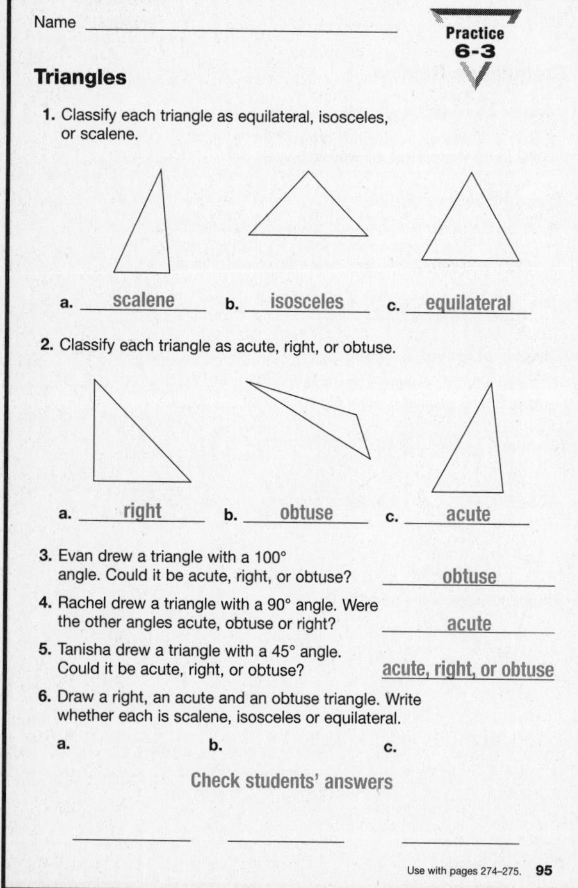

Name ______________________

Practice 6-3

Triangles

1. Classify each triangle as equilateral, isosceles, or scalene.

a. scalene b. isosceles c. equilateral

2. Classify each triangle as acute, right, or obtuse.

a. right b. obtuse c. acute

3. Evan drew a triangle with a 100° angle. Could it be acute, right, or obtuse? obtuse
4. Rachel drew a triangle with a 90° angle. Were the other angles acute, obtuse or right? acute
5. Tanisha drew a triangle with a 45° angle. Could it be acute, right, or obtuse? acute, right, or obtuse
6. Draw a right, an acute and an obtuse triangle. Write whether each is scalene, isosceles or equilateral.

a. b. c.

Check students' answers

Use with pages 274–275. 95

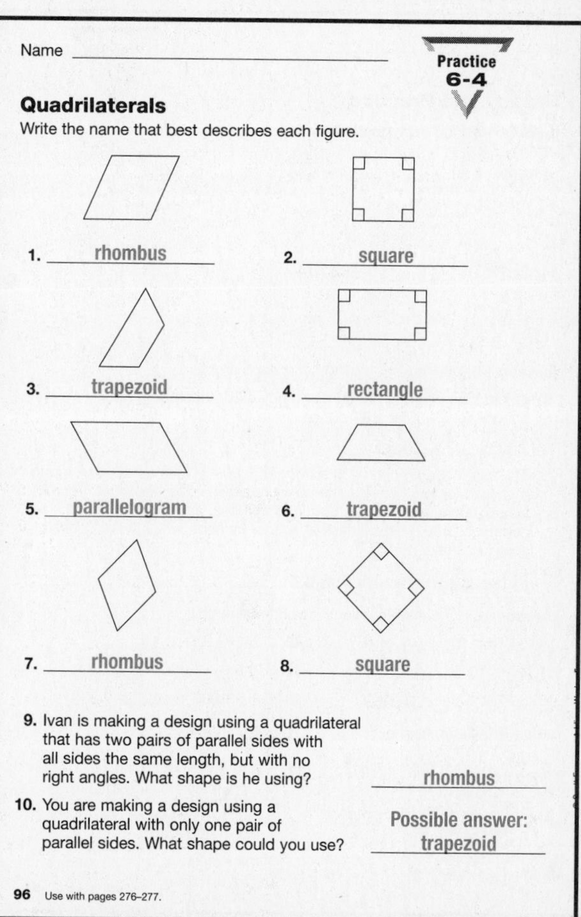

Name ______________________

Practice 6-4

Quadrilaterals

Write the name that best describes each figure.

1. rhombus
2. square
3. trapezoid
4. rectangle
5. parallelogram
6. trapezoid
7. rhombus
8. square
9. Ivan is making a design using a quadrilateral that has two pairs of parallel sides with all sides the same length, but with no right angles. What shape is he using? rhombus
10. You are making a design using a quadrilateral with only one pair of parallel sides. What shape could you use? Possible answer: trapezoid

96 Use with pages 276–277.

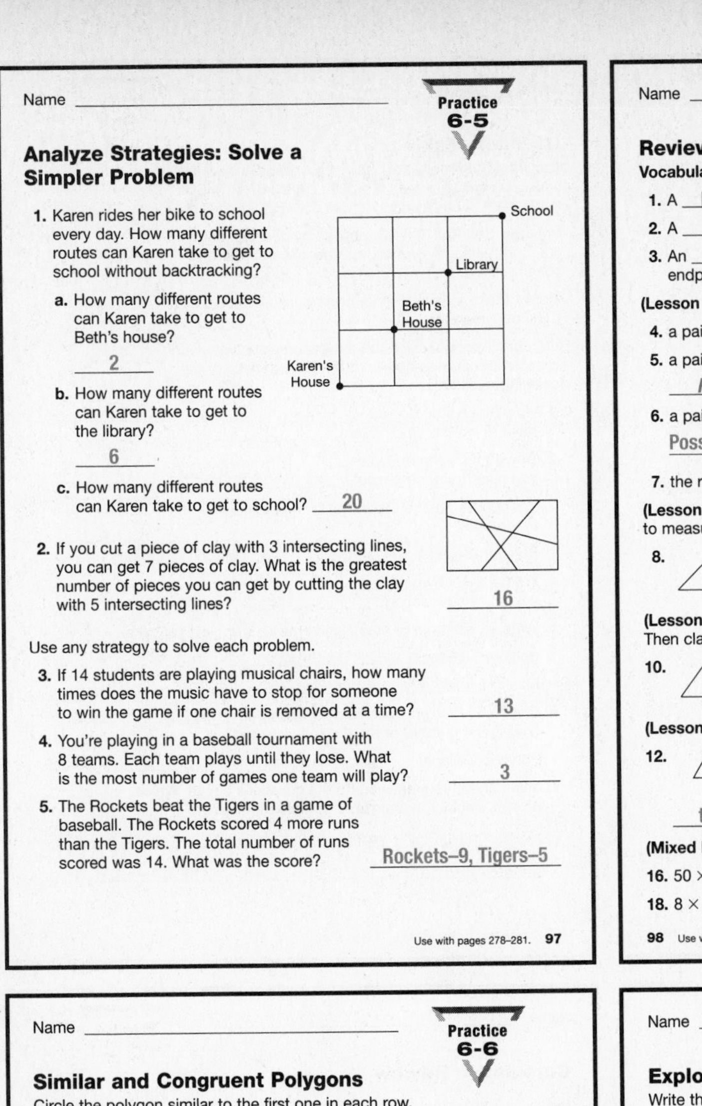

Name ______________________

Practice 6-5

Analyze Strategies: Solve a Simpler Problem

1. Karen rides her bike to school every day. How many different routes can Karen take to get to school without backtracking?

   a. How many different routes can Karen take to get to Beth's house? 2

   b. How many different routes can Karen take to get to the library? 6

   c. How many different routes can Karen take to get to school? 20

2. If you cut a piece of clay with 3 intersecting lines, you can get 7 pieces of clay. What is the greatest number of pieces you can get by cutting the clay with 5 intersecting lines? 16

Use any strategy to solve each problem.

3. If 14 students are playing musical chairs, how many times does the music have to stop for someone to win the game if one chair is removed at a time? 13

4. You're playing in a baseball tournament with 8 teams. Each team plays until they lose. What is the most number of games one team will play? 3

5. The Rockets beat the Tigers in a game of baseball. The Rockets scored 4 more runs than the Tigers. The total number of runs scored was 14. What was the score? Rockets–9, Tigers–5

Use with pages 278–281. 97

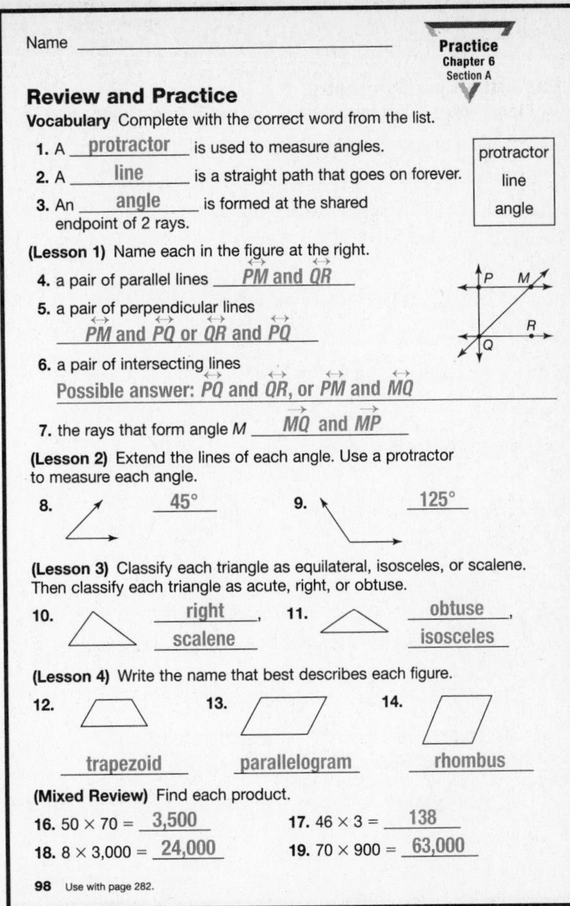

Name ______________________

Practice Chapter 6 Section A

Review and Practice

Vocabulary Complete with the correct word from the list.

protractor
line
angle

1. A protractor is used to measure angles.
2. A line is a straight path that goes on forever.
3. An angle is formed at the shared endpoint of 2 rays.

(Lesson 1) Name each in the figure at the right.

4. a pair of parallel lines $\overleftrightarrow{PM}$ and $\overleftrightarrow{QR}$
5. a pair of perpendicular lines $\overleftrightarrow{PM}$ and $\overleftrightarrow{PQ}$ or $\overleftrightarrow{QR}$ and $\overleftrightarrow{PQ}$
6. a pair of intersecting lines Possible answer: $\overleftrightarrow{PQ}$ and $\overleftrightarrow{QR}$, or $\overleftrightarrow{PM}$ and $\overleftrightarrow{MQ}$
7. the rays that form angle M $\overrightarrow{MQ}$ and $\overrightarrow{MP}$

(Lesson 2) Extend the lines of each angle. Use a protractor to measure each angle.

8. 45°
9. 125°

(Lesson 3) Classify each triangle as equilateral, isosceles, or scalene. Then classify each triangle as acute, right, or obtuse.

10. right, scalene
11. obtuse, isosceles

(Lesson 4) Write the name that best describes each figure.

12. trapezoid
13. parallelogram
14. rhombus

(Mixed Review) Find each product.

16. 50 × 70 = 3,500
17. 46 × 3 = 138
18. 8 × 3,000 = 24,000
19. 70 × 900 = 63,000

98 Use with page 282.

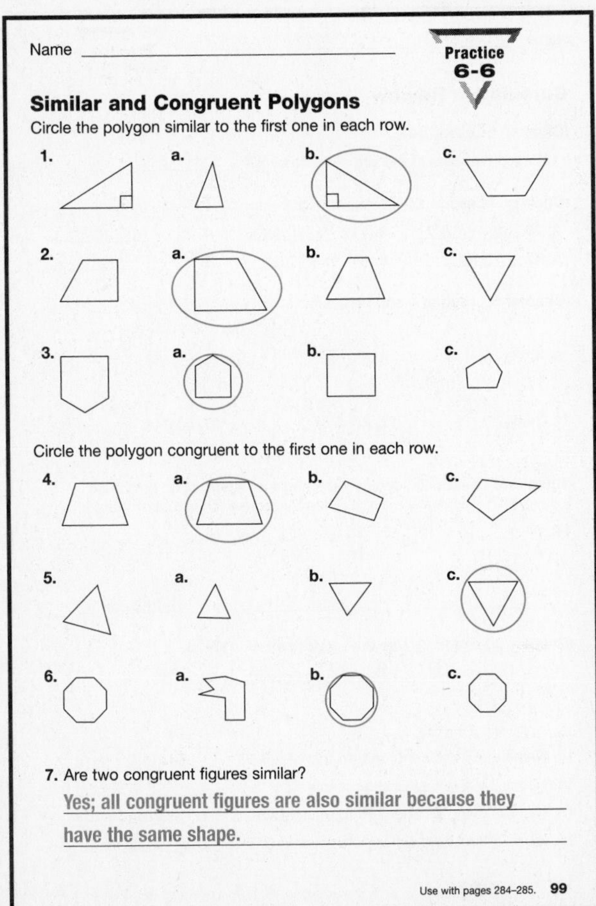

Name ______________________

Practice 6-6

Similar and Congruent Polygons

Circle the polygon similar to the first one in each row.

1. a. b. c.
2. a. b. c.
3. a. b. c.

Circle the polygon congruent to the first one in each row.

4. a. b. c.
5. a. b. c.
6. a. b. c.

7. Are two congruent figures similar? Yes; all congruent figures are also similar because they have the same shape.

Use with pages 284–285. 99

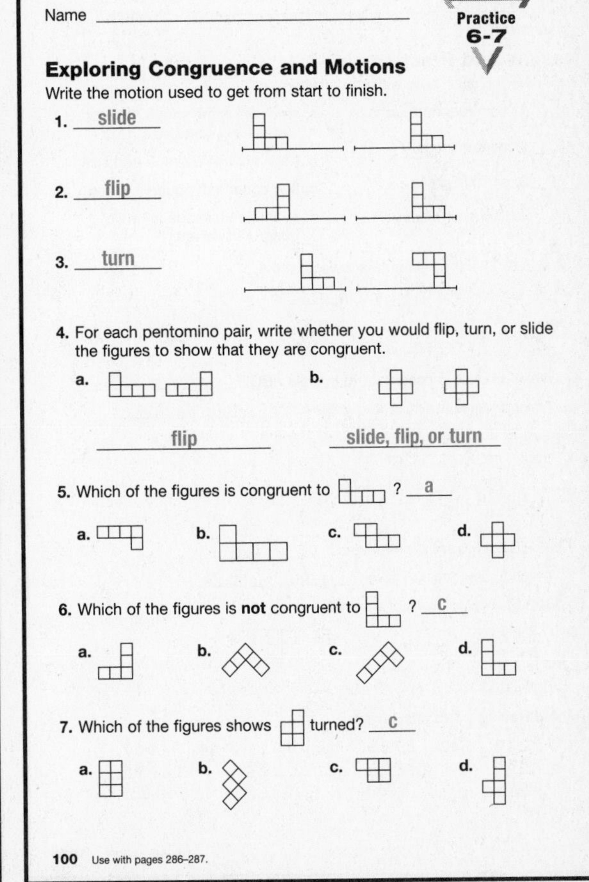

Name ______________________

Practice 6-7

Exploring Congruence and Motions

Write the motion used to get from start to finish.

1. slide
2. flip
3. turn

4. For each pentomino pair, write whether you would flip, turn, or slide the figures to show that they are congruent.

   a. flip
   b. slide, flip, or turn

5. Which of the figures is congruent to [figure]? a

   a. b. c. d.

6. Which of the figures is **not** congruent to [figure]? c

   a. b. c. d.

7. Which of the figures shows [figure] turned? c

   a. b. c. d.

100 Use with pages 286–287.

Name ______________________

Practice 6-8

Exploring Line Symmetry

1. Explain how tracing a figure can help you find its lines of symmetry.
Possible answer: By tracing a figure and cutting it out, you can fold it to find lines of symmetry. If the two sides match exactly, the fold line is a line of symmetry.

Draw all lines of symmetry.

2. 3.

Use the line of symmetry to complete each figure.

4. 5.

Use flips, turns, or slides. Is each pair of figures congruent? Explain.

6. Yes, figure is turned.
7. Yes, figure is turned.

8. Draw three hexominoes that have at least 1 line of symmetry.
Possible answers

Use with pages 288–289. 101

Name ______________________

Practice 6-9

Decision Making

You want to complete an art project over the weekend. You have to decide between 2 project choices. You will be working by yourself. Here are the 2 project choices:

Polygon Collage: Make a collage by drawing, cutting out, and pasting polygons. Include some similar and congruent figures.

Mask: Make a mask that is symmetrical. It should have 1 line of symmetry.

In order to decide which project to complete, you need to think about some details of the project. Answer the following questions:

1. How much time do you have to work on the project? 2 days
2. Do you have the materials you need for each project? Answers may vary.
3. Will you be able to use either of the projects in the future?
Polygon Collage: Possibly Mask: Possibly
4. Which project would you enjoy completing? Answers may vary.
5. Write an estimate of how much time each project will take.
Polygon Collage: Possible answer: 4 hours
Mask: Possible answer: 3 hours
6. Divide the time you will need for each project equally among the number of days in the weekend.
Polygon Collage: 2 hours each day Mask: $1\frac{1}{2}$ hours each day
7. Think about your answers to the questions above. Which project would you choose to complete? Why?
Possible answer: I would choose to make the mask because it takes less time to make and I could use it for a party.

102 Use with pages 290–291.

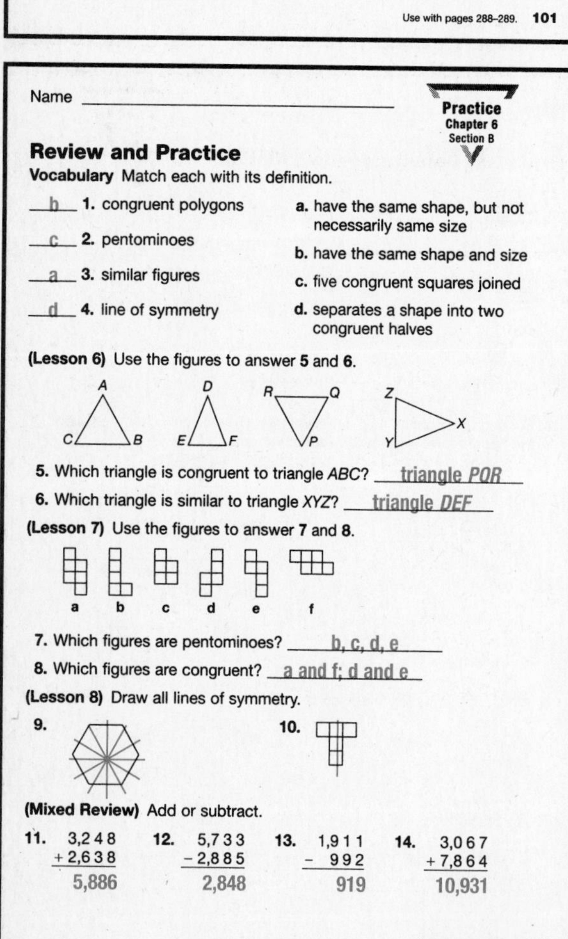

Name ______________________

Practice Chapter 6 Section B

Review and Practice

Vocabulary Match each with its definition.

b 1. congruent polygons
c 2. pentominoes
a 3. similar figures
d 4. line of symmetry

a. have the same shape, but not necessarily same size
b. have the same shape and size
c. five congruent squares joined
d. separates a shape into two congruent halves

(Lesson 6) Use the figures to answer **5** and **6**.

5. Which triangle is congruent to triangle *ABC*? triangle *PQR*
6. Which triangle is similar to triangle *XYZ*? triangle *DEF*

(Lesson 7) Use the figures to answer **7** and **8**.

a b c d e f

7. Which figures are pentominoes? b, c, d, e
8. Which figures are congruent? a and f; d and e

(Lesson 8) Draw all lines of symmetry.

9. 10.

(Mixed Review) Add or subtract.

11. 3,248 + 2,638 = 5,886
12. 5,733 − 2,885 = 2,848
13. 1,911 − 992 = 919
14. 3,067 + 7,864 = 10,931

Use with page 292. 103

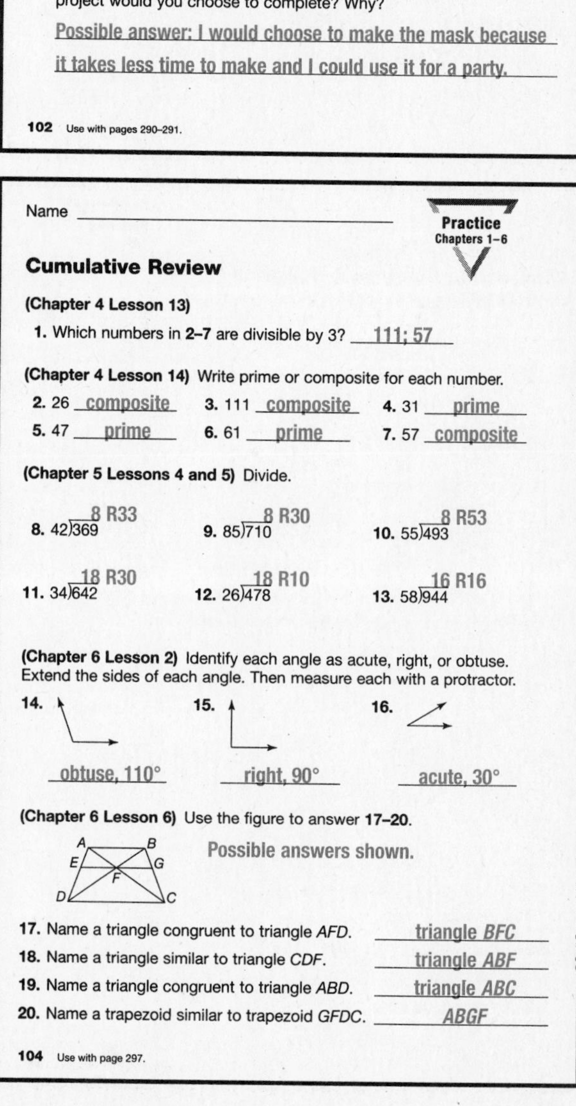

Name ______________________

Practice Chapters 1–6

Cumulative Review

(Chapter 4 Lesson 13)

1. Which numbers in **2–7** are divisible by 3? 111; 57

(Chapter 4 Lesson 14) Write prime or composite for each number.

2. 26 composite 3. 111 composite 4. 31 prime
5. 47 prime 6. 61 prime 7. 57 composite

(Chapter 5 Lessons 4 and 5) Divide.

8. 42)369 = 8 R33 9. 85)710 = 8 R30 10. 55)493 = 8 R53
11. 34)642 = 18 R30 12. 26)478 = 18 R10 13. 58)944 = 16 R16

(Chapter 6 Lesson 2) Identify each angle as acute, right, or obtuse. Extend the sides of each angle. Then measure each with a protractor.

14. obtuse, 110° 15. right, 90° 16. acute, 30°

(Chapter 6 Lesson 6) Use the figure to answer **17–20**.

Possible answers shown.

17. Name a triangle congruent to triangle *AFD*. triangle *BFC*
18. Name a triangle similar to triangle *CDF*. triangle *ABF*
19. Name a triangle congruent to triangle *ABD*. triangle *ABC*
20. Name a trapezoid similar to trapezoid *GFDC*. *ABGF*

104 Use with page 297.

Name ____________

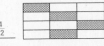

Practice 7-1

Whole and Parts

Write the fraction that names each shaded part.

1. 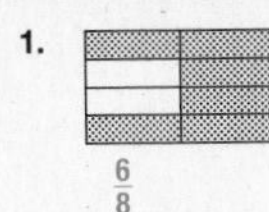
$\frac{6}{8}$

2. 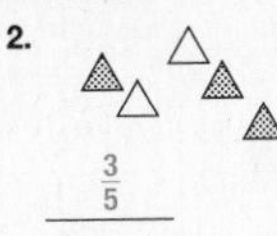
$\frac{3}{5}$

What part of each set is square?

3. 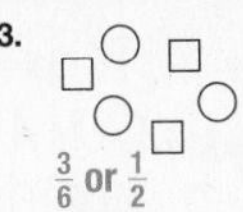
$\frac{3}{6}$ or $\frac{1}{2}$

4. 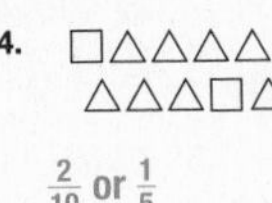
$\frac{2}{10}$ or $\frac{1}{5}$

5. Which shows three fourths? B

A. 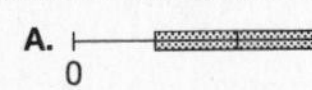
0 1

B. 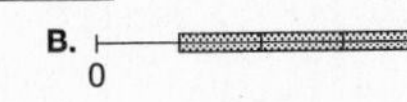
0 1

6. Estimate the fraction of the figure that is shaded. B

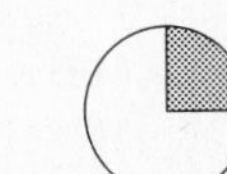

A. $\frac{1}{8}$  B. $\frac{1}{4}$ C. $\frac{1}{2}$ 

7. During an art contest at your school, you and a classmate each won blue ribbons for $\frac{1}{3}$ of the pieces you entered in the contest. You won 2 blue ribbons and your classmate won 3 blue ribbons. Explain how this could be.
Possible answer: I entered 6 pieces of art and my classmate entered 9.

Name ____________

Practice 7-2

Exploring Equivalent Fractions

1. Which shadings show fractions equivalent to $\frac{2}{3}$? A

A. 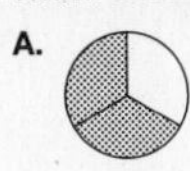 B. 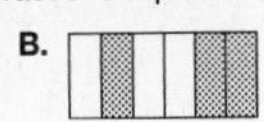 C. 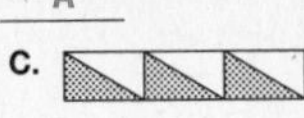

Write two fractions that name the shaded part.

2. 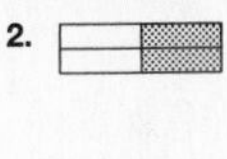
$\frac{2}{4}, \frac{1}{2}$

3. 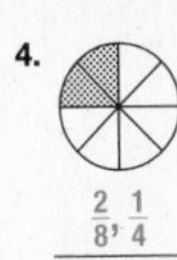
$\frac{2}{4}, \frac{1}{2}$

4. $\frac{2}{8}, \frac{1}{4}$

5. Write a fraction for the shaded part of each picture. Which fractions are equivalent to $\frac{1}{3}$?

A. 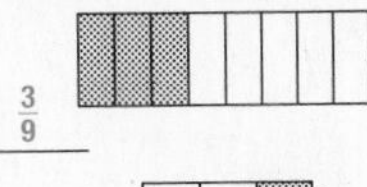
$\frac{3}{9}$

B. $\frac{3}{6}$

C. 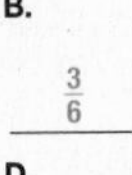
$\frac{2}{6}$

D. 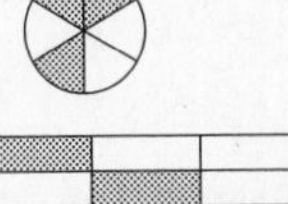
$\frac{4}{12}$

Fractions A, C, and D are all equivalent to $\frac{1}{3}$.

6. John's mother baked a lasagna in a rectangular pan and cut it into 6 pieces. John ate 2 pieces.

a. Draw a picture to represent the lasagna and shade in the pieces that John ate.

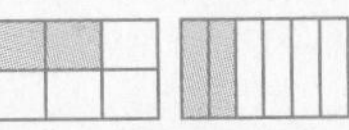

b. Write 2 fractions that describe how much lasagna is left. $\frac{4}{6}, \frac{2}{3}$

7. Gina said she would share half a pack of baseball cards with Joe. Joe ended up with $\frac{5}{10}$ of the pack. Did Joe get half? Explain.
Yes, $\frac{5}{10} = \frac{1}{2}$

Name ____________

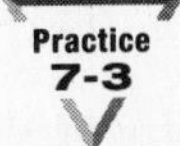

Practice 7-3

Patterns with Equivalent Fractions

Find equivalent fractions with a denominator of 8.

1. $\frac{1}{2}$ $\frac{4}{8}$
2. $\frac{3}{4}$ $\frac{6}{8}$
3. $\frac{9}{24}$ $\frac{3}{8}$
4. $\frac{25}{40}$ $\frac{5}{8}$

Find equivalent fractions with a denominator of 12.

5. $\frac{2}{3}$ $\frac{8}{12}$
6. $\frac{5}{6}$ $\frac{10}{12}$
7. $\frac{8}{24}$ $\frac{4}{12}$
8. $\frac{9}{36}$ $\frac{3}{12}$

Name the fractions in the box equivalent to each fraction below.

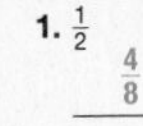

$\frac{12}{16}$	$\frac{3}{6}$	$\frac{9}{12}$	$\frac{2}{4}$	$\frac{3}{9}$	$\frac{6}{8}$	$\frac{4}{8}$	$\frac{2}{6}$	$\frac{4}{12}$

9. $\frac{1}{3}$ $\frac{3}{9}, \frac{2}{6}, \frac{4}{12}$
10. $\frac{3}{4}$ $\frac{12}{16}, \frac{9}{12}, \frac{6}{8}$
11. $\frac{1}{2}$ $\frac{3}{6}, \frac{2}{4}, \frac{4}{8}$
12. $\frac{2}{6}$ $\frac{3}{9}, \frac{2}{6}, \frac{4}{12}$

Write whether each pair is equivalent. Explain how you decided.

13. $\frac{1}{4}$ and $\frac{3}{12}$
Yes; $1 \times 3 = 3$ and $4 \times 3 = 12$

14. $\frac{12}{18}$ and $\frac{3}{9}$
No; $12 \div 4 = 3$ and $18 \div 4 \neq 9$

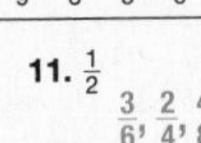

15. $\frac{4}{5}$ and $\frac{12}{15}$
Yes; $4 \times 3 = 12$ and $5 \times 3 = 15$

16. Three-ninths of a soccer game is over. Is this half-time? Explain.
No; $\frac{3}{9} = \frac{1}{3}$

Name ____________

Practice 7-4

Greatest Common Factor

Find the greatest common factor for each pair.

1. 4 and 8 — 4
2. 6 and 9 — 3
3. 12 and 18 — 6
4. 10 and 15 — 5
5. 6 and 12 — 6
6. 14 and 21 — 7
7. 6 and 18 — 6
8. 16 and 24 — 8
9. 6 and 15 — 3
10. 4 and 10 — 2
11. 3 and 7 — 1
12. 9 and 15 — 3
13. 5 and 12 — 1
14. 7 and 4 — 1
15. 2 and 5 — 1
16. 12 and 9 — 3

17. Find two numbers that have 6 as the greatest common factor.
Possible answer: 12, 18

18. Find two numbers that have 10 as the greatest common factor.
Possible answer: 20 and 30

19. Find the factors of 12 and 16.
12: 1,2,3,4,6,12
16: 1,2,4,8,16

20. Find the factors of 8 and 20
8: 1, 2, 4, 8
20: 1, 2, 4, 5, 10, 20

21. Could 7 be the greatest common factor of 21 and 35? Explain.
Yes, 21 and 35 are divisible by 7.

22. The common factors of two numbers are 2 and 4. The two numbers could be 12 and 16 or 8 and 24. Explain how.
Factors of 12 and 16 include 2 and 4. Factors of 8 and 24 include 2 and 4.

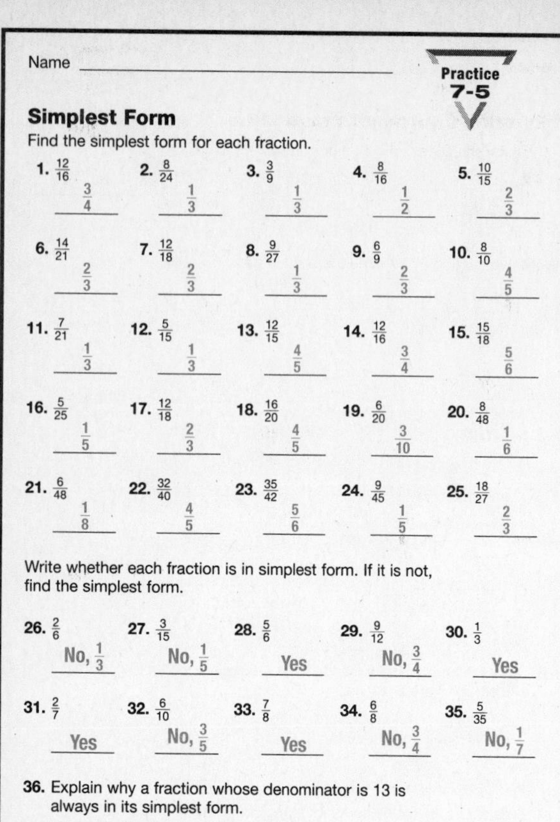

Name ______________________

Practice 7-5

Simplest Form

Find the simplest form for each fraction.

1. $\frac{12}{16}$ $\frac{3}{4}$
2. $\frac{8}{24}$ $\frac{1}{3}$
3. $\frac{3}{9}$ $\frac{1}{3}$
4. $\frac{8}{16}$ $\frac{1}{2}$
5. $\frac{10}{15}$ $\frac{2}{3}$
6. $\frac{14}{21}$ $\frac{2}{3}$
7. $\frac{12}{18}$ $\frac{2}{3}$
8. $\frac{9}{27}$ $\frac{1}{3}$
9. $\frac{6}{9}$ $\frac{2}{3}$
10. $\frac{8}{10}$ $\frac{4}{5}$
11. $\frac{7}{21}$ $\frac{1}{3}$
12. $\frac{5}{15}$ $\frac{1}{3}$
13. $\frac{12}{15}$ $\frac{4}{5}$
14. $\frac{12}{16}$ $\frac{3}{4}$
15. $\frac{15}{18}$ $\frac{5}{6}$
16. $\frac{5}{25}$ $\frac{1}{5}$
17. $\frac{12}{18}$ $\frac{2}{3}$
18. $\frac{16}{20}$ $\frac{4}{5}$
19. $\frac{6}{20}$ $\frac{3}{10}$
20. $\frac{8}{48}$ $\frac{1}{6}$
21. $\frac{6}{48}$ $\frac{1}{8}$
22. $\frac{32}{40}$ $\frac{4}{5}$
23. $\frac{35}{42}$ $\frac{5}{6}$
24. $\frac{9}{45}$ $\frac{1}{5}$
25. $\frac{18}{27}$ $\frac{2}{3}$

Write whether each fraction is in simplest form. If it is not, find the simplest form.

26. $\frac{2}{6}$ No, $\frac{1}{3}$
27. $\frac{3}{15}$ No, $\frac{1}{5}$
28. $\frac{5}{6}$ Yes
29. $\frac{9}{12}$ No, $\frac{3}{4}$
30. $\frac{1}{3}$ Yes
31. $\frac{2}{7}$ Yes
32. $\frac{6}{10}$ No, $\frac{3}{5}$
33. $\frac{7}{8}$ Yes
34. $\frac{6}{8}$ No, $\frac{3}{4}$
35. $\frac{5}{35}$ No, $\frac{1}{7}$
36. Explain why a fraction whose denominator is 13 is always in its simplest form.
    The only factors of 13 are 13 and 1.

Use with pages 310–311. 109

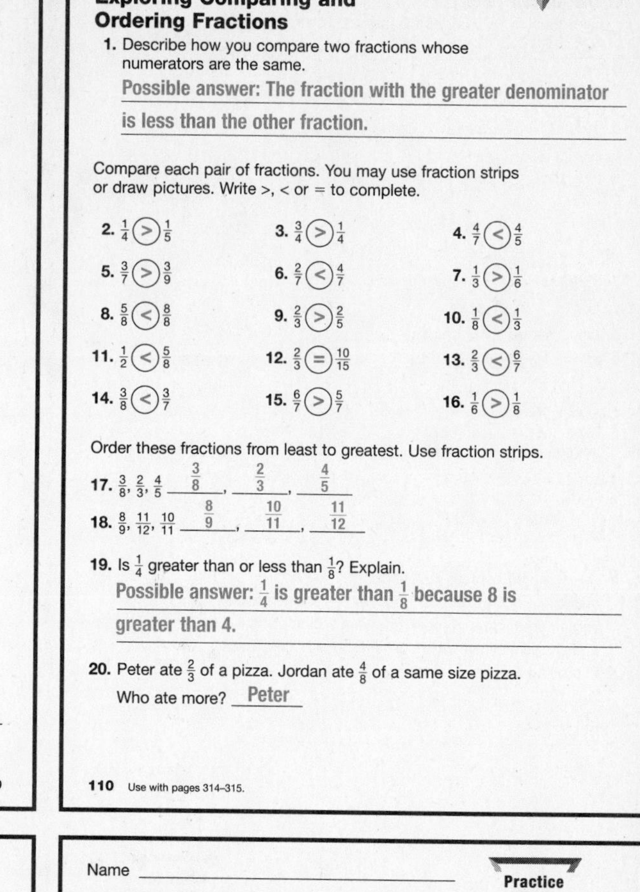

Name ______________________

Practice 7-6

Exploring Comparing and Ordering Fractions

1. Describe how you compare two fractions whose numerators are the same.
   Possible answer: The fraction with the greater denominator is less than the other fraction.

Compare each pair of fractions. You may use fraction strips or draw pictures. Write >, < or = to complete.

2. $\frac{1}{4} > \frac{1}{5}$
3. $\frac{3}{4} > \frac{1}{4}$
4. $\frac{4}{7} < \frac{4}{5}$
5. $\frac{3}{7} > \frac{3}{9}$
6. $\frac{2}{7} < \frac{4}{7}$
7. $\frac{1}{3} > \frac{1}{6}$
8. $\frac{5}{8} < \frac{8}{8}$
9. $\frac{2}{3} > \frac{2}{5}$
10. $\frac{1}{8} < \frac{1}{3}$
11. $\frac{1}{2} < \frac{5}{8}$
12. $\frac{2}{3} = \frac{10}{15}$
13. $\frac{2}{3} < \frac{6}{7}$
14. $\frac{3}{8} < \frac{3}{7}$
15. $\frac{6}{7} > \frac{5}{7}$
16. $\frac{1}{6} > \frac{1}{8}$

Order these fractions from least to greatest. Use fraction strips.

17. $\frac{3}{8}, \frac{2}{3}, \frac{4}{5}$ $\frac{3}{8}$, $\frac{2}{3}$, $\frac{4}{5}$
18. $\frac{8}{9}, \frac{11}{12}, \frac{10}{11}$ $\frac{8}{9}$, $\frac{10}{11}$, $\frac{11}{12}$
19. Is $\frac{1}{4}$ greater than or less than $\frac{1}{8}$? Explain.
    Possible answer: $\frac{1}{4}$ is greater than $\frac{1}{8}$ because 8 is greater than 4.
20. Peter ate $\frac{2}{3}$ of a pizza. Jordan ate $\frac{4}{8}$ of a same size pizza.
    Who ate more? Peter

110 Use with pages 314–315.

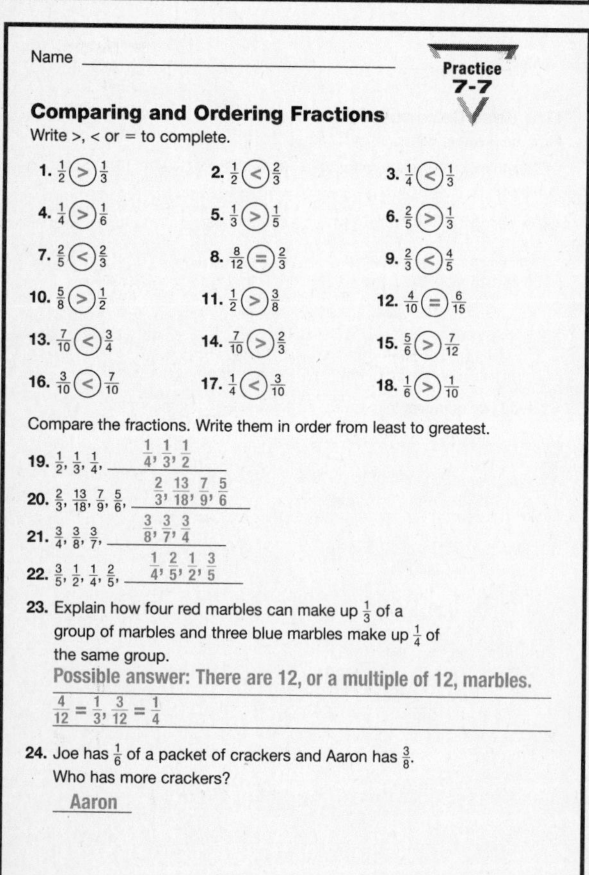

Name ______________________

Practice 7-7

Comparing and Ordering Fractions

Write >, < or = to complete.

1. $\frac{1}{2} > \frac{1}{3}$
2. $\frac{1}{2} < \frac{2}{3}$
3. $\frac{1}{4} < \frac{1}{3}$
4. $\frac{1}{4} > \frac{1}{6}$
5. $\frac{1}{3} > \frac{1}{5}$
6. $\frac{2}{5} > \frac{1}{3}$
7. $\frac{2}{5} < \frac{2}{3}$
8. $\frac{8}{12} = \frac{2}{3}$
9. $\frac{2}{3} < \frac{4}{5}$
10. $\frac{5}{8} > \frac{1}{2}$
11. $\frac{1}{2} > \frac{3}{8}$
12. $\frac{4}{10} = \frac{6}{15}$
13. $\frac{7}{10} < \frac{3}{4}$
14. $\frac{7}{10} > \frac{2}{3}$
15. $\frac{5}{6} > \frac{7}{12}$
16. $\frac{3}{10} < \frac{7}{10}$
17. $\frac{1}{4} < \frac{3}{10}$
18. $\frac{1}{6} > \frac{1}{10}$

Compare the fractions. Write them in order from least to greatest.

19. $\frac{1}{2}, \frac{1}{3}, \frac{1}{4}$, $\frac{1}{4}, \frac{1}{3}, \frac{1}{2}$
20. $\frac{2}{3}, \frac{13}{18}, \frac{7}{9}, \frac{5}{6}$, $\frac{2}{3}, \frac{13}{18}, \frac{7}{9}, \frac{5}{6}$
21. $\frac{3}{4}, \frac{3}{8}, \frac{3}{7}$, $\frac{3}{8}, \frac{3}{7}, \frac{3}{4}$
22. $\frac{3}{5}, \frac{1}{2}, \frac{1}{4}, \frac{2}{5}$, $\frac{1}{4}, \frac{2}{5}, \frac{1}{2}, \frac{3}{5}$
23. Explain how four red marbles can make up $\frac{1}{3}$ of a group of marbles and three blue marbles make up $\frac{1}{4}$ of the same group.
    Possible answer: There are 12, or a multiple of 12, marbles.
    $\frac{4}{12} = \frac{1}{3}, \frac{3}{12} = \frac{1}{4}$
24. Joe has $\frac{1}{6}$ of a packet of crackers and Aaron has $\frac{3}{8}$.
    Who has more crackers?
    Aaron

Use with pages 316–317. 111

Name ______________________

Practice 7-8

Analyze Strategies: Make a Table

Make a table or use another strategy to solve each problem.

1. For every 10 videos Video Palace rents, 5 are comedy videos. If they rent 30 videos, how many were comedy videos? 15 comedy videos
2. For every 2 hours Karen does yard work, her brother, Jeff works 4 hours cleaning the house. If Jeff works in the house for 12 hours a month, how many hours would Karen work on the yard? 6 hours
3. José used his new telescope to view the stars. On his first night he observed 7 stars. Every night that followed he discovered 3 new stars he hadn't seen before. On the fifth night how many stars did José observe altogether? 19 stars
4. The local ice cream shop was selling 20 shakes in a day. Then they advertised a special on their shakes, and their sales doubled every day. On the fourth day how many shakes did they sell? 160 shakes
5. Mrs. Gupta came home from the mall with \$14. At her last stop before coming home she bought some paint and paint brushes at an art supply store for \$9.50. Earlier she had purchased some overalls for \$23.50. How much money did Mrs Gupta take with her to the mall? \$47
6. Lana drives 6 miles every day, and Fred drives 7 miles every day. If Fred has driven 56 miles, how many miles has Lana driven? 48 miles

112 Use with pages 318–319.

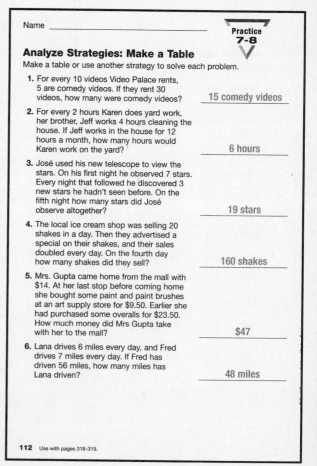

Name ______________________

Practice Chapter 7 Section A

Review and Practice

Vocabulary Write true or false for each statement.

1. The denominator is the bottom number in a fraction. true
2. A fraction is in simplest form when the GCF of the numerator and denominator is less than 3. false
3. $\frac{2}{3}$ and $\frac{3}{4}$ are equivalent fractions. false

(Lesson 1) Write the fraction that names each shaded part.

4. 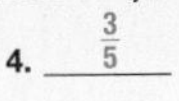 $\frac{3}{5}$

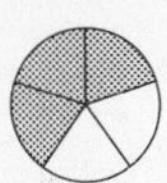

5. $\frac{4}{6}$ or $\frac{2}{3}$

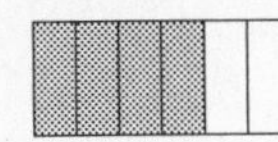

(Lessons 2 and 3) Complete.

6. $\frac{3}{4} = \frac{9}{12} = \frac{6}{8} = \frac{12}{16}$
7. $\frac{5}{6} = \frac{10}{12} = \frac{50}{60}$

(Lesson 4) Find the greatest comon factor for each pair.

8. 12 and 8 4
9. 20 and 9 1

(Lesson 5) Find the simplest form for each fraction.

10. $\frac{22}{66} = \frac{1}{3}$
11. $\frac{36}{48} = \frac{3}{4}$
12. $\frac{14}{16} = \frac{7}{8}$

(Lessons 6 and 7) Write each set of fractions in order from least to greatest.

13. $\frac{1}{6}, \frac{2}{3}, \frac{1}{5}$ $\frac{1}{6}, \frac{1}{5}, \frac{2}{3}$
14. $\frac{5}{6}, \frac{9}{12}, \frac{5}{8}$ $\frac{5}{8}, \frac{9}{12}, \frac{5}{6}$

(Lesson 8) Solve. You may make a table to help.

15. On Monday, Megan found a 3-leaf plant. On Tuesday, she found a 4-leaf plant and on Wednesday she found a 5-leaf plant. If she continues to find plants in the same pattern, on what day of the week would she find a 10-leaf plant? Monday

(Mixed Review) Complete each number sentence.

16. 36 ÷ 9 = 4
17. 48 ÷ 6 = 8
18. 8 × 7 = 56

Name ______________________

Practice 7-9

Exploring Mixed Numbers

Match each with its definition.

a 1. mixed number — a. a whole number and a fraction

b 2. improper fraction — b. a fraction greater than, or equal to, 1

Write the mixed or whole number and the improper fraction that name each shaded part.

3. $2\frac{1}{4}, \frac{9}{4}$

4. 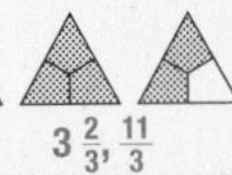 $3\frac{2}{3}, \frac{11}{3}$

5. $4\frac{3}{8}, \frac{35}{8}$

6. $2, \frac{6}{3}$ or $\frac{2}{1}$

7. $3\frac{3}{6}$ or $3\frac{1}{2}, \frac{21}{6}$ or $\frac{7}{2}$

8. $2\frac{2}{4}$ or $2\frac{1}{2}, \frac{10}{4}$ or $\frac{5}{2}$

9. 0 1 2 — $1\frac{2}{6}$ or $1\frac{1}{3}, \frac{8}{6}$ or $\frac{4}{3}$

10. $3, \frac{24}{8}$ or $\frac{3}{1}$

Make a drawing that shows each fraction.

11. $2\frac{3}{5}$

12. $\frac{15}{3}$

13. $2\frac{2}{3}$

14. $\frac{7}{2}$

Name ______________________

Practice 7-10

Mixed Numbers

Write each improper fraction as a mixed number in simplest form, or as a whole number.

1. $\frac{11}{3} = 3\frac{2}{3}$
2. $\frac{19}{5} = 3\frac{4}{5}$
3. $\frac{25}{3} = 8\frac{1}{3}$
4. $\frac{42}{6} = 7$
5. $\frac{43}{8} = 5\frac{3}{8}$
6. $\frac{49}{6} = 8\frac{1}{6}$
7. $\frac{36}{4} = 9$
8. $\frac{68}{9} = 7\frac{5}{9}$
9. $\frac{23}{4} = 5\frac{3}{4}$
10. $\frac{96}{8} = 12$
11. $\frac{23}{5} = 4\frac{3}{5}$
12. $\frac{34}{3} = 11\frac{1}{3}$
13. $\frac{72}{5} = 14\frac{2}{5}$
14. $\frac{46}{6} = 7\frac{2}{3}$
15. $\frac{49}{7} = 7$

Write each mixed number as an improper fraction.

16. $3\frac{1}{2} = \frac{7}{2}$
17. $5\frac{3}{4} = \frac{23}{4}$
18. $6\frac{7}{8} = \frac{55}{8}$
19. $5\frac{5}{12} = \frac{65}{12}$
20. $4\frac{1}{6} = \frac{25}{6}$
21. $6\frac{2}{3} = \frac{20}{3}$
22. $12\frac{2}{3} = \frac{38}{3}$
23. $9\frac{1}{4} = \frac{37}{4}$
24. $8\frac{2}{5} = \frac{42}{5}$
25. $25\frac{1}{4} = \frac{101}{4}$
26. $22\frac{1}{2} = \frac{45}{2}$
27. $6\frac{4}{5} = \frac{34}{5}$
28. $11\frac{3}{8} = \frac{91}{8}$
29. $16\frac{5}{6} = \frac{101}{6}$
30. $9\frac{8}{9} = \frac{89}{9}$

Complete.

31. $2 = \frac{40}{20}$
32. $6 = \frac{18}{3}$
33. $8 = \frac{40}{5}$
34. $7\frac{1}{2} = \frac{45}{6}$
35. $4\frac{3}{5} = \frac{23}{5}$
36. $11\frac{1}{2} = \frac{23}{2}$

37. The pizza at Ryan's party is divided into eighths. Ryan usually eats 3 slices and the rest of his family usually eats 13. Are 2 pizzas enough? Explain.
Yes. The family eats $1\frac{5}{8}$ pizzas. Ryan's 3 slices finish the second pizza.

Name ______________________

Practice 7-11

Exploring Comparing and Ordering Mixed Numbers

1. How do you know $2\frac{1}{3}$ is greater than $1\frac{5}{6}$ without comparing the fractions?
Since 2 > 1, $2\frac{1}{3} > 1\frac{5}{6}$.
2. Can you just compare the whole numbers when comparing $1\frac{3}{4}$ and $1\frac{1}{3}$? Explain. No; 1 = 1, so you have to compare the fractions to see which is greater.

Give a mixed number for the shaded part of each picture. Use > and < to compare each pair of mixed numbers.

3.    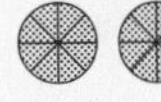

$2\frac{3}{4}$ > $2\frac{5}{8}$

4.  

$1\frac{2}{3}$ > $1\frac{1}{2}$

5. 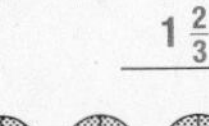 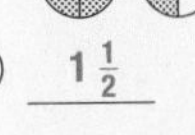

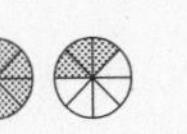

$3\frac{3}{8}$ < $3\frac{5}{6}$

Compare. Use > or <.

6. $4\frac{3}{8} < 5\frac{1}{6}$
7. $2\frac{2}{3} > 2\frac{1}{4}$
8. $3\frac{1}{8} < 3\frac{1}{6}$
9. $2\frac{5}{6} < 2\frac{3}{4}$
10. $6\frac{2}{3} > 4\frac{7}{8}$
11. $3\frac{7}{10} < \frac{17}{4}$

Write in order from least to greatest.

12. $2\frac{1}{2}, \frac{9}{4}, \frac{8}{3}, 1\frac{4}{5}$ $1\frac{4}{5}, \frac{9}{4}, 2\frac{1}{2}, \frac{8}{3}$

Name ______________________

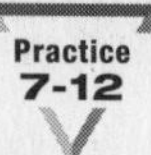

Understanding Percent

Write the fraction and the percent shaded in each picture.

1. 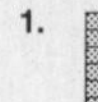 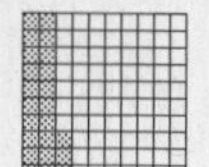 $\frac{23}{100}$; 23%

2. $\frac{27}{100}$; 27%

3. 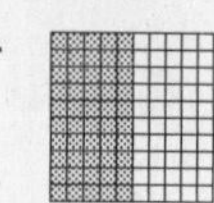 $\frac{50}{100}$; 50%

Write each as a percent.

4. 78 out of 100 78%
5. 83 out of 100 83%
6. 55 out of 100 55%
7. $\frac{25}{100}$ 25%

Write each as a hundredths fraction.

8. 82% $\frac{82}{100}$
9. 6% $\frac{6}{100}$
10. 59% $\frac{59}{100}$
11. 60% $\frac{60}{100}$

For each set, decide which does **not** belong.

12. **A.** 32% **B.** 32 out of 100 **C.** $\frac{3}{100}$ **D.** $\frac{32}{100}$ C
13. **A.** $\frac{49}{100}$ **B.** $\frac{4}{9}$ **C.** 49 out of 100 **D.** 49% B

Estimation Estimate the percent of each figure that is shaded.

14.  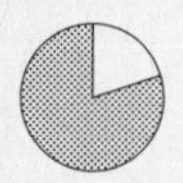 accept 75%-85%

15. 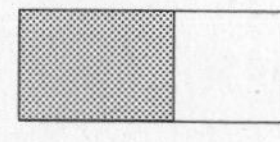 accept 65%-75%

Name ______________________

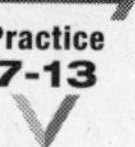

Connecting Fractions, Decimals and Percents

Write a fraction, a decimal, and a percent that name each shaded part.

1. 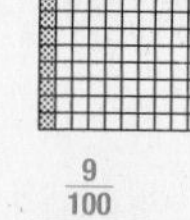 $\frac{9}{100}$, 0.09, 9%

2. $\frac{80}{100}$, 0.8, 80%

3. 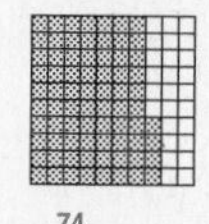 $\frac{74}{100}$, 0.74, 74%

Write each as a percent.

4. 5 out of 100 5%
5. 89 out of 100 89%
6. 0.65 65%
7. 0.09 9%
8. $\frac{4}{100}$ 4%
9. $\frac{57}{100}$ 57%

Write each as a fraction and a decimal.

10. 3% $\frac{3}{100}$, 0.03
11. 59% $\frac{59}{100}$, 0.59
12. 35% $\frac{35}{100}$ or $\frac{7}{20}$, 0.35
13. 41% $\frac{41}{100}$, 0.41
14. 5% $\frac{5}{100}$ or $\frac{1}{20}$, 0.05
15. 37% $\frac{37}{100}$, 0.37

16. Which is less: $\frac{1}{3}$ or 50%? $\frac{1}{3}$
17. Which is greater: 0.06 or 60%? 60%

Name ______________________

Decision Making

It's the start of football season. Suppose you read a survey of favorite teams taken at Sandburg School. You decide to survey 50 students at your own school.

Favorite Football Teams Sandburg School		Votes for Favorite Teams at Your School	
Cowboys	10%	Cowboys	5
49ers	30%	49ers	10
Steelers	25%	Steelers	20
Eagles	25%	Eagles	5
Broncos	10%	Broncos	10

1. Write fractions, decimals, and percents to describe the survey results at your school.

	Fraction	Decimal	Percent
a. Cowboys	$\frac{5}{50} = \frac{1}{10}$	0.1	10%
b. 49ers	$\frac{10}{50} = \frac{1}{5}$	0.2	20%
c. Steelers	$\frac{20}{50} = \frac{2}{5}$	0.4	40%
d. Eagles	$\frac{5}{50} = \frac{1}{10}$	0.1	10%
e. Broncos	$\frac{10}{50} = \frac{1}{5}$	0.2	20%

2. Which team is the favorite at Sandburg School? 49ers
3. Which team is the least favorite overall? Cowboys
4. Which team has the biggest difference between the two surveys? Eagles and Steelers
5. Draw a circle graph for each survey.

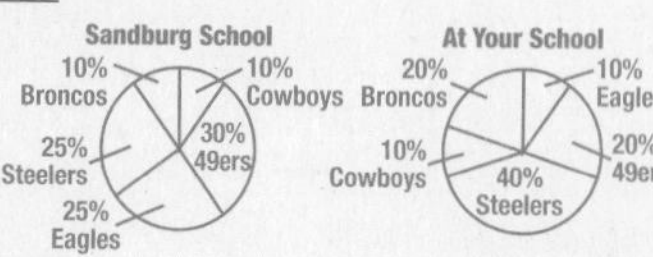

Name ______________________

Review and Practice

Vocabulary Match each with its example.

$2\frac{1}{5}$, $\frac{12}{7}$, 15%

1. percent 15%
2. improper fraction $\frac{12}{7}$
3. mixed number $2\frac{1}{5}$

(Lesson 9) Write the mixed or whole number and the improper fraction that name each shaded part.

4. 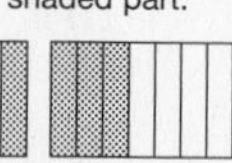 $1\frac{3}{7}$, $\frac{10}{7}$

5. 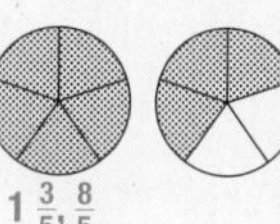 $1\frac{3}{5}$, $\frac{8}{5}$

(Lesson 10) Write each improper fraction as a mixed number in simplest form or a whole number. Write each mixed number as an improper fraction.

6. $\frac{24}{15} =$ $1\frac{3}{5}$
7. $\frac{36}{12} =$ 3
8. $2\frac{4}{5} =$ $\frac{14}{5}$

(Lesson 11) Write >, <, or = to complete.

9. $3\frac{2}{3}$ (>) $1\frac{4}{5}$
10. $6\frac{4}{8}$ (=) $6\frac{3}{6}$
11. $2\frac{6}{9}$ (>) $2\frac{1}{5}$

(Lessons 12 and 14) Use the circle graph to answer **12** and **13**.

12. What fractional part of those surveyed favored red? $\frac{60}{100}$ or $\frac{3}{5}$
13. What percent favored green or blue? 40%

Favorite Colors: Red 60%, Green 25%, Blue 15%

(Mixed Review) Add or subtract.

14. 69,294 + 13,920 = 83,214
15. 18,517 − 9,368 = 9,149
16. 806 + 736 = 1,542
17. 99 − 45 = 54

Name ______________________

Practice
Chapters 1–7

Cumulative Review

(Chapter 1 Lesson 6) Tell which operation you would use. Then solve.

1. There are 28 people on a hike. Each person carried a backpack weighing 5 pounds. How many pounds were carried in all?
   multiplication, 140 pounds

(Chapter 3 Lesson 10) Multiply.

2. $3.69 × 3 = $11.07
3. 37.1 × 8 = 296.8
4. $9.01 × 6 = $54.06
5. 0.159 × 7 = 1.113

(Chapter 6 Lesson 3) Name each triangle by its sides and angles.

6.  equilateral, acute
7.  scalene, obtuse
8. 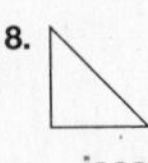 isosceles, right

(Chapter 6 Lesson 8) Draw all lines of symmetry.

9. 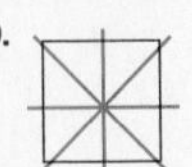
10. 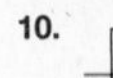 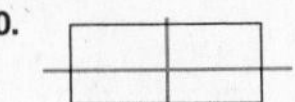
11. 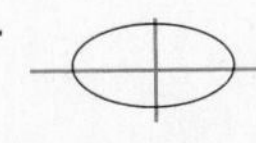

(Chapter 7 Lesson 5) Write the simplest form for each fraction.

12. $\frac{8}{16} = \frac{1}{2}$
13. $\frac{12}{32} = \frac{3}{8}$
14. $\frac{6}{14} = \frac{3}{7}$
15. $\frac{15}{35} = \frac{3}{7}$
16. $\frac{20}{30} = \frac{2}{3}$
17. $\frac{33}{99} = \frac{1}{3}$

(Chapter 7 Lesson 11) Write in order from least to greatest.

18. $2\frac{1}{4}, 1\frac{5}{6}, 1\frac{1}{4}$ — $1\frac{1}{4}$, $1\frac{5}{6}$, $2\frac{1}{4}$
19. $2\frac{2}{3}, 5\frac{1}{5}, 2\frac{1}{5}$ — $2\frac{1}{5}$, $2\frac{2}{3}$, $5\frac{1}{5}$

Name ______________________

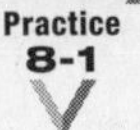
Practice
8-1

Adding and Subtracting Fractions with Like Denominators

Find each sum or difference. Simplify.

1. $\frac{4}{6} + \frac{1}{6} = \frac{5}{6}$
2. $\frac{7}{8} - \frac{4}{8} = \frac{3}{8}$
3. $\frac{8}{10} - \frac{5}{10} = \frac{3}{10}$
4. $\frac{2}{3} + \frac{2}{3} = 1\frac{1}{3}$
5. $\frac{2}{6} - \frac{1}{6} = \frac{1}{6}$
6. $\frac{7}{8} + \frac{1}{8} = 1$
7. $\frac{6}{9} - \frac{3}{9} = \frac{1}{3}$
8. $\frac{2}{7} + \frac{6}{7} = 1\frac{1}{7}$
9. $\frac{8}{9} - \frac{5}{9} = \frac{1}{3}$
10. $\frac{7}{8} + \frac{3}{8} = 1\frac{1}{4}$
11. $\frac{8}{10} - \frac{3}{10} = \frac{1}{2}$
12. $\frac{2}{12} + \frac{10}{12} = 1$
13. $\frac{7}{8} + \frac{7}{8} = 1\frac{3}{4}$
14. $\frac{6}{10} - \frac{2}{10} = \frac{2}{5}$
15. $\frac{3}{9} + \frac{3}{9} + \frac{3}{9} = 1$
16. $\frac{2}{10} + \frac{5}{10} + \frac{6}{10} = 1\frac{3}{10}$
17. $\frac{7}{12} + \frac{3}{12} + \frac{4}{12} = 1\frac{1}{6}$
18. $\frac{2}{8} + \frac{4}{8} + \frac{6}{8} = 1\frac{1}{2}$
19. $\frac{2}{6} + \frac{3}{6} + \frac{4}{6} = 1\frac{1}{2}$
20. $\frac{1}{2} + \frac{1}{2} + \frac{1}{2} = 1\frac{1}{2}$
21. $\frac{4}{5} + \frac{1}{5} + \frac{2}{5} = 1\frac{2}{5}$
22. Find the sum of $\frac{8}{9}$ and $\frac{4}{9}$. $1\frac{1}{3}$
23. Why does $\frac{3}{9} + \frac{6}{9} = \frac{6}{9} + \frac{3}{9}$? Explain.
    You can add in any order.

Name ______________________

Practice
8-2

Exploring Adding Fractions

1. $\frac{1}{2} + \frac{1}{4}$

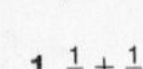
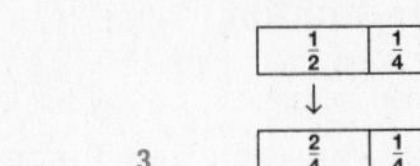

$\frac{2}{4} + \frac{1}{4} = \frac{3}{4}$

Find each sum.

2. $\frac{2}{3} + \frac{1}{6}$ 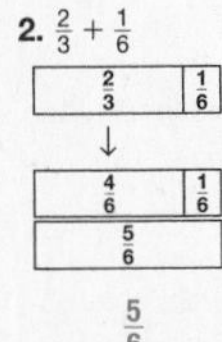 $\frac{5}{6}$
3. $\frac{1}{2} + \frac{3}{8}$ $\frac{7}{8}$
4. $\frac{4}{9} + \frac{1}{3}$ 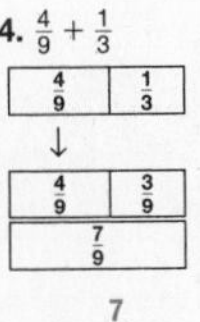 $\frac{7}{9}$

Find each sum. You may use fraction strips or draw pictures to help.

5. $\frac{4}{5} + \frac{1}{10} = \frac{9}{10}$
6. $\frac{2}{3} + \frac{2}{9} = \frac{8}{9}$
7. $\frac{2}{5} + \frac{1}{2} = \frac{9}{10}$
8. $\frac{1}{3} + \frac{1}{6} = \frac{3}{6} = \frac{1}{2}$
9. $\frac{2}{9} + \frac{1}{3} = \frac{5}{9}$
10. $\frac{2}{3} + \frac{5}{6} = 1\frac{3}{6} = 1\frac{1}{2}$
11. $\frac{2}{5} + \frac{2}{3} = 1\frac{1}{15}$
12. $\frac{2}{9} + \frac{1}{3} = \frac{5}{9}$
13. $\frac{1}{8} + \frac{1}{2} + \frac{3}{4} = 1\frac{3}{8}$
14. $\frac{2}{3} + \frac{1}{3} + \frac{5}{6} = 1\frac{5}{6}$
15. $\frac{1}{2} + \frac{2}{8} + \frac{1}{4} = \frac{8}{8} = 1$
16. Find the sum of $\frac{2}{5}$ and $\frac{7}{10}$. $1\frac{1}{10}$
17. Find the sum of $\frac{1}{3}$ and $\frac{5}{9}$. $\frac{8}{9}$

Name ______________________

Practice
8-3

Least Common Denominator

Find the LCD for each pair of fractions.

1. $\frac{3}{5}$ and $\frac{1}{2}$ — 10
2. $\frac{2}{3}$ and $\frac{3}{5}$ — 15
3. $\frac{3}{4}$ and $\frac{3}{8}$ — 8
4. $\frac{5}{12}$ and $\frac{1}{4}$ — 12
5. $\frac{1}{3}$ and $\frac{2}{5}$ — 15
6. $\frac{1}{4}$ and $\frac{3}{10}$ — 20
7. $\frac{4}{9}$ and $\frac{5}{12}$ — 36
8. $\frac{3}{8}$ and $\frac{5}{12}$ — 24
9. $\frac{9}{12}$ and $\frac{3}{9}$ — 36
10. $\frac{3}{5}$ and $\frac{2}{7}$ — 35
11. $\frac{2}{3}$ and $\frac{1}{4}$ — 12
12. $\frac{2}{9}$ and $\frac{1}{8}$ — 72
13. $\frac{1}{6}$ and $\frac{4}{9}$ — 18
14. $\frac{1}{4}$ and $\frac{3}{9}$ — 36
15. $\frac{2}{6}$ and $\frac{1}{8}$ — 24
16. $\frac{2}{7}$ and $\frac{3}{4}$ — 28
17. Why is the LCD of $\frac{3}{4}$ and $\frac{4}{8}$ not the product of 4 and 8?
    8 is a multiple of 4, so the LCD is 8.
18. Why is the LCD of $\frac{5}{9}$ and $\frac{7}{12}$ not the product of 9 and 12?
    9 and 12 share the multiple 36, so the LCD is 36.
19. If you know that the least common multiple (LCM) of 3 and 7 is 21, what do you also know about the least common denominator (LCD) of $\frac{2}{3}$ and $\frac{4}{7}$?
    The LCD is also 21.
20. If you know that the least common multiple (LCM) of 4 and 6 is 12, what do you also know about the least common denominator (LCD) of $\frac{3}{4}$ and $\frac{5}{6}$?
    The LCD is also 12.

Name ______________________

Practice 8-4

Adding Fractions

Find each sum. Simplify.

1. $\frac{1}{4} + \frac{4}{5}$ $1\frac{1}{20}$
2. $\frac{2}{5} + \frac{2}{3}$ $1\frac{1}{15}$
3. $\frac{3}{8} + \frac{2}{3}$ $1\frac{1}{24}$
4. $\frac{2}{3} + \frac{4}{5}$ $1\frac{7}{15}$
5. $\frac{7}{8} + \frac{2}{3}$ $1\frac{13}{24}$
6. $\frac{7}{12} + \frac{7}{8}$ $1\frac{11}{24}$
7. $\frac{3}{4} + \frac{5}{12}$ $1\frac{1}{6}$
8. $\frac{2}{5} + \frac{7}{8}$ $1\frac{11}{40}$
9. $\frac{5}{9} + \frac{5}{6}$ $1\frac{7}{18}$
10. $\frac{7}{9} + \frac{1}{2}$ $1\frac{5}{18}$
11. $\frac{5}{6} + \frac{3}{4}$ $1\frac{7}{12}$
12. $\frac{4}{5} + \frac{3}{4}$ $1\frac{11}{20}$
13. $\frac{1}{5} + \frac{2}{3} + \frac{5}{6}$ $1\frac{21}{30}$
14. $\frac{1}{3} + \frac{1}{6} + \frac{8}{9}$ $1\frac{7}{18}$
15. $\frac{5}{8} + \frac{3}{4} + \frac{3}{10}$ $1\frac{27}{40}$
16. Find the sum of $\frac{1}{3}$ and $\frac{7}{8}$. $1\frac{5}{24}$
17. Add $\frac{3}{5}$ and $\frac{7}{10}$. $1\frac{3}{10}$
18. Find $\frac{1}{3} + \frac{1}{6} + \frac{1}{9} + \frac{1}{12}$ using mental math $\frac{25}{36}$
19. Do you get the same sum when you use 18 rather than 9 as a common denominator for $\frac{2}{3}$ and $\frac{4}{9}$? Explain.
    Yes, $\frac{6}{9} + \frac{4}{9} = \frac{10}{9} = 1\frac{1}{9}$ and $\frac{12}{18} + \frac{8}{18} = \frac{20}{18} = 1\frac{2}{18} = 1\frac{1}{9}$
20. What extra step will you have to perform if you do not use the **least common denominator** when adding fractions? Explain your response.
    When you do not use the LCD, you have to simplify your answer.

Name ______________________

Practice 8-5

Exploring Subtracting Fractions

1. $\frac{3}{4} - \frac{1}{8} = n$

$\frac{6}{8} - \frac{1}{8} = \frac{5}{8}$

Find each difference. Simplify.

2. $\frac{9}{10} - \frac{3}{5}$ $\frac{3}{10}$
3. $\frac{3}{8} - \frac{1}{4}$ $\frac{1}{8}$
4. $\frac{5}{6} - \frac{3}{4}$ $\frac{1}{12}$
5. $\frac{7}{8} - \frac{1}{6}$ $\frac{17}{24}$

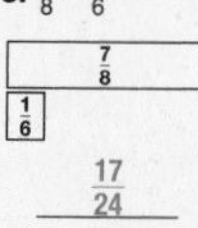

Find each difference. You may use fraction strips or draw pictures to help.

6. $\frac{4}{5} - \frac{1}{10}$ $\frac{7}{10}$
7. $\frac{2}{3} - \frac{2}{9}$ $\frac{4}{9}$
8. $\frac{4}{5} - \frac{8}{15}$ $\frac{4}{15}$
9. $\frac{1}{3} - \frac{1}{6}$ $\frac{1}{6}$
10. $\frac{3}{4} - \frac{1}{6}$ $\frac{7}{12}$
11. $\frac{5}{9} - \frac{1}{3}$ $\frac{2}{9}$
12. $\frac{9}{10} - \frac{3}{5}$ $\frac{3}{10}$
13. $\frac{5}{6} - \frac{1}{4}$ $\frac{7}{12}$
14. $\frac{7}{9} - \frac{2}{3}$ $\frac{1}{9}$
15. $\frac{5}{6} - \frac{1}{2}$ $\frac{1}{3}$
16. $\frac{5}{7} - \frac{3}{14}$ $\frac{1}{2}$
17. $\frac{1}{2} - \frac{1}{8}$ $\frac{3}{8}$
18. Find the difference of $\frac{5}{6}$ and $\frac{1}{2}$. Write the answer in simplest form. $\frac{1}{3}$

Name ______________________

Practice 8-6

Subtracting Fractions

Find each difference. Simplify.

1. $\frac{3}{4} - \frac{1}{3} = \frac{5}{12}$
2. $\frac{2}{3} - \frac{1}{2} = \frac{1}{6}$
3. $\frac{4}{5} - \frac{3}{10} = \frac{1}{2}$
4. $\frac{3}{5} - \frac{1}{10} = \frac{1}{2}$
5. $\frac{7}{8} - \frac{1}{2} = \frac{3}{8}$
6. $\frac{5}{6} - \frac{2}{3} = \frac{1}{6}$
7. $\frac{2}{5} - \frac{1}{5} = \frac{1}{5}$
8. $\frac{5}{6} - \frac{3}{4} = \frac{1}{12}$
9. $\frac{7}{8} - \frac{2}{3} = \frac{5}{24}$
10. $\frac{3}{5} - \frac{1}{2}$ $\frac{1}{10}$
11. $\frac{7}{12} - \frac{1}{6}$ $\frac{5}{12}$
12. $\frac{3}{10} - \frac{1}{5}$ $\frac{1}{10}$
13. $\frac{3}{4} - \frac{2}{3}$ $\frac{1}{12}$
14. $\frac{7}{8} - \frac{1}{4}$ $\frac{5}{8}$
15. $\frac{7}{10} - \frac{2}{5}$ $\frac{3}{10}$
16. $\frac{5}{6} - \frac{3}{5}$ $\frac{7}{30}$
17. $\frac{5}{7} - \frac{1}{3}$ $\frac{8}{21}$
18. Find the difference between $\frac{5}{8}$ and $\frac{1}{6}$. $\frac{11}{24}$
19. If $\frac{1}{3}$ is subtracted from $\frac{5}{6}$, will the difference be greater or less than $\frac{1}{3}$? Explain.
    The difference is greater than $\frac{1}{3}$. $\frac{5}{6}$ is greater than $\frac{4}{6}$. $\frac{4}{6} = \frac{2}{3}$
    $\frac{2}{3} - \frac{1}{3} = \frac{1}{3}$
20. If $\frac{2}{3}$ is subtracted from $\frac{5}{6}$, will the difference be greater or less than $\frac{1}{3}$? Explain.
    The difference is less than $\frac{1}{3}$. $\frac{2}{3} = \frac{4}{6}$. $\frac{5}{6} - \frac{4}{6} = \frac{1}{6}$ and $\frac{1}{6}$ is less than $\frac{1}{3}$.

Name ______________________

Practice 8-7

Analyze Word Problems: Too Much or Too Little Information

Write if each problem has too much or too little information. Solve, or if possible, tell what is needed to solve.

1. During one week, $\frac{1}{3}$ of the hotel rooms were available. The clerk took 20 additional reservations. How many rooms are still available?
   too little information; need to know the total number of rooms
2. The school is $\frac{2}{3}$ mi from the library. Jessie lives $\frac{3}{5}$ mi from school. John lives $\frac{1}{10}$ mi closer than Jessie. How far from school is John?
   too much information; $\frac{5}{10}$ or $\frac{1}{2}$ mile
3. Cary cut a hero sandwich into 10 pieces. Only 8 pieces were eaten. His 3 sisters had ravioli. What fraction of the hero sandwich was left?
   too much information; $\frac{1}{5}$
4. Mom built a shelf. She used $\frac{1}{2}$ a board for the shelf and $\frac{2}{5}$ of the board for the braces. How many inches of the board were left?
   too little information; need to know the length of the board before it was cut
5. John rode with his mom in the car $\frac{1}{3}$ mi. He walked the rest of the way to Jim's house. How far did he have to walk?
   too little information; need to know the distance from John's house to Jim's house
6. For a recipe Lee needs $\frac{1}{3}$ cup of sugar, $\frac{3}{4}$ cup of flour, and twice as much milk as sugar. How many cups of milk does she need?
   too much information; $\frac{2}{3}$ cup

Name ______________________

Practice
Chapter 8
Section A

Review and Practice

Vocabulary Write true or false.

1. The least common denominator (LCD) is the least common multiple of the two demoninators. true

(Lesson 1) Find each sum or difference. Simplify.

2. $\frac{1}{6} + \frac{1}{6} = \frac{2}{6} = \frac{1}{3}$
3. $\frac{5}{9} - \frac{2}{9} = \frac{3}{9} = \frac{1}{3}$
4. $\frac{10}{11} - \frac{8}{11} = \frac{2}{11}$
5. $\frac{1}{6} + \frac{5}{6} = \frac{6}{6} = 1$

6. What number must be added to $\frac{3}{7}$ to get a sum of 1? $\frac{4}{7}$

(Lessons 2–4) Find each sum. Simplify.

7. $\frac{2}{3} + \frac{1}{9} =$ $\frac{7}{9}$
8. $\frac{1}{4} + \frac{1}{8} =$ $\frac{3}{8}$
9. $\frac{2}{5} + \frac{8}{10} =$ $\frac{12}{10} = 1\frac{1}{5}$
10. $\frac{1}{20} + \frac{1}{5} =$ $\frac{5}{20} = \frac{1}{4}$

11. On three days Wendy rode her bike $\frac{2}{5}$ mi, $\frac{1}{2}$ mi and $\frac{4}{5}$ mi. How far did she ride? $\frac{17}{10} = 1\frac{7}{10}$ mi

(Lessons 5–6) Find each difference. Simplify.

12. $\frac{8}{9} - \frac{1}{4} = \frac{23}{36}$
13. $\frac{5}{7} - \frac{1}{3} = \frac{8}{21}$
14. $\frac{6}{10} - \frac{1}{3} = \frac{8}{30} = \frac{4}{15}$
15. $\frac{5}{8} - \frac{2}{5} = \frac{9}{40}$

(Lesson 7) Write if the problem has too much or too little information. Solve if possible. Tell what is needed if you can't solve.

16. Sue needed boat line that costs $5 for 6 ft. How much did she spend?
can't solve; need to know how much she buys

(Mixed Review) Order each list from least to greatest.

17. $\frac{3}{4}, \frac{1}{2}, \frac{4}{6}$ $\frac{1}{2}, \frac{4}{6}, \frac{3}{4}$
18. $\frac{3}{5}, \frac{2}{7}, \frac{4}{8}$ $\frac{2}{7}, \frac{4}{8}, \frac{3}{5}$
19. $\frac{5}{7}, \frac{5}{8}, \frac{1}{2}$ $\frac{1}{2}, \frac{5}{8}, \frac{5}{7}$

Name ______________________

Practice
8-8

Exploring Adding and Subtracting Mixed Numbers

Find each sum or difference. Use fraction strips or drawings to help. Simplify.

1. [1] [1] [$\frac{2}{3}$] / [1] [$\frac{3}{4}$] $2\frac{2}{3} + 1\frac{3}{4} =$ $4\frac{5}{12}$

2. [1] [$\frac{1}{2}$] / [$\frac{2}{3}$] [?] $1\frac{1}{2} - \frac{2}{3} =$ $1\frac{1}{6}$

3. $2\frac{2}{3} - 1\frac{1}{2} = 1\frac{1}{6}$
4. $3\frac{1}{6} + 2\frac{2}{3} = 5\frac{5}{6}$
5. $1\frac{3}{4} + \frac{1}{12} = 1\frac{5}{6}$
6. $2\frac{3}{10} + \frac{2}{5} = 2\frac{7}{10}$
7. $4 - 2\frac{1}{3} = 1\frac{2}{3}$
8. $3\frac{1}{4} - \frac{2}{16} = 3\frac{1}{8}$

9. $3\frac{1}{6} + 1\frac{2}{3} =$ $4\frac{5}{6}$
10. $3\frac{3}{5} - 2\frac{3}{10} =$ $1\frac{3}{10}$

11. Find the sum of $2\frac{1}{8}$ and $3\frac{3}{4}$. $5\frac{7}{8}$
12. Find the difference of $5\frac{4}{9}$ and $2\frac{1}{3}$. $3\frac{1}{9}$
13. How much longer is the pen than the piece of chalk? $3\frac{3}{4}$

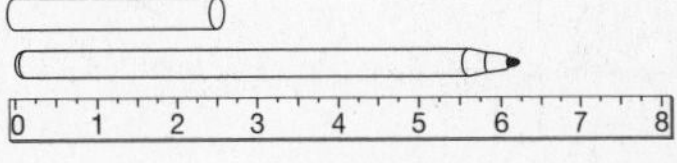

Name ______________________

Practice
8-9

Estimating Sums and Differences

Estimate each sum or difference.

Possible answers are shown.

1. $1\frac{1}{3} + 1\frac{1}{6}$ 2–3
2. $5\frac{1}{8} + 2\frac{1}{2}$ 7–8
3. $8\frac{1}{2} - 1\frac{1}{4}$ 7–8
4. $7\frac{4}{5} - 5\frac{1}{4}$ 2–3
5. $2\frac{3}{4} + 3\frac{2}{3}$ 6–7
6. $7\frac{3}{4} - 3\frac{1}{2}$ 4–5
7. $2\frac{1}{2} - 1\frac{1}{8}$ 1–2
8. $1\frac{1}{3} + 6\frac{1}{12}$ 7–8
9. $2\frac{3}{5} + 1\frac{2}{3}$ 4–5
10. $2\frac{3}{4} + 3\frac{5}{8}$ 6–7
11. $4\frac{1}{4} - 1\frac{5}{6}$ 2–3
12. $9\frac{1}{10} - 8\frac{4}{5}$ 0–1
13. $5\frac{7}{8} + 1\frac{1}{3}$ 7–8
14. $6\frac{2}{3} - 1\frac{5}{6}$ 4–5
15. $9\frac{1}{4} - 5$ 4–5
16. $8\frac{7}{8} + 3\frac{1}{4} + 2\frac{1}{2}$ 14–15
17. $4\frac{1}{5} + 3\frac{2}{3} + 8\frac{5}{8}$ 16–17

18. Estimate the difference between $5\frac{1}{8}$ and $2\frac{2}{3}$. 2–3

Name ______________________

Practice
8-10

Adding and Subtracting Mixed Numbers

Find each sum or difference. Simplify.

1. $4\frac{1}{8} + 3\frac{1}{4} = 7\frac{3}{8}$
2. $4\frac{2}{3} - 2\frac{1}{4} = 2\frac{5}{12}$
3. $5\frac{1}{2} - 1\frac{1}{5} = 4\frac{3}{10}$
4. $5\frac{1}{3} + 4\frac{1}{8} = 9\frac{11}{24}$
5. $10\frac{3}{10} + 9\frac{4}{5} = 20\frac{1}{10}$
6. $14\frac{1}{8} + \frac{1}{4} = 14\frac{3}{8}$
7. $6\frac{2}{10} - 3\frac{1}{5} = 3$
8. $7\frac{1}{3} - 5 = 2\frac{1}{3}$
9. $3\frac{2}{3} + 4\frac{1}{4} = 7\frac{11}{12}$
10. $6\frac{3}{8} - 2\frac{1}{8} = 4\frac{1}{4}$
11. $6\frac{5}{6} - 5\frac{1}{3} = 1\frac{1}{2}$
12. $6\frac{5}{6} + 2\frac{1}{3} = 9\frac{1}{6}$

13. $7\frac{2}{3} - 2\frac{1}{6} =$ $5\frac{1}{2}$
14. $20\frac{1}{5} + 4\frac{7}{10} =$ $24\frac{9}{10}$
15. $8\frac{1}{3} + 8\frac{3}{4} =$ $17\frac{1}{12}$
16. $4\frac{5}{8} - 1\frac{1}{2} =$ $3\frac{1}{8}$
17. $23\frac{3}{10} + \frac{2}{5} =$ $23\frac{7}{10}$
18. $9\frac{3}{8} - 8 =$ $1\frac{3}{8}$

19. Find the sum of $6\frac{2}{3}$ and $7\frac{3}{5}$. $14\frac{4}{15}$
20. Find the difference of $8\frac{7}{8}$ and $2\frac{3}{4}$. $6\frac{1}{8}$
21. How do you simplify $8\frac{9}{6}$?
Possible answer: $\frac{9}{6} = 1\frac{3}{6} = 1\frac{1}{2}$, $8 + 1\frac{1}{2} = 9\frac{1}{2}$

Name ______________________

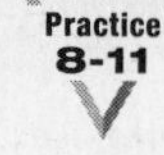

Practice 8-11

Adding Mixed Numbers

Find each sum. Simplify, if possible.

1. $2\frac{1}{8} + 1\frac{1}{2} + 3\frac{3}{4}$ $7\frac{3}{8}$
2. $5\frac{1}{3} + 2\frac{1}{2} + 1\frac{2}{3}$ $9\frac{1}{2}$
3. $3\frac{1}{4} + 4\frac{1}{2} + 1\frac{3}{4}$ $9\frac{1}{2}$
4. $6\frac{1}{4} + 1\frac{1}{2} + \frac{3}{8}$ $8\frac{1}{8}$
5. $9\frac{2}{3} + \frac{1}{4} + 4\frac{5}{6}$ $14\frac{3}{4}$
6. $2\frac{1}{5} + 4\frac{3}{10} + 3\frac{3}{5}$ $10\frac{1}{10}$
7. $3\frac{3}{8} + 2\frac{1}{2} + 3\frac{1}{8}$ 9
8. $13\frac{5}{12} + 8\frac{1}{2} + 11$ $32\frac{11}{12}$
9. $7 + 4\frac{1}{4} + 6\frac{7}{10} =$ $17\frac{19}{20}$
10. $\frac{2}{5} + 4\frac{3}{10} + 1\frac{1}{5} =$ $5\frac{9}{10}$
11. $8\frac{1}{8} + 4\frac{7}{10} + \frac{3}{5} =$ $13\frac{17}{40}$
12. $3\frac{1}{7} + 21\frac{3}{4} + 3\frac{5}{7} =$ $28\frac{17}{28}$
13. $2\frac{1}{2} + 3\frac{1}{4} + 5\frac{1}{8} =$ $10\frac{7}{8}$
14. Add $\frac{1}{3}$, $3\frac{3}{5}$, and $7\frac{1}{3}$. $11\frac{4}{15}$
15. When adding several fractions you can combine those with common denominators first to make addition easier. How can you combine fractions first to add $2\frac{1}{5}$, $4\frac{1}{4}$, and $3\frac{3}{5}$?

    First combine $\frac{1}{5}$ and $\frac{3}{5}$ to make $\frac{4}{5}$. Then the only fractions you have to add are $\frac{4}{5}$ and $\frac{1}{4}$. $\frac{4}{5} + \frac{1}{4} = \frac{21}{20} = 1\frac{1}{20}$. $1\frac{1}{20} + 2 + 4 + 3 = 10\frac{1}{20}$.
16. **Estimation** What is $3\frac{5}{7} + 4\frac{1}{8} + 2\frac{3}{4}$ to the nearest whole number?

    11
17. What is the sum of the answers for **1–4**? $34\frac{1}{2}$

Name ______________________

Practice 8-12

Subtracting Mixed Numbers

Find each difference. Simplify.

1. $6\frac{1}{3} - 2\frac{3}{4}$ $3\frac{7}{12}$
2. $7\frac{3}{4} - 1\frac{3}{8}$ $6\frac{3}{8}$
3. $9\frac{1}{2} - \frac{1}{3}$ $9\frac{1}{6}$
4. $6\frac{3}{4} - 4\frac{1}{2}$ $2\frac{1}{4}$
5. $7 - \frac{3}{5}$ $6\frac{2}{5}$
6. $22\frac{1}{3} - 13\frac{3}{8}$ $8\frac{23}{24}$
7. $7 - 2\frac{1}{3}$ $4\frac{2}{3}$
8. $6\frac{7}{10} - \frac{5}{8}$ $6\frac{3}{40}$
9. $3\frac{3}{4} - 2\frac{1}{2}$ $1\frac{1}{4}$
10. $5 - 3\frac{3}{4}$ $1\frac{1}{4}$
11. $17\frac{4}{9} - 11\frac{5}{6}$ $5\frac{11}{18}$
12. $7\frac{1}{8} - 4\frac{4}{5}$ $2\frac{13}{40}$
13. $15 - 7\frac{2}{5} =$ $7\frac{3}{5}$
14. $11\frac{1}{4} - \frac{5}{8} =$ $10\frac{5}{8}$
15. $8\frac{7}{12} - 3\frac{3}{4} =$ $4\frac{5}{6}$
16. $5\frac{2}{3} - 2\frac{1}{2} =$ $3\frac{1}{6}$
17. $8 - 2\frac{1}{3} =$ $5\frac{2}{3}$
18. $17\frac{1}{8} - 4\frac{1}{2} =$ $12\frac{5}{8}$
19. Find the difference of $13\frac{2}{5}$ and $3\frac{3}{4}$. $9\frac{13}{20}$
20. **Estimation** What is $4\frac{1}{8} - 2\frac{2}{3}$ to the nearest whole number? 1
21. Bridget added $\frac{1}{5}$ to both 12 and $6\frac{4}{5}$ when subtracting $12 - 6\frac{4}{5}$. Tell why.

    Possible answer: Bridget added $\frac{1}{5}$ to $6\frac{4}{5}$ to make it a whole number. So that the problem wasn't changed, Bridget added $\frac{1}{5}$ to 12. $12\frac{1}{5} - 7 = 5\frac{1}{5}$, $12 - 6\frac{4}{5} = 5\frac{1}{5}$.

Name ______________________

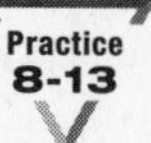

Practice 8-13

Compare Strategies: Work Backward/Draw a Picture

Work backward or use any strategy to solve the problem.

1. Stacey, Kiesha, and Maria planned their trip to band camp. Maria had to travel 5 more miles than Kiesha. Stacey had to travel $\frac{1}{2}$ the distance Kiesha traveled. Stacey traveled 50 miles. How far did Maria travel?

   105 miles
2. Sven and Ryan hiked a desert trail for their scout badge. They followed the trail $1\frac{1}{4}$ miles west, then turned north for $\frac{5}{8}$ mile. Finally they headed east for $1\frac{5}{8}$ mile to join the troop for camp. The next morning they hiked back over the same trail. How many miles in all did they hike? 7 miles
3. Students voted to raise money for new soccer goals for their school. The goals cost $450. Students raised $\frac{1}{3}$ of the money. The school's PTA contributed $50 more than the students. Parents organized an additional fundraiser for the extra funds needed. How much did each group contribute?

   Students: $150; PTA: $200; Parents: $100
4. Carly, Courtney, and Ashley went to the skating party for their school. Courtney skated three times as many laps as Ashley. Carly skated $\frac{2}{3}$ of the distance Courtney skated. Ashley skated 50 laps. How many laps did Courtney and Carly skate?

   Courtney: 150 laps; Carly: 100 laps
5. Max invited his friends over for pizza. Matt ate 12 slices. Cole ate half as much as Matt but twice as much as Sergio. Max ate 2 more slices than Sergio. How much pizza did Cole, Sergio, and Max each eat?

   Cole: 6 slices; Sergio: 3 slices; Max: 5 slices

Name ______________________

Practice Chapter 8 Section B

Review and Practice

(Lessons 8–12) Find each sum or difference. Simplify.

1. $5\frac{1}{3} + 3\frac{1}{6}$ $8\frac{3}{6} = 8\frac{1}{2}$
2. $4\frac{7}{9} - 1\frac{2}{9}$ $3\frac{5}{9}$
3. $6\frac{5}{8} - 2\frac{2}{4}$ $4\frac{1}{8}$
4. $8\frac{2}{3} + 1\frac{1}{9}$ $9\frac{7}{9}$
5. $9 - \frac{1}{8}$ $8\frac{7}{8}$
6. $7\frac{2}{5} + 1\frac{3}{10}$ $8\frac{7}{10}$
7. $6\frac{2}{9} - 4\frac{2}{3}$ $1\frac{5}{9}$
8. $8\frac{5}{7} - 2\frac{5}{6}$ $5\frac{37}{42}$
9. $2\frac{1}{10} - 1\frac{7}{8}$ $\frac{9}{40}$
10. $13\frac{6}{9} + 12\frac{1}{5}$ $25\frac{39}{45} = 25\frac{13}{15}$
11. $16\frac{4}{5} - 12\frac{3}{4}$ $4\frac{1}{20}$
12. $9\frac{1}{4} + 1\frac{3}{8}$ $10\frac{5}{8}$
13. Ms. Whitney bought $2\frac{1}{4}$ yd of red checked material, $1\frac{3}{4}$ yd of blue material, and 3 yd of red material. How many yards of material did she buy in all? 7 yd

(Lesson 13) Solve. Use any strategy.

14. Leroy gave half of his crayons to a friend. He then lost 2. He had 10 left. How many crayons did he have to begin with? 24
15. Trish has a total of 36 colored pencils and chalks. She has 8 more pencils than chalks. How many chalks does she have? 14 chalks

(Mixed Review) Tell whether the each is prime or composite.

16. 6 composite
17. 5 prime
18. 27 composite
19. 21 composite
20. 38 composite
21. 31 prime

Name ______________________

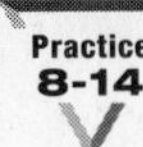

Linear Measure

Find the length to the nearest $\frac{1}{4}$-inch.

1. 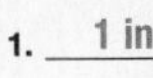 1 in.

2. 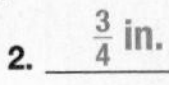 $\frac{3}{4}$ in.

Find the length to the nearest $\frac{1}{8}$-inch.

3. $1\frac{1}{4}$ in.

4. $3\frac{1}{2}$ in.

5. Mario broke a pane of glass in a window. The opening measured $7\frac{1}{4}$ in. by $9\frac{1}{2}$ in. At the hardware store, they sold him a pane of glass that was $7\frac{1}{4}$ in. by $9\frac{1}{2}$ in. to the nearest $\frac{1}{4}$ in. Can Mario be sure the glass will fit the window? Explain.
No; to the nearest $\frac{1}{4}$-inch is an approximation.

Use your ruler to draw a line segment for each length.

6. $1\frac{3}{4}$ in.

7. $2\frac{1}{8}$ in.

8. $3\frac{1}{4}$ in.

9. $1\frac{1}{8}$ in.

Name ______________________

Practice
8-15

Feet, Yards, and Miles

Complete.

1. 12 yd = 36 ft
2. 3 mi = 15,840 ft
3. 192 in. = 16 ft
4. 2 mi = 3,520 yd
5. 180 in. = 15 ft
6. 87 in. = 7 ft 3 in.
7. 15 ft 3 in. = 183 in.
8. 21,120 ft = 4 mi
9. 7 ft 4 in. = 88 in.
10. 5 yd 2 ft = 17 ft
11. 63 in. = 5 ft 3 in.
12. 15,840 yd = 9 mi
13. 38 yd = 114 ft
14. 7 mi = 36,960 ft
15. 420 in. = 35 ft
16. 3 yd 1 ft = 10 ft
17. Kevin and Reggie are on the track team. Kevin's best high jump is 4 ft 9 in. Reggie's best jump is 56 in. Who has the better record? Kevin
18. Complete.

a. Number of feet	21	24	18	12	36	45
b. Number of yards	7	8	6	4	12	15

c. To change feet to yards, you must divide the number of feet by 3.

d. To change yards to feet, you must multiply the number of yards by 3.

19. Complete.

a. Number of inches	12	24	36	60	120	300
b. Number of feet	1	2	3	5	10	25

c. To change inches to feet you must divide the number of inches by 12.

d. To change feet to inches you must multiply the number of feet by 12.

Name ______________________

Practice
8-16

Analyze Word Problems: Exact or Estimate?

Decide whether you need an exact answer or an estimate. Solve.

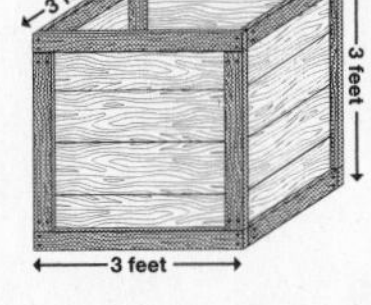

1. Kathy wants to build a storage box 3 ft wide, 3 ft high, and 3 ft deep. Would three 2 × 4's that are each 8 ft long be enough to build the box? Explain your answer.
estimate; No, Kathy would need
 36 ft of wood. She only has 24 ft.

2. If Kathy wanted to make the cage 2 ft on each side, would she have enough wood?
estimate; Yes, she would need 24 ft of wood.

3. Carly usually does gymnastics for three hours on Monday through Friday, and for two hours on Saturday. About how many hours does she do gymnastics in a month?
estimate; between 68 to 72 hours

4. Donald needs to be at school band practice by 7:30 A.M. He wants to get to school at least 15 minutes early. School is about a $\frac{1}{2}$ –hr bike ride away. What time should Donald leave for school?
estimate; 6:45 A.M.

5. Sharish saved $210 for a stereo for her room. The stereo costs $186. Sharish also wanted to purchase two CD's at $11 each. While at the store, Sharish found another CD she wanted for $13. Did Sharish have enough money to pay for everything she wanted? Tell what strategy you used.
exact; No, she had $210 and her purchases cost $221; work backward.

Name ______________________

Review and Practice

(Lesson 14) Find the length to the nearest $\frac{1}{8}$-inch.

1. $2\frac{1}{2}$ in.

2. $3\frac{3}{8}$ in.

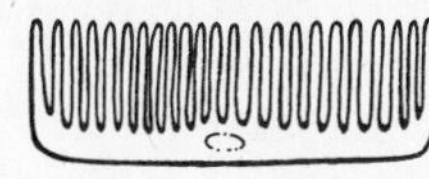

Use your ruler to draw a line segment for each length.

3. $2\frac{3}{4}$ inches
4. $3\frac{7}{8}$ inches

(Lesson 15) Complete.

5. 5 yd = 15 ft
6. 8 ft 7 in. = 103 in.
7. 137 in. = 11 ft 5 in.
8. 3 mi = 15,840 ft
9. 5 mi = 8,800 yd
10. 96 in. = 8 ft
11. 6 yd 2 ft = 20 ft
12. 15,840 ft = 3 mi
13. Which is longer, 526 ft or 150 yd? 526 ft

(Lesson 16) Tell whether you need an exact answer or an estimate. Then solve.

14. Betty went to the library at 8:30 A.M. She wants to be at her friend's house by 10:30 A.M. It takes her about 20 minutes to walk to her friend's house. What time should she leave the library?
Estimate, she should leave between 10 and 10:10.

15. Philip has $12. Does he have enough money to treat himself and two friends a movie that costs $4? exact, yes

(Mixed Review) Divide.

16. 400 ÷ 2 200
17. 390 ÷ 3 130
18. 400 ÷ 20 20
19. 100 ÷ 50 2

Name ______________________

Cumulative Review

(Chapter 4 Lesson 5) Divide.

1. $6\overline{)726}$ **121** **2.** $8\overline{)2488}$ **311** **3.** $5\overline{)834}$ **166 R4**

(Chapter 7 Lesson 7) Write in order from least to greatest.

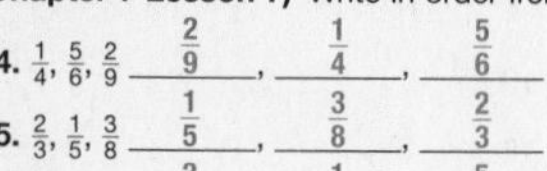

4. $\frac{1}{4}, \frac{5}{6}, \frac{2}{9}$ **$\frac{2}{9}$, $\frac{1}{4}$, $\frac{5}{6}$**

5. $\frac{2}{3}, \frac{1}{5}, \frac{3}{8}$ **$\frac{1}{5}$, $\frac{3}{8}$, $\frac{2}{3}$**

6. $\frac{1}{2}, \frac{5}{9}, \frac{2}{5}$ **$\frac{2}{5}$, $\frac{1}{2}$, $\frac{5}{9}$**

(Chapter 7 Lesson 13) Write each as a percent.

7. 12 out of 100 **12%** **8.** $\frac{31}{100}$ **31%**

Write each as a hundredths fraction and as a decimal.

9. $\frac{15}{25} =$ **$\frac{60}{100}$**, **0.60**

10. $\frac{2}{50} =$ **$\frac{4}{100}$**, **0.04**

(Chapter 8 Lessons 4, 6, and 10) Add or subtract.

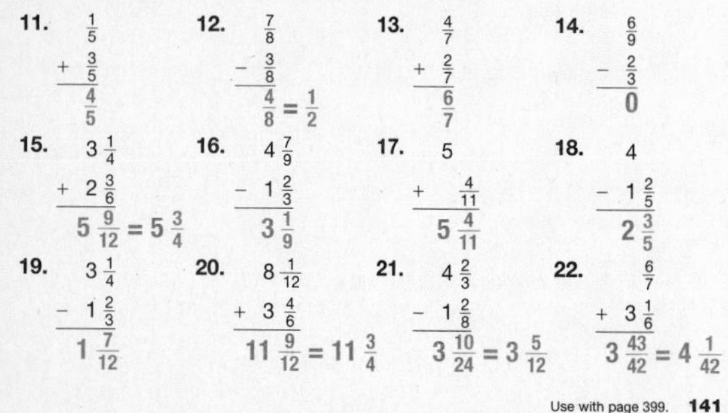

11. $\frac{1}{5} + \frac{3}{5} =$ **$\frac{4}{5}$**

12. $\frac{7}{8} - \frac{3}{8} =$ **$\frac{4}{8} = \frac{1}{2}$**

13. $\frac{4}{7} + \frac{2}{7} =$ **$\frac{6}{7}$**

14. $\frac{6}{9} - \frac{2}{3} =$ **0**

15. $3\frac{1}{4} + 2\frac{3}{6} =$ **$5\frac{9}{12} = 5\frac{3}{4}$**

16. $4\frac{7}{9} - 1\frac{2}{3} =$ **$3\frac{1}{9}$**

17. $5 + \frac{4}{11} =$ **$5\frac{4}{11}$**

18. $4 - 1\frac{2}{5} =$ **$2\frac{3}{5}$**

19. $3\frac{1}{4} - 1\frac{2}{3} =$ **$1\frac{7}{12}$**

20. $8\frac{1}{12} + 3\frac{4}{6} =$ **$11\frac{9}{12} = 11\frac{3}{4}$**

21. $4\frac{2}{3} - 1\frac{2}{8} =$ **$3\frac{10}{24} = 3\frac{5}{12}$**

22. $\frac{6}{7} + 3\frac{1}{6} =$ **$3\frac{43}{42} = 4\frac{1}{42}$**

Name ______________________

Practice 9-1

Exploring Multiplication of Whole Numbers by Fractions

Use division to help you find the fraction of each number.

1. To find $\frac{3}{4}$ of 12, think:

a. $\frac{1}{4}$ of 12 is **3**.

b. $\frac{3}{4}$ is 3 times as much as **$\frac{1}{4}$**.

c. $3 \times 3 =$ **9** so $\frac{3}{4}$ of 12 is **9**.

Find each product. You may use counters to help.

2. $\frac{1}{2}$ of 20 **10** **3.** $\frac{1}{4}$ of 16 **4** **4.** $\frac{3}{4}$ of 24 **18**

5. $\frac{1}{9}$ of 27 **3** **6.** $\frac{2}{9}$ of 36 **8** **7.** $\frac{1}{5}$ of 45 **9**

8. $\frac{1}{3}$ of 18 **6** **9.** $\frac{4}{5}$ of 15 **12** **10.** $\frac{2}{3}$ of 15 **10**

11. Find two-fifths of ten. **4**

12. Find four-ninths of 27. **12**

13. Find one-third of 21. **7**

14. Find two-sevenths of 28. **8**

15. Which of the number lines below shows $\frac{1}{5}$ of 50? **b**

a. 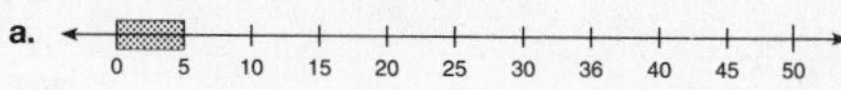

b. 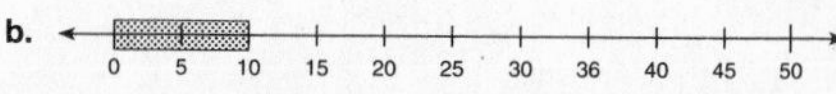

c. 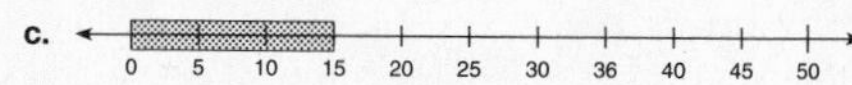

Name ______________________

Practice 9-2

Multiplying with Fractions

Find each product. Use mental math.

1. $\frac{1}{4}$ of 28 **7** **2.** $\frac{1}{9}$ of 63 **7** **3.** $\frac{2}{5}$ of 35 **14**

4. $\frac{2}{3}$ of 27 **18** **5.** $\frac{3}{8}$ of 24 **9** **6.** $\frac{4}{7}$ of 70 **40**

7. $\frac{1}{3}$ of 18 **6** **8.** $\frac{1}{5}$ of 45 **9** **9.** $\frac{5}{8}$ of 32 **20**

10. $\frac{1}{8}$ of 48 **6** **11.** $\frac{4}{9}$ of 54 **24** **12.** $\frac{3}{4}$ of 40 **30**

13. $\frac{1}{2}$ of 18 **9** **14.** $\frac{4}{5}$ of 30 **24** **15.** $\frac{2}{7}$ of 14 **4**

16. $\frac{3}{8}$ of 32 **9** **17.** $\frac{2}{7}$ of 21 **24** **18.** $\frac{4}{5}$ of 45 **4**

19. Multiply one-sixth and sixty. **10**

20. Multiply three-fifths and thirty. **18**

21. Multiply three-fourths and forty. **30**

22. Multiply two-ninths and forty-five. **10**

23. Complete the table. Use patterns to help you find each product.

$\frac{1}{6}$ of 36	6	$\frac{4}{6}$ of 36	24
$\frac{2}{6}$ of 36	12	$\frac{5}{6}$ of 36	30
$\frac{3}{6}$ of 36	18	$\frac{6}{6}$ of 36	36

24. How could you use the product of $\frac{1}{3}$ and 300 to find the product of $\frac{1}{6}$ and 300?

Possible answer: $\frac{1}{6}$ is half of $\frac{1}{3}$, so the product of $\frac{1}{6}$ and 300 is half the product of $\frac{1}{3}$ and 300.

25. How could you use the product of $\frac{1}{2}$ and 200 to find the product of $\frac{1}{8}$ and 200?

Possible answer: $\frac{1}{8}$ is a quarter of $\frac{1}{2}$, so the product of $\frac{1}{8}$ and 200 is a quarter of the product of $\frac{1}{2}$ and 200.

Name ______________________

Practice 9-3

Estimating Products

Use rounding, benchmarks, or compatible numbers to estimate each products.

1. $7 \times 2\frac{8}{9}$ **20–21** **2.** $\frac{1}{8} \times 17$ **2–3** **3.** $\frac{5}{8} \times 10$ **5–10**

4. $\frac{3}{8} \times 22$ **9–11** **5.** $1\frac{4}{5} \times 6$ **9–12** **6.** $\frac{2}{9} \times 28$ **6–8**

7. $\frac{2}{7} \times 48$ **13–16** **8.** $\frac{4}{9} \times 30$ **12–15** **9.** $\frac{4}{7} \times 15$ **7–8**

10. $1\frac{7}{8} \times 10$ **17–20** **11.** $\frac{4}{5} \times 11$ **8–11** **12.** $3\frac{3}{4} \times 4$ **15–16**

13. $\frac{5}{6} \times 25$ **20–25** **14.** $\frac{3}{8} \times 33$ **12–18** **15.** $2\frac{1}{9} \times 34$ **57–68**

16. Estimate the product of $1\frac{9}{10}$ and 15. Describe your method.

30; Possible answer: Round $1\frac{9}{10}$ to 2.

17. Estimate the product of $\frac{2}{3}$ and 31. Describe your method.

20; Possible answer: Use compatible number–30.

18. Estimate the product of $3\frac{7}{8}$ and 25. Describe your method.

100; Possible answer: Round $3\frac{7}{8}$ to 4.

Use rounding, benchmarks, or compatible numbers to estimate each product. Write the letter of the estimate that is closer to the actual product.

19. $6 \times 3\frac{7}{8}$ **b** a. more than 24 b. less than 24

20. $\frac{3}{8} \times 25$ **a** a. more than 9 b. less than 9

21. $\frac{5}{9} \times 17$ **b** a. more than 10 b. less than 10

22. $2\frac{1}{7} \times 22$ **a** a. more than 44 b. less than 44

23. $3\frac{2}{3} \times 10$ **b** a. more than 40 b. less than 40

Name ______________________

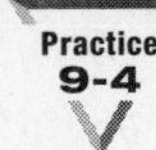
Practice 9-4

Exploring Multiplication of Fractions by Fractions

Use the drawing to help you complete each sentence.

1. $\frac{1}{3} \times \frac{1}{4}$ means $\frac{1}{3}$ of $\frac{1}{4}$

The parts of the rectangle show that $\frac{1}{4} \times \frac{1}{3} =$ $\underline{\frac{1}{12}}$

2. $\frac{1}{2} \times \frac{1}{8}$ means $\frac{1}{2}$ of $\frac{1}{8}$

The parts of the rectangle show that $\underline{\frac{1}{2}} \times \underline{\frac{1}{8}} = \underline{\frac{1}{16}}$

3. Which of the drawings below shows $\frac{1}{5} \times \frac{1}{3}$? d

a. 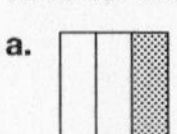

b. 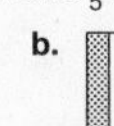

c. 

d. 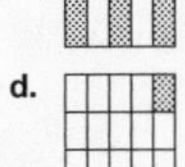

Use each drawing to help you complete each sentence.

4. $\frac{1}{4}$ is shaded.
$\frac{1}{2}$ of $\frac{1}{4}$ is $\underline{\frac{1}{8}}$.

5. $\frac{2}{5}$ is shaded.
$\frac{1}{3}$ of $\frac{2}{5}$ is $\underline{\frac{2}{15}}$.

Draw pictures or use paper folding to find each product.

6. What is $\frac{1}{3} \times \frac{1}{5}$? $\underline{\frac{1}{15}}$
7. What is $\frac{2}{3}$ of $\frac{1}{5}$? $\underline{\frac{2}{15}}$
8. $\frac{1}{4} \times \frac{1}{4} = \underline{\frac{1}{16}}$
9. $\frac{1}{6} \times \frac{1}{2} = \underline{\frac{1}{12}}$
10. $\frac{3}{4} \times \frac{1}{3} = \underline{\frac{1}{4}}$
11. $\frac{1}{2} \times \frac{1}{8} = \underline{\frac{1}{16}}$
12. $\frac{1}{3} \times \frac{1}{7} = \underline{\frac{1}{21}}$
13. $\frac{2}{3} \times \frac{1}{7} = \underline{\frac{2}{21}}$

Name ______________________

Practice 9-5

Multiplying Fractions

Find each product. Simplify.

1. What is $\frac{3}{4} \times \frac{1}{3}$? $\underline{\frac{1}{4}}$
2. What is $\frac{7}{10} \times \frac{1}{2}$? $\underline{\frac{7}{20}}$
3. What is $\frac{1}{5} \times \frac{2}{3}$? $\underline{\frac{2}{15}}$
4. What is $\frac{2}{3} \times \frac{1}{5}$? $\underline{\frac{2}{15}}$
5. What is $\frac{1}{9} \times \frac{2}{3}$? $\underline{\frac{2}{27}}$
6. What is $\frac{2}{5} \times \frac{3}{6}$? $\underline{\frac{1}{5}}$
7. $\frac{1}{7} \times \frac{7}{8} = \underline{\frac{1}{8}}$
8. $\frac{3}{8} \times \frac{1}{4} = \underline{\frac{3}{32}}$
9. $\frac{2}{3} \times \frac{3}{5} = \underline{\frac{2}{5}}$
10. $\frac{3}{4} \times \frac{4}{5} = \underline{\frac{3}{5}}$
11. $\frac{1}{9} \times \frac{9}{10} = \underline{\frac{1}{10}}$
12. $\frac{3}{7} \times \frac{1}{3} = \underline{\frac{1}{7}}$
13. $\frac{1}{2} \times \frac{3}{5} = \underline{\frac{3}{10}}$
14. $\frac{1}{3} \times \frac{3}{8} = \underline{\frac{1}{8}}$
15. $\frac{5}{6} \times \frac{1}{4} = \underline{\frac{5}{24}}$
16. $\frac{2}{5} \times \frac{1}{2} = \underline{\frac{1}{5}}$
17. $\frac{1}{6} \times \frac{6}{7} = \underline{\frac{1}{7}}$
18. $\frac{2}{9} \times \frac{1}{2} = \underline{\frac{1}{9}}$
19. $\frac{4}{9} \times \frac{9}{12} = \underline{\frac{1}{3}}$
20. $\frac{1}{7} \times \frac{5}{7} = \underline{\frac{5}{49}}$
21. $\frac{11}{12} \times \frac{6}{11} = \underline{\frac{1}{2}}$
22. $\frac{1}{2}$ is multiplied by a fraction and the product is $\frac{3}{8}$. What is the fraction? $\underline{\frac{3}{4}}$
23. $\frac{4}{5}$ is multiplied by a fraction and the product is $\frac{4}{15}$. What is the fraction? $\underline{\frac{1}{3}}$
24. What is the product of $\frac{2}{3}$ and $\frac{3}{3}$? $\underline{\frac{2}{3}}$
25. Multiply $\frac{1}{2}$ and $\frac{2}{2}$. $\underline{\frac{1}{2}}$
26. Multiply $\frac{3}{4}$ and $\frac{4}{4}$. $\underline{\frac{3}{4}}$
27. Multiply $\frac{2}{5}$ and $\frac{5}{5}$. $\underline{\frac{2}{5}}$
28. Multiply $\frac{8}{8}$ and $\frac{7}{8}$. $\underline{\frac{7}{8}}$
29. If $\frac{3}{4}$ is multiplied by itself, will the product be greater than $\frac{3}{4}$? Explain.
No. It will be less than $\frac{3}{4}$, because the product is a part of $\frac{3}{4}$.

Name ______________________

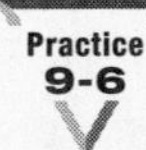
Practice 9-6

Analyze Word Problems: Overestimating and Underestimating

Use overestimating and underestimating to solve the problem.

1. Paula's class washed 22 cars on Saturday afternoon. Each customer paid $4.25 for a car wash. Did the class earn the $75 they need for a field trip?
   a. Can the problem be solved with an estimate or does it require an exact answer? estimate
   b. Should you overestimate or underestimate? Why?
   Underestimate; if the underestimate is over $75, they earned enough.
   c. Did the class earn enough?
   Possible answer: 20 × 4 = 80. 80 > 75, so they earned enough.
   d. If the field trip costs $80 instead of $75, how can the class be sure that they earned enough? How do you know?
   Solve the problem for an exact answer. The estimate may not make sure that the class earned enough.

Estimate to solve. Tell whether you overestimated or underestimated. Explain your reasoning.

2. Marlene invited 34 people to a party. She will serve salad, corn, and $\frac{1}{4}$-pound burgers. How many pounds of meat should she buy?
Possible answer: 9 pounds; overestimate, so there is enough of food for everyone.

Name ______________________

Practice Chapter 9 Section A

Review and Practice

Vocabulary Fill-in each blank with a word from the word bank.

factor unit fraction whole number numerator denominator

1. The numerator is the top number of a fraction.
2. A unit fraction has a 1 as the numerator.
3. One factor of 8 is 4. Others are 1, 2, and 8.

(Lessons 1 and 2) Find each product.

4. $\frac{1}{3}$ of 24 8
5. $\frac{1}{9}$ of 36 4
6. $\frac{10}{11} \times 22 =$ 20
7. $\frac{5}{6} \times 18 =$ 15
8. Find two-thirds of thirty. 20

(Lesson 3) Estimate each product. Use rounding, benchmarks, or compatible numbers.

9. $\frac{3}{4} \times 18$ 12–18
10. $3\frac{2}{5} \times 32$ 96–120
11. $2\frac{7}{20} \times 41$ 80–120
12. $\frac{6}{11} \times 12$ 6–12
13. $\frac{1}{8}$ of a small box of detergent cleans 1 load of laundry. How many loads could you wash with 5 boxes of detergent?
40 loads

(Lessons 4 and 5) Find each product.

14. $\frac{8}{9} \times \frac{1}{4} = \underline{\frac{2}{9}}$
15. $\frac{5}{7} \times \frac{3}{4} = \underline{\frac{15}{28}}$
16. $\frac{6}{10} \times \frac{5}{12} = \underline{\frac{1}{4}}$
17. $\frac{3}{8} \times \frac{8}{9} = \underline{\frac{1}{3}}$

Complete.

18. $\frac{1}{3}$ of $\underline{\frac{1}{3}} = \frac{1}{9}$
19. $\frac{1}{6}$ of $\underline{\frac{5}{7}} = \frac{5}{42}$

(Mixed Review) Round each to the nearest whole number.

20. $2\frac{1}{3}$ 2
21. $6\frac{3}{8}$ 6
22. 5.75 6
23. 6.09 6
24. $14\frac{7}{8}$ 15
25. 2.49 2

Name ______________________

Practice 9-7

Multiplying Whole Numbers by Fractions

Complete.

1. $\frac{5}{8} \times 3 = \frac{\boxed{15}}{8} = 1\frac{7}{8}$
2. $\frac{2}{7} \times 5 = \frac{\boxed{10}}{7} = 1\frac{3}{7}$
3. $\frac{3}{5} \times 9 = \frac{\boxed{27}}{5} = \boxed{5\frac{2}{5}}$
4. $\frac{3}{4} \times 7 = \frac{\boxed{21}}{4} = \boxed{5\frac{1}{4}}$
5. $\frac{3}{4} \times 8 = \frac{\boxed{24}}{\boxed{4}} = \boxed{6}$
6. $5 \times \frac{8}{10} = \frac{\boxed{40}}{\boxed{10}} = \boxed{4}$
7. $9 \times \frac{5}{9} = \frac{\boxed{45}}{\boxed{9}} = \boxed{5}$
8. $4 \times \frac{9}{12} = \frac{\boxed{36}}{\boxed{12}} = \boxed{3}$

Find each product.

9. $\frac{7}{6} \times 6 =$ 7
10. $\frac{2}{3} \times 9 =$ 6
11. $\frac{8}{9} \times 7 =$ $6\frac{2}{9}$
12. $\frac{3}{7} \times 49 =$ 21
13. $\frac{1}{3} \times 96 =$ 32
14. $\frac{9}{8} \times 11 =$ $12\frac{3}{8}$
15. $\frac{4}{5} \times 30 =$ 24
16. $\frac{2}{9} \times 54 =$ 12
17. $\frac{4}{3} \times 24 =$ 32
18. $\frac{8}{7} \times 63 =$ 72
19. $\frac{6}{7} \times 28 =$ 24
20. $\frac{3}{5} \times 60 =$ 36

21. Explain how you can find the product of 5 and $\frac{3}{4}$.
Possible answer: $5 \times \frac{1}{4} = \frac{5}{4}$, so $5 \times \frac{3}{4} = \frac{15}{4} = 3\frac{3}{4}$

22. Complete. $4 \times \frac{3}{4} = 3$, so $\frac{3}{4} \times 4 = \boxed{3}$.

23. James says that he knows all the answers to the following problems are mixed numbers, even without solving them. Explain how he knows.
$\frac{3}{5} \times 248$ $\frac{5}{9} \times 366$ $\frac{7}{8} \times 450$
Possible answer: Each whole number cannot be divided evenly by each denominator.

Name ______________________

Practice 9-8

Multiplying Whole Numbers and Mixed Numbers

Complete.

1. $8\frac{2}{3} \times 7 = \frac{\boxed{26}}{3} \times 7$
2. $4\frac{1}{8} \times 6 = \frac{\boxed{33}}{8} \times 6$
3. $4 \times 5\frac{1}{3} = 4 \times \frac{\boxed{16}}{3}$
4. $9 \times 6\frac{7}{8} = 9 \times \frac{\boxed{55}}{8}$
5. $7\frac{7}{8} \times 3\frac{3}{4} = \frac{\boxed{63}}{8} \times \frac{\boxed{15}}{4}$
6. $3\frac{4}{7} \times 2\frac{7}{9} = \frac{\boxed{25}}{7} \times \frac{\boxed{25}}{9}$

Find each product. Simplify. Use estimation to check.

7. $7\frac{8}{9} \times 3 =$ $23\frac{2}{3}$
8. $8 \times 2\frac{2}{3} =$ $21\frac{1}{3}$
9. $2\frac{3}{4} \times 12 =$ 33
10. $2\frac{7}{9} \times 4 =$ $11\frac{1}{9}$
11. $2\frac{7}{8} \times 8 =$ 23
12. $4 \times 3\frac{1}{6} =$ $12\frac{2}{3}$
13. $10 \times 4\frac{1}{8} =$ $41\frac{1}{4}$
14. $3\frac{5}{6} \times 7 =$ $26\frac{5}{6}$
15. $\frac{2}{3} \times 1\frac{7}{10} =$ $1\frac{2}{15}$
16. $2\frac{1}{4} \times \frac{8}{9} =$ 2
17. $3\frac{1}{2} \times \frac{7}{8} =$ $3\frac{1}{16}$
18. $5\frac{2}{3} \times \frac{2}{5} =$ $2\frac{4}{15}$
19. $3\frac{1}{2} \times 2\frac{2}{5} =$ $8\frac{2}{5}$
20. $3\frac{3}{8} \times 4\frac{1}{3} =$ $14\frac{5}{8}$
21. $\frac{2}{9} \times 4\frac{3}{8} =$ $\frac{35}{36}$
22. $4\frac{5}{7} \times 2\frac{8}{9} =$ $13\frac{13}{21}$
23. Find the product of $2\frac{1}{3}$ and $3\frac{1}{8}$. $7\frac{7}{24}$
24. Find the product of $4\frac{2}{3}$ and $7\frac{5}{6}$. $36\frac{5}{9}$
25. Find the product of $1\frac{3}{7}$ and 9. $12\frac{6}{7}$
26. Multiply $2\frac{2}{3}$ and $7\frac{3}{8}$. $19\frac{2}{3}$
27. Multiply $3\frac{9}{10}$ and $2\frac{2}{5}$. $9\frac{9}{25}$
28. Multiply $8\frac{6}{7}$ and $3\frac{2}{7}$. $29\frac{5}{49}$

Name ______________________

Practice 9-9

Compare Strategies: Logical Reasoning/Draw a Picture

Use logical reasoning to solve the problem.

1. Rosa, Gina, Bryan, and Patrick are each wearing their favorite color shirt: blue, pink, green, or red. No one likes a color that begins with the same letter as his or her name. Neither Gina nor Bryan likes red. Gina's pink shoes match her shirt. Which person is wearing each color?

	Rosa	Gina	Bryan	Patrick
Red	no	no	no	yes
Green	no	no	yes	no
Blue	yes	no	no	no
Pink	no	yes	no	no

Use logical reasoning or any strategy to solve each problem.

2. Luis said, "Guess my birthday. I was born in a summer month whose name does not begin with J. The day is a 2-digit number that is a multiple of 7. My birthday is close to the middle of the month." When is Luis's birthday?

August 14

3. Amy's ancestors came to America in the 1800s. Amy asked her mom what the exact year was. Her mom said, "The digit in the tens place is half the digit in the hundreds place. The digit in the ones place is 3 more than the digit in the tens place." What year did they come to America?
1847

4. LaVonne goes to bed at 9:00. She has 2 hours of homework. Dinner will take 30 minutes, and washing the dishes will take 15 minutes. She wants to watch $1\frac{1}{2}$ hours of TV and work on the computer for 45 minutes.
a. What time should she start doing all these things? 4:00
b. What strategy did you use to solve this problem?
Possible answer: Work Backward.

Name ______________________

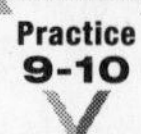

Practice 9-10

Exploring Division of Fractions

Complete the drawings to find each quotient.

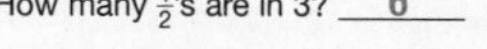

1. How many $\frac{1}{2}$'s are in 3? 6

2. How many $\frac{1}{3}$'s are in 2? 6
3. How many $\frac{1}{4}$'s are in 4? 16
4. How many $\frac{1}{6}$'s are in 5? 30

Find each quotient.

5. How many $\frac{1}{2}$'s are in 9? 18
6. How many $\frac{1}{6}$'s are in 5? 30
7. How many $\frac{1}{4}$'s are in 14? 56
8. $10 \div \frac{1}{8} =$ 80
9. $11 \div \frac{1}{4} =$ 44
10. $4 \div \frac{1}{11} =$ 44
11. $6 \div \frac{1}{3} =$ 18
12. $8 \div \frac{1}{10} =$ 80
13. $15 \div \frac{1}{4} =$ 60
14. $9 \div \frac{1}{6} =$ 54
15. $12 \div \frac{1}{5} =$ 60
16. $7 \div \frac{1}{4} =$ 28
17. $7 \div \frac{1}{7} =$ 49
18. Cheesy Pizza cuts all large pizzas into twelfths. How many pieces of pizza would Alicia get if she orders 3 large pizzas? 36 pieces
19. Stan cuts 3 pans of lasagne into eighths. How many servings does he have? 24 servings
20. For a fruit plate, Jay cuts 6 apples into sixths. How many pieces of apple does he have? 36 pieces

Name ______________________

Practice
Chapter 9
Section B

Review and Practice

(Lessons 7 and 8) Find each product. Simplify.

1. $\frac{2}{3} \times 9 =$ 6
2. $\frac{7}{9} \times \frac{9}{10} =$ $\frac{7}{10}$
3. $\frac{5}{8} \times \frac{4}{5} =$ $\frac{1}{2}$
4. $\frac{2}{7} \times \frac{1}{4} =$ $\frac{1}{14}$
5. $2\frac{1}{2} \times 6 =$ 15
6. $\frac{1}{7} \times 6\frac{2}{9} =$ $\frac{8}{9}$
7. $2\frac{2}{5} \times \frac{4}{6} =$ $1\frac{3}{5}$
8. $2\frac{2}{7} \times 1\frac{3}{4} =$ 4
9. Kim can walk $\frac{2}{3}$ of a mile in 15 minutes. How far can she walk in $\frac{1}{3}$ of the time? $\frac{2}{9}$ mile

(Lesson 9) Solve each problem.

10. Phil, Mel, Shel, and Cal are a pharmacist, machinist, secretary, and chef. No one has an occupation that begins with the same letter as his or her name. Neither Phil nor Mel is a chef. Cal is a secretary. What is the occupation of each person?
    Phil is a machinist; Mel is a pharmacist; Shel is a chef; and Cal is a secretary.
11. What fraction of an hour is 40 minutes? $\frac{2}{3}$

(Lesson 10) Find each quotient.

12. $4 \div \frac{1}{3} =$ 12
13. $5 \div \frac{1}{4} =$ 20
14. $20 \div \frac{1}{10} =$ 200
15. $17 \div \frac{1}{2} =$ 34
16. $18 \div \frac{1}{5} =$ 90
17. $13 \div \frac{1}{7} =$ 91
18. How many $\frac{1}{4}$'s are in 9? 36
19. How many $\frac{1}{3}$'s are in 12? 36

(Mixed Review) Find each sum.

20. $\frac{6}{9} + \frac{1}{9} =$ $\frac{7}{9}$
21. $\frac{2}{5} + \frac{3}{5} =$ 1
22. $\frac{1}{8} + \frac{5}{8} =$ $\frac{3}{4}$
23. $\frac{2}{7} + \frac{3}{7} =$ $\frac{5}{7}$

Name ______________________

Practice
Chapters 1–9

Cumulative Review

(Chapter 5 Lesson 10) Divide. Round each answer to the nearest cent if needed.

1. 16)$7.26 $0.45
2. 28)$244.88 $8.75
3. 35)$68.34 $1.95

(Chapter 7 Lesson 3) Write each as an equivalent fraction with a denominator of 12.

4. $\frac{2}{3}$ $\frac{8}{12}$
5. $\frac{12}{24}$ $\frac{6}{12}$
6. $\frac{5}{6}$ $\frac{10}{12}$
7. $\frac{3}{4}$ $\frac{9}{12}$

(Chapter 8 Lesson 12) Find each difference.

8. $3\frac{1}{4} - 2\frac{3}{6}$ = $\frac{3}{4}$
9. $3\frac{5}{9} - 1\frac{2}{3}$ = $\frac{25}{27}$
10. $5\frac{6}{7} - \frac{4}{5}$ = $5\frac{2}{35}$
11. $3\frac{3}{4} - 1\frac{1}{3}$ = $2\frac{5}{12}$
12. $6\frac{1}{3} - 3\frac{4}{6}$ = $2\frac{2}{3}$
13. $4\frac{2}{5} - 1\frac{2}{8}$ = $3\frac{3}{20}$

(Chapter 8 Lesson 15) Complete.

14. 12 yd = 36 ft
15. 2 mi = 10,560 ft
16. 13 ft 7 in. = 163 in.
17. 3 yd 2 ft = 11 ft
18. 34 in. = 2 ft 10 in.

(Chapter 9 Lessons 7 and 8) Find each product.

19. $\frac{4}{5} \times 15 =$ 12
20. $\frac{3}{7} \times \frac{7}{8} =$ $\frac{3}{8}$
21. $\frac{7}{9} \times \frac{3}{14} =$ $\frac{1}{6}$
22. $\frac{1}{6} \times \frac{3}{4} =$ $\frac{1}{8}$
23. $3\frac{1}{2} \times 16 =$ 56
24. $2\frac{4}{5} \times 2\frac{1}{7} =$ 6
25. $3\frac{1}{3} \times 3\frac{3}{8} =$ $11\frac{1}{4}$
26. $4\frac{1}{6} \times \frac{2}{3} =$ $2\frac{7}{9}$

Name ______________________

Practice
10-1

Exploring Estimating and Measuring Length

Draw a line to match each distance estimate to the most appropriate unit of measurement listed.

1. The distance covered by driving from St. Louis, Missouri to Louisville, Kentucky
2. The distance between 2 leaves on the same branch of a tree
3. The distance you cover when crossing a parking lot
4. The distance between two rows of desks in a classroom

a. centimeters
b. decimeters
c. meters
d. kilometers

Choose the most appropriate unit of measure to estimate the length or height of each. Write cm, dm, or m.

5.   m
6.  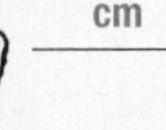 cm
7.   m
8. 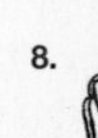 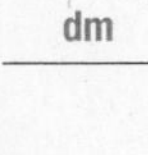 dm

Choose the most appropriate unit of measure to estimate the length or height of each. Write m or km.

9.   m
10.   km
11. 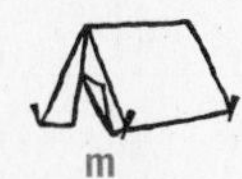 m
12. 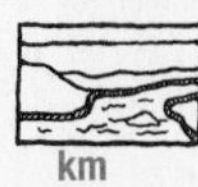 km

Name ______________________

Practice
10-2

Millimeters

Complete.

1. 90 mm = 9 cm
2. 3 dm = 300 mm
3. 1,400 mm = 140 cm
4. 6 m = 60 dm
5. 50 cm = 500 mm
6. 200 cm = 20 dm
7. 9 m = 90 dm
8. 8,000 mm = 8 m
9. 40 mm = 4 cm
10. 3,000 mm = 30 dm
11. 200 cm = 20 dm
12. 4,000 mm = 400 cm
13. 900 cm = 9,000 mm
14. 50 dm = 5,000 mm
15. 6 m = 600 cm
16. 7,000 mm = 7 m
17. 20 m = 2,000 cm
18. 8 cm = 80 mm
19. 17 cm = 170 mm
20. 5 m = 5,000 mm
21. 100 cm = 1 m
22. 6 dm = 60 cm
23. The width of a hockey puck is 44 mm. Is this length shorter or longer than 5 cm? Explain.
    shorter; 44 mm = 4.4 cm, 4.4 cm < 5 cm
24. Old Faithful, Yellowstone National Park's most famous geyser, shoots a spray of steam and hot water 50 m into the air. Is this height greater or less than 5,000 mm? Explain.
    greater; 5,000 mm = 5 m, 50 m > 5 m

Name ______________________

Practice 10-3

Centimeters, Meters, and Decimals

Complete.

1. 0.42 m = 42 cm
2. 76 cm = 0.76 m
3. 388 cm = 3.88 m
4. 56 m = 5,600 cm
5. 6.76 m = 676 cm
6. 552 cm = 5.52 m

Write each measurement, first in centimeters only and then in meters only.

7. 6 m 80 cm 680 cm, 6.8 m
8. 5 m 29 cm 529 cm, 5.29 m
9. 6 m 17 cm 617 cm, 6.17 m
10. 8 m 67 cm 867 cm, 8.67 m

Write the longer distance.

11. The length of a football field (91 m) or the distance from the pitcher's mound to home plate (1,844 cm)
    the football field
12. The length of a kangaroo's hop (7.6 m) or the length of a frog's jump (1,000 cm)
    the frog's jump
13. The length of the longest dinosaur (3,000 cm) or the length of the ocean liner Queen Elizabeth II (293.5 m)
    the ocean liner
14. The height of the Eiffel Tower in Paris (300.5 m) or the height of the Empire State Building in New York City (38,100 cm)
    the Empire State Building

Name ______________________

Practice 10-4

Millimeters, Centimeters, and Decimals

Complete.

1. 4.7 cm = 47 mm
2. 46 cm = 460 mm
3. 42 cm = 420 mm
4. 80 mm = 8 cm
5. 3 mm = 0.3 cm
6. 49 m = 4,900 cm
7. 9.78 cm = 97.8 mm
8. 32.1 cm = 321 mm
9. 4,321 cm = 43.21 m
10. 82.4 mm = 8.24 cm
11. 9.10 m = 910 cm
12. 849.2 cm = 8,492 mm

13. Which length is the longest? C
    A. 94 mm
    B. 9.4 cm
    C. 9.40 m
14. Which length is the longest? C
    A. 6.7 m
    B. 67 cm
    C. 670 m
15. Which length is the shortest? B
    A. 0.19 m
    B. 1.9 cm
    C. 190 mm
16. Which length is the shortest? C
    A. 6,205 mm
    B. 6.205 m
    C. 62.05 cm
17. Which two lengths are equal? A and B
    A. 2.3 m
    B. 230 cm
    C. 230 mm
18. Which two lengths are equal? A and B
    A. 4,867 mm
    B. 486.7 cm
    C. 48.67 m

Name ______________________

Practice Chapter 10 Section A

Review and Practice

Vocabulary Fill in each blank with the correct word.

meter decimeter centimeter

1. One tenth of a meter is equal to 1 decimeter.
2. 1,000 millimeters is equal to one meter.
3. One meter is equal to 100 centimeters.

(Lesson 1) Circle the most appropriate unit of measure to estimate each.

4. length of a golf club mm (m) km
5. thickness of a dime (mm) cm dm
6. distance to a museum dm m (km)

(Lesson 2) Complete.

7. 8 m = 800 cm
8. 500 cm = 5 m
9. 90 dm = 9 m
10. 3,000 mm = 3 m

(Lesson 3) Write each measurement, first in centimeters only and then in meters only.

11. 9 m 15 cm 915 cm, 9.15 m
12. 4 m 30 cm 430 cm, 4.3 m
13. 12 m 8 cm 1,208 cm, 12.08 m

(Lesson 4) Complete.

14. 2.5 mm = 0.25 cm
15. 6.3 cm = 63 mm
16. 16.03 m = 1,603 cm
17. 9.8 m = 980 cm

(Mixed Review) Find each product.

18. $3 \times \frac{3}{5} = 1\frac{4}{5}$
19. $\frac{2}{3} \times \frac{6}{7} = \frac{4}{7}$
20. 3.58 × 10 = 35.8
21. 46.17 × 100 = 4,617
22. 2.75 × 0.0004 = 0.0011
23. 3.22 × 0.005 = 0.0161
24. 5.86 × 0.00003 = 0.0001758

Name ______________________

Practice 10-5

Exploring Perimeter of Polygons

Write a multiplication number sentence describing the perimeter of each polygon.

1. 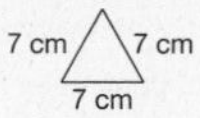

7 cm × 3 = 21 cm

2. 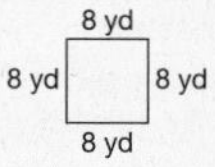

8 yd × 4 = 32 yd

3. 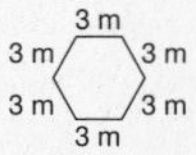

3 m × 6 = 18 m

Find each perimeter.

4. 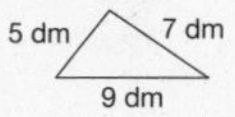

21 dm

5. 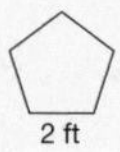

10 ft

6. 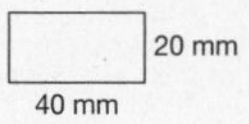

120 mm

7. 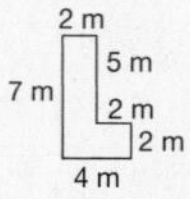

22 m

8. 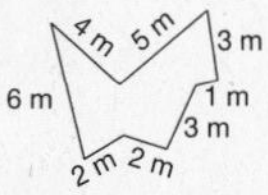

26 m

9. 

12 km

10. a regular pentagon with sides of 9 cm 45 cm
11. a triangle with sides of 8 dm, 8 dm and 10 dm 26 dm
12. a regular hexagon with sides of 5 mm 30 mm
13. an equilateral triangle with sides of 4 cm 12 cm
14. When finding the perimeter of a regular polygon, will you get the same answer if you add each side as when you multiply the length of one side by the total number of sides? Explain.
    yes; Possible answer: because regular polygons have sides of equal length

Name ______________________

Practice 10-6

Exploring Perimeter of Rectangles

Use the formula $P = 2 \times (l + w)$ to find the perimeter of each rectangle. Fill in the missing numbers.

1. 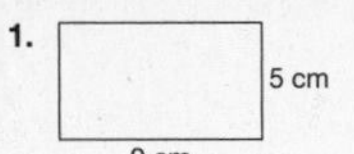
5 cm
9 cm

$P = 2 \times ($ 9 + 5 $)$
$P = 2 \times ($ 14 $)$
$P =$ 28 cm

2. 4 m
17 m

$P = 2 \times ($ 17 + 4 $)$
$P = 2 \times ($ 21 $)$
$P =$ 42 m

Find the perimeter of each rectangle.

3. 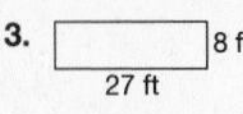
8 ft
27 ft
70 ft

4. 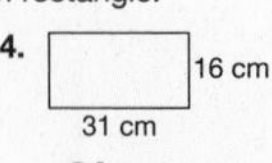
16 cm
31 cm
94 cm

5. 2.3 m
3.4 m
11.4 m

6. l = 26 ft
w = 24 ft
$P =$ 100 ft

7. l = 246 mi
w = 93 mi
$P =$ 678 mi

8. l = 4.25 m
w = 3.85 m
$P =$ 16.2 m

Estimate the perimeter of each rectangle.

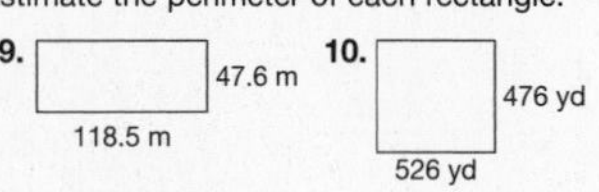

9. 47.6 m
118.5 m
about 340 m

10. 476 yd
526 yd
about 2,000 yd

11. 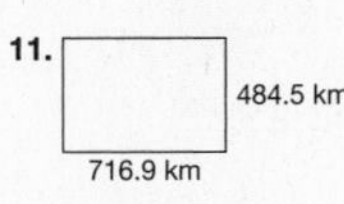
484.5 km
716.9 km
about 2,400 km

12. What is the perimeter of a rectangular rose garden 5.3 meters long and 3.7 meters wide? 18 m

Name ______________________

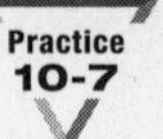
Practice 10-7

Converting Units to Find Perimeter

Find each sum.

1. 3 yd 2 ft + 2 yd 1 ft = 6 yd
2. 8 ft 8 in. + 2 ft 4 in. = 11 ft
3. 6 yd 31 in. + 7 yd 5 in. = 14 yd
4. 3 yd 2 ft + 5 yd 2 ft = 9 yd 1 ft
5. 9 ft 3 in. + 8 ft 11 in. = 18 ft 2 in.
6. 11 yd 1 ft + 3 yd 2 ft = 15 yd

Find each product.

7. 3×4 ft 6 in. = 13 ft 6 in.
8. 2×6 ft 5 in. = 12 ft 10 in.
9. 5×2 yd 9 in. = 11 yd 9 in.
10. 6×3 yd 2 ft = 22 yd
11. 4×11 yd 2 ft = 46 yd 2 ft
12. 7×4 yd 9 in. = 29 yd 2 ft 3 in.

13. Find the perimeter of a bird house 2 ft 7 in. by 1 ft 5 in. 8 ft

14. Find the perimeter of a square sandbox with sides measuring 7 ft 8 in. 30 ft 8 in.

Find each perimeter.

15. a rectangle 6 ft 10 in. long and 4 ft 11 in. wide 23 ft 6 in.
16. a square with sides measuring 2 mi 25 ft 8 mi 100 ft
17. a rectangle 31 yd 2 ft long and 17 yd 2 ft wide 98 yd 2 ft

18. Which rectangle has the greater perimeter? Explain how you know.

a. 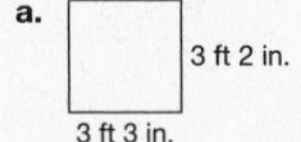
3 ft 2 in.
3 ft 3 in.

b. 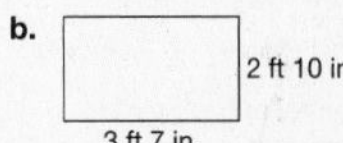
2 ft 10 in.
3 ft 7 in.

neither; They have equal perimeters of 12 ft 10 in.

Name ______________________

Practice 10-8

Exploring Area of Rectangles

Use the formula $A = l \times w$ to find the area of each rectangle. Fill in the missing numbers.

1. 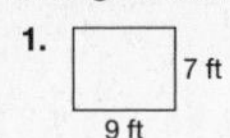
7 ft
9 ft

$A =$ 9 $\times$ 7
$A =$ 63 ft^2

2. 6 yd
8 yd

$A =$ 8 $\times$ 6
$A =$ 48 yd^2

Find the area of each square.

Use the formula $A = s^2$ to find the area of each square. Fill in the missing numbers.

3. 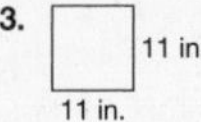
11 in.
11 in.

a. $A = 11^2$
b. $A =$ 121 in^2

4. 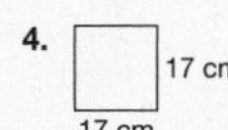
17 cm
17 cm

a. $A = 17^2$
b. $A =$ 289 cm^2

Find the area of each rectangle.

5. l = 14 mi
w = 8 mi
$A =$ 112 mi^2

6. l = 3.9 m
w = 5 m
$A =$ 19.5 m^2

7. l = 16 m
w = 0.5 m
$A =$ 8 m^2

8. s = 13 cm
$A =$ 169 cm^2

9. l = 18 ft
w = 12 ft
$A =$ 216 ft^2

10. s = 15 yd
$A =$ 225 yd^2

11. A rectangle has an area of 91 m^2 and a length of 13 m. What is its width? 7 m

12. A square has an area of 144 cm^2. What is the measure of its side? 12 cm

Name ______________________

Practice 10-9

Decision Making

You would like to participate in an after-school activity. The following is a list of things you might do.

Activity	Cost	Time
Sports Team	$50 for uniform	3:45 P.M. – 5 P.M., Mon., Wed., Fri., Sat.
Dance Class	$12.75 a class	3:45 P.M. – 5 P.M., Tue., Thur.
Music Lesson	$30 a week	3 P.M. – 4 P.M., Mon., Wed.
Arts and Crafts	$40 a month	12 P.M. – 5 P.M., Sat.

1. Which activity is the most expensive for a month? the least?
most—music lesson; least—sports team

2. If you wanted to participate in as many activities as you could, which activities could you choose? Explain.
dance, music, and arts and crafts; The times of these activities do not conflict.

3. How much would it cost in a month to participate in these activities? Find the cost for each.
Dance—$12.75 × 8 = $102; Music—$30 × 4 = $120; Arts and Crafts—$40; Sports—1 uniform fee of $50

4. a. Which activities would you choose?
Answers will vary. Look for answers that show a balanced schedule and understanding of costs.

b. How much would it cost for one month?
Check students' answers.

Name ___

Practice
Chapter 10
Section B

Review and Practice

Vocabulary Write a definition for each word.

1. perimeter The perimeter is the distance around a figure.
2. area Area is the measure of the surface of a region in square units.

(Lessons 5–7) Find each perimeter.

3. 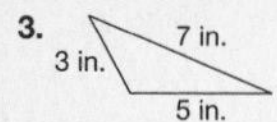

4. 9 cm, 2 cm
5. 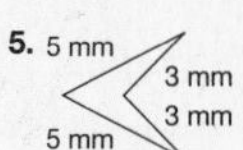

15 in. or 1 ft 3 in. | 22 cm | 16 mm

6. $\frac{1}{3}$ in., $\frac{1}{3}$ in.
7. 14 ft 3 in., 3 ft 2 in.
8. 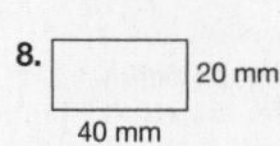

$\frac{4}{3}$ or $1\frac{1}{3}$ in. | 34 ft 10 in. | 120 mm or 12 cm

(Lesson 8) Find each area.

9. 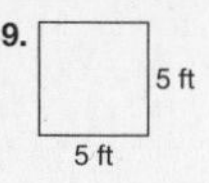

10. 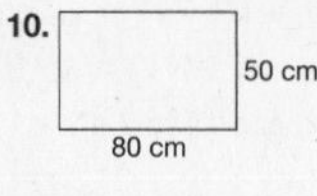

11. 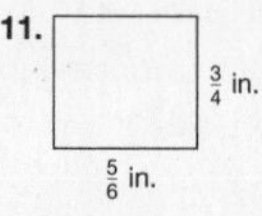

25 ft^2 | 4,000 cm^2 | $\frac{15}{24}$ in^2 or $\frac{5}{8}$ in^2

(Mixed Review) Complete.

12. 300 × 6 = 1,800
13. 36,000 ÷ 9 = 4,000
14. 16 × 20 = 320
15. 45,000 × 900 = 50

Name ___

Practice
10-10

Exploring Area of Right Triangles

Use the formula $A = \frac{1}{2} \times (b \times h)$ to find the area of each right triangle. Fill in the missing numbers.

1. 5 in., 4 in.

$A = \frac{1}{2} \times (5 \times 4)$
$A = \frac{1}{2} \times (20)$
$A = 10$ in^2

2. 2 m, 8 m

$A = \frac{1}{2} \times (2 \times 8)$
$A = \frac{1}{2} \times (16)$
$A = 8$ m^2

Find each area.

3. 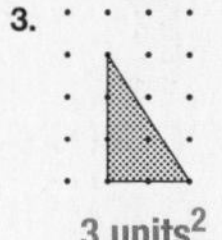
3 units^2

4. 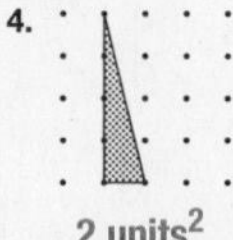
2 units^2

5. 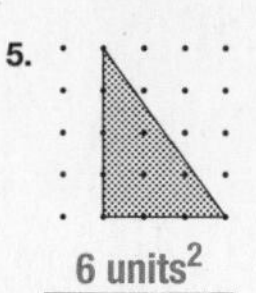
6 units^2

6. 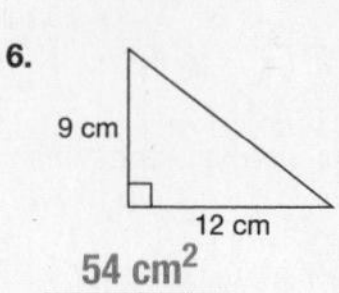

54 cm^2

7. 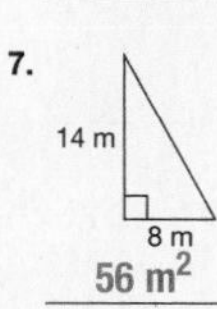

56 m^2

8. 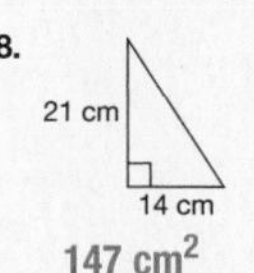

147 cm^2

Name ___

Practice
10-11

Exploring Area of Triangles

Use the formula $A = \frac{1}{2} \times (b \times h)$ to find the area of each triangle. Fill in the missing numbers.

1. 5 in., 8 in.

$A = \frac{1}{2} \times (8 \times 5)$
$A = \frac{1}{2} \times (40)$
$A = 20$ in^2

2. 11 cm, 8 cm

$A = \frac{1}{2} \times (8 \times 11)$
$A = \frac{1}{2} \times (88)$
$A = 44$ cm^2

Find each area.

3. 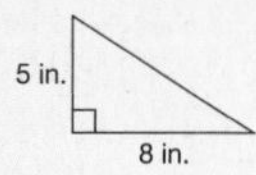
$A = 32.5$ units^2

4. 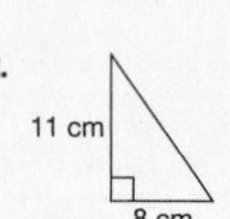
$A = 27$ units^2

5. 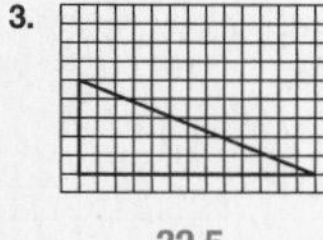

$A = 45.5$ in^2

6. 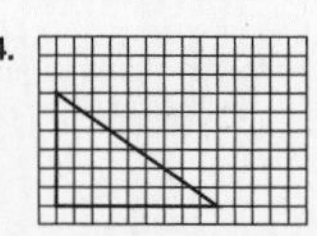

$A = 8$ cm^2

7. Alyson planted a garden area in the shape of a triangle. The base was 9 ft and the height was 7 ft. What was the area of the triangular garden? $31\frac{1}{2}$ ft^2
8. Rosey embroidered triangles on a pillow cover. Each triangle has a base of 2 in. and a height of 3 in. What is the area of each triangle? 3 in^2

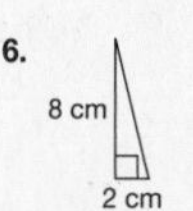

Name ___

Practice
10-12

Exploring Area of Other Polygons

Find each area.

1. 6 square units
2. 6 square units
3. 12 square units

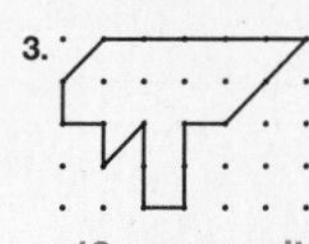

Find each area.

4. 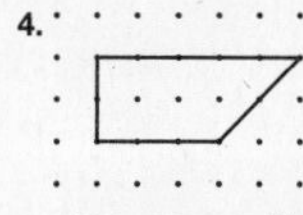
8 square units
5. 8 square units
6. 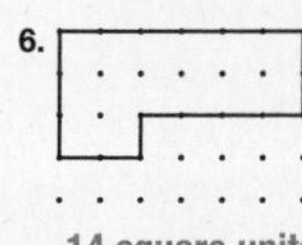
14 square units

7. Order the figures from least to greatest area. B, D, A, C

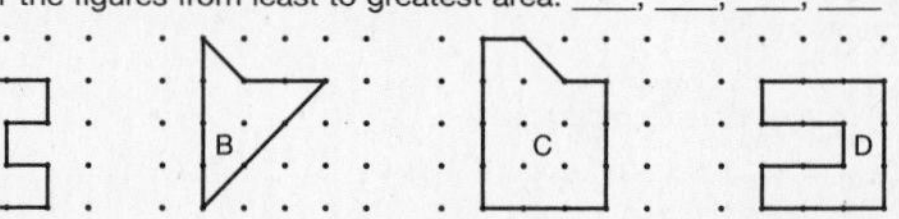

On dot paper below, draw a polygon with each area. Possible answers:

8. 6 square units
9. 7 square units
10. $4\frac{1}{2}$ square units

Check students' drawings.

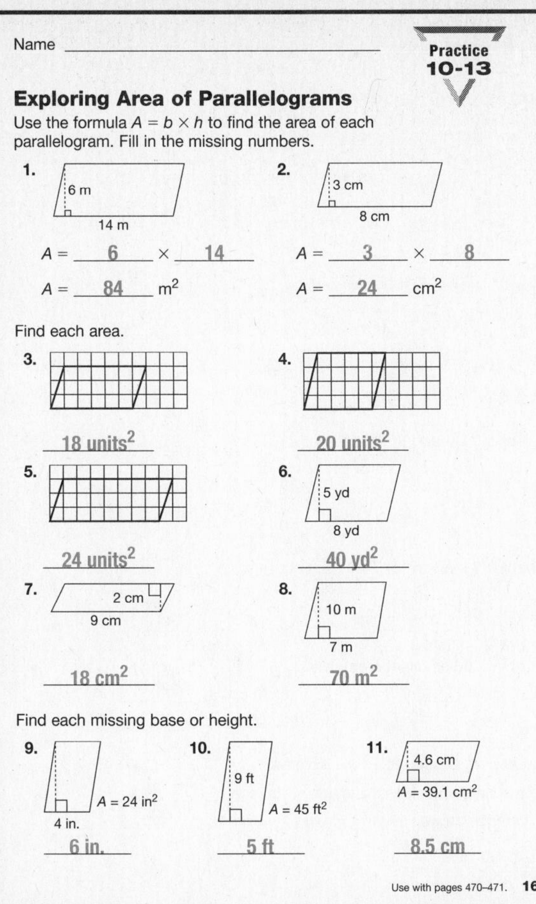

Name ____________________

Practice 10-13

Exploring Area of Parallelograms

Use the formula $A = b \times h$ to find the area of each parallelogram. Fill in the missing numbers.

1. 6 m, 14 m

$A =$ 6 $\times$ 14

$A =$ 84 m^2

2. 3 cm, 8 cm

$A =$ 3 $\times$ 8

$A =$ 24 cm^2

Find each area.

3. 18 $units^2$

4. 20 $units^2$

5. 24 $units^2$

6. 5 yd, 8 yd — 40 yd^2

7. 2 cm, 9 cm — 18 cm^2

8. 10 m, 7 m — 70 m^2

Find each missing base or height.

9. $A = 24$ in^2, 4 in. — 6 in.

10. 9 ft, $A = 45$ ft^2 — 5 ft

11. 4.6 cm, $A = 39.1$ cm^2 — 8.5 cm

Use with pages 470–471. 169

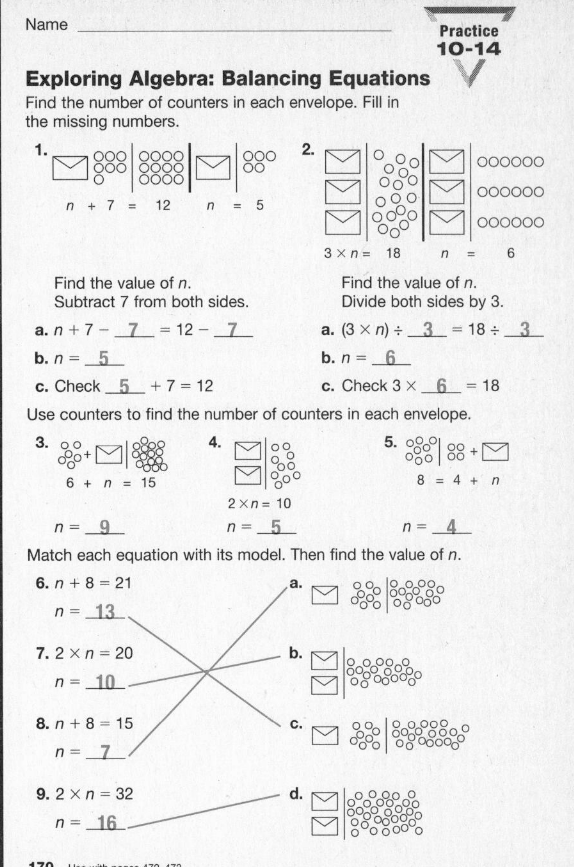

Name ____________________

Practice 10-14

Exploring Algebra: Balancing Equations

Find the number of counters in each envelope. Fill in the missing numbers.

1. $n + 7 = 12 \quad n = 5$

2. $3 \times n = 18 \quad n = 6$

Find the value of n.
Subtract 7 from both sides.

a. $n + 7 -$ 7 $= 12 -$ 7

b. $n =$ 5

c. Check 5 $+ 7 = 12$

Find the value of n.
Divide both sides by 3.

a. $(3 \times n) \div$ 3 $= 18 \div$ 3

b. $n =$ 6

c. Check $3 \times$ 6 $= 18$

Use counters to find the number of counters in each envelope.

3. $6 + n = 15$ — $n =$ 9

4. $2 \times n = 10$ — $n =$ 5

5. $8 = 4 + n$ — $n =$ 4

Match each equation with its model. Then find the value of n.

6. $n + 8 = 21$, $n =$ 13

7. $2 \times n = 20$, $n =$ 10

8. $n + 8 = 15$, $n =$ 7

9. $2 \times n = 32$, $n =$ 16

a. b. c. d.

170 Use with pages 472–473.

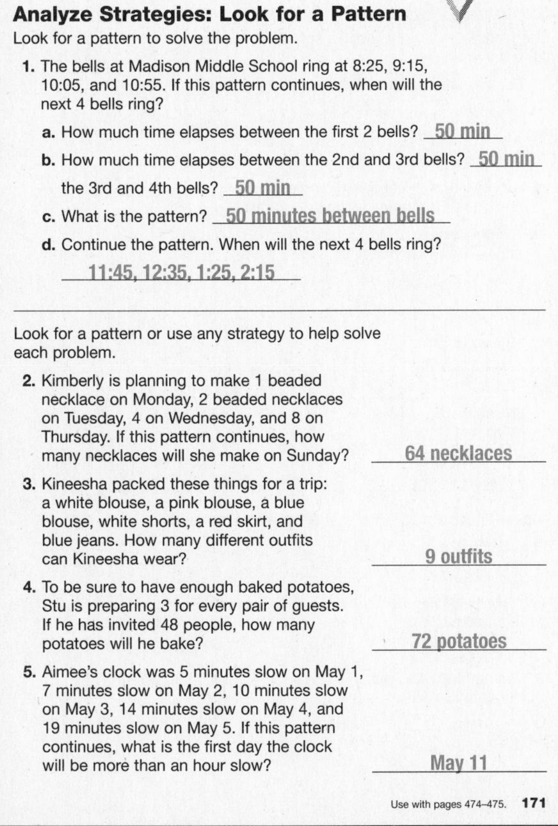

Name ____________________

Practice 10-15

Analyze Strategies: Look for a Pattern

Look for a pattern to solve the problem.

1. The bells at Madison Middle School ring at 8:25, 9:15, 10:05, and 10:55. If this pattern continues, when will the next 4 bells ring?
   a. How much time elapses between the first 2 bells? 50 min
   b. How much time elapses between the 2nd and 3rd bells? 50 min
   the 3rd and 4th bells? 50 min
   c. What is the pattern? 50 minutes between bells
   d. Continue the pattern. When will the next 4 bells ring?
   11:45, 12:35, 1:25, 2:15

Look for a pattern or use any strategy to help solve each problem.

2. Kimberly is planning to make 1 beaded necklace on Monday, 2 beaded necklaces on Tuesday, 4 on Wednesday, and 8 on Thursday. If this pattern continues, how many necklaces will she make on Sunday? 64 necklaces
3. Kineesha packed these things for a trip: a white blouse, a pink blouse, a blue blouse, white shorts, a red skirt, and blue jeans. How many different outfits can Kineesha wear? 9 outfits
4. To be sure to have enough baked potatoes, Stu is preparing 3 for every pair of guests. If he has invited 48 people, how many potatoes will he bake? 72 potatoes
5. Aimee's clock was 5 minutes slow on May 1, 7 minutes slow on May 2, 10 minutes slow on May 3, 14 minutes slow on May 4, and 19 minutes slow on May 5. If this pattern continues, what is the first day the clock will be more than an hour slow? May 11

Use with pages 474–475. 171

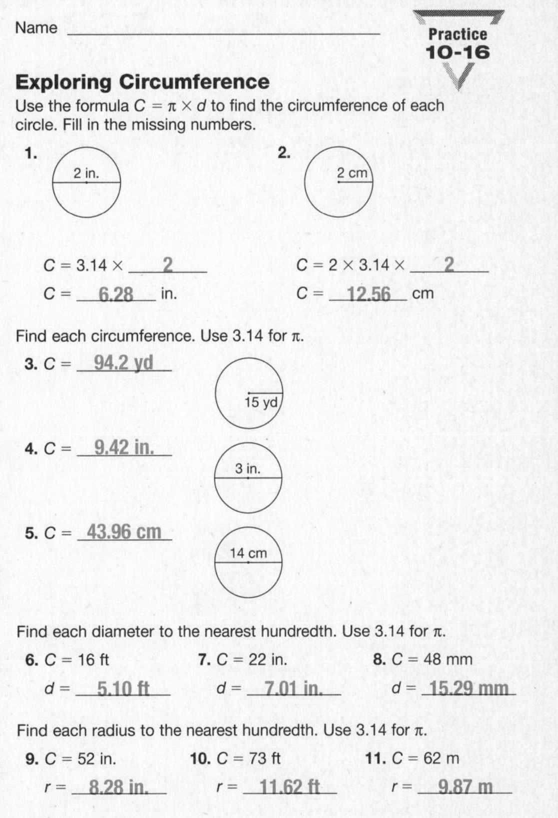

Name ____________________

Practice 10-16

Exploring Circumference

Use the formula $C = \pi \times d$ to find the circumference of each circle. Fill in the missing numbers.

1. 2 in.

$C = 3.14 \times$ 2

$C =$ 6.28 in.

2. 2 cm

$C = 2 \times 3.14 \times$ 2

$C =$ 12.56 cm

Find each circumference. Use 3.14 for π.

3. $C =$ 94.2 yd (15 yd)

4. $C =$ 9.42 in. (3 in.)

5. $C =$ 43.96 cm (14 cm)

Find each diameter to the nearest hundredth. Use 3.14 for π.

6. $C = 16$ ft, $d =$ 5.10 ft
7. $C = 22$ in., $d =$ 7.01 in.
8. $C = 48$ mm, $d =$ 15.29 mm

Find each radius to the nearest hundredth. Use 3.14 for π.

9. $C = 52$ in., $r =$ 8.28 in.
10. $C = 73$ ft, $r =$ 11.62 ft
11. $C = 62$ m, $r =$ 9.87 m

172 Use with pages 476–477.

Name ______________________

Practice
Chapter 10
Section C

Review and Practice

Vocabulary Draw an example of each on a separate sheet of paper.

1. diameter **2.** radius **3.** height of a triangle

Check students' drawings.

(Lessons 10–13) Find the area of each figure.

4. 5 square units

5. 3.1 cm, 6 cm — 9.3 cm^2

6. 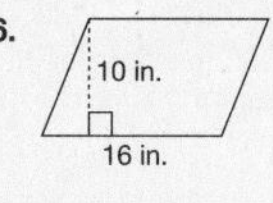

160 in^2

(Lesson 14) Find the value of *n*. You may use counters to help.

7. $n + 8 = 11$ $n =$ 3

8. $5 + n = 13$ $n =$ 8

(Lesson 16) Find each circumference. Use 3.14 for π.

9. 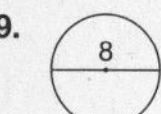

$C =$ 25.12

10. 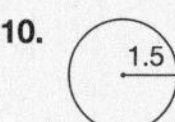

$C =$ 9.42

11. 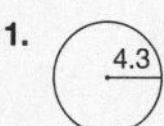

$C =$ 27.004

(Mixed Review) Divide.

12. $7\overline{)945}$ 135 **13.** $6\overline{)735}$ 122 R3 **14.** $5\overline{)862}$ 172 R2

Use with page 478. 173

Name ______________________

Practice
Chapters 3–10

Cumulative Review

(Chapter 3 Lesson 13) Find each product. Round to the nearest cent where necessary.

1. 16.2×2.4 = 38.88 **2.** $\$38.15 \times 5.7$ = \$217.46 **3.** $\$4.02 \times 53$ = \$213.06 **4.** 3.041×7.8 = 23.7198

(Chapter 8 Lesson 15) Complete.

5. 6 yd = 18 ft

6. 9 ft 3 in. = 111 in.

7. 28 in. = 2 ft 4 in.

8. 133 in. 11 ft 1 in.

(Chapter 9 Lesson 5) Find each product.

9. $\frac{3}{4} \times \frac{2}{7} = \frac{3}{14}$ **10.** $\frac{2}{3} \times \frac{9}{21} = \frac{2}{7}$

11. $\frac{3}{8} \times \frac{8}{7} = \frac{3}{7}$ **12.** $\frac{6}{10} \times \frac{20}{30} = \frac{2}{5}$

(Chapter 9 Lesson 10) Find each quotient.

13. $6 \div \frac{1}{2} =$ 12 **14.** $9 \div \frac{1}{4} =$ 36

15. $15 \div \frac{1}{3} =$ 45 **16.** $8 \div \frac{1}{10} =$ 80

(Chapter 10 Lesson 4) Complete.

17. 38 mm = 3.8 cm **18.** 18 cm = 180 mm

19. 9.3 m = 930 cm **20.** 472 cm = 4.72 m

(Chapter 10 Lesson 8) Find each area.

21. a square with sides that measure 12 feet 144 ft^2

22. a rectangle with length 1.5 m and width 5 m 7.5 m^2

174 Use with page 483.

Name ______________________

Practice
11-1

Exploring Solids

Complete the table comparing a pyramid and a prism.

	Solid	Number of Bases	Shape of Side Faces
1.		1	triangle
2.		2	rectangle

Write the name of the solid suggested in each drawing.

3. 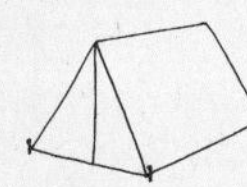
triangular prism

4. 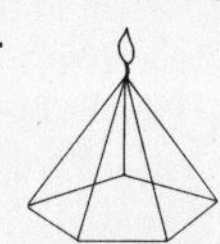
pentagonal pyramid

5. 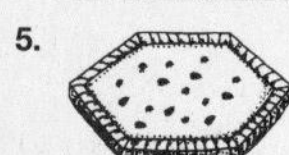
hexagonal prism

6. 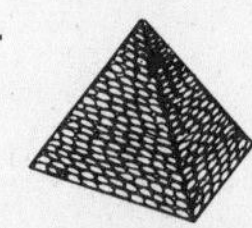
rectangular pyramid

Decide if each statement is true *always*, *sometimes*, or *never*.

7. A pyramid has 2 bases. never

8. A prism has 2 bases. always

9. A pyramid has 4 faces. sometimes

10. A pentagonal pyramid has 5 triangular faces. always

11. A triangular prism has 3 square faces. sometimes

12. The side faces of a pyramid are triangles. always

Use with pages 488–489. 175

Name ______________________

Practice
11-2

Exploring Patterns with Solids

Complete the rule you discovered for prisms. Then solve the problems.

1. For any prism, number of faces + number of vertices = number of edges + 2.

2. A pentagonal prism has 7 faces and 10 vertices. How many edges does it have? 15

3. An octagonal prism has 16 vertices and 24 edges. How many faces does it have? 10

4. A hexagonal prism has 8 faces and 18 edges. How many vertices does it have? 12

5. Complete the table.

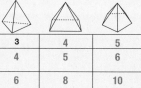

Pyramid			
Edges of Base	3	4	5
Number of Vertices	4	5	6
Total Number of Edges	6	8	10

Decide if each statement is true or false.

6. A hexagonal pyramid has a total of 13 edges. false

7. A pyramid with 7 edges on its base has a total of 14 edges. true

8. The number of edges on the base of a pyramid is twice the total number of edges. false

176 Use with pages 490–491.

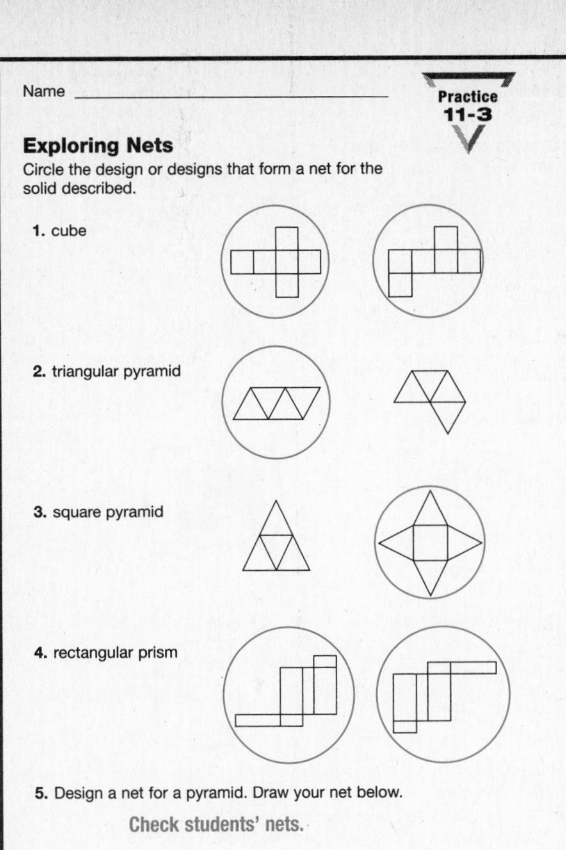

Name ____________________

Practice 11-3

Exploring Nets

Circle the design or designs that form a net for the solid described.

1. cube

2. triangular pyramid

3. square pyramid

4. rectangular prism

5. Design a net for a pyramid. Draw your net below.

Check students' nets.

Use with pages 492–493. **177**

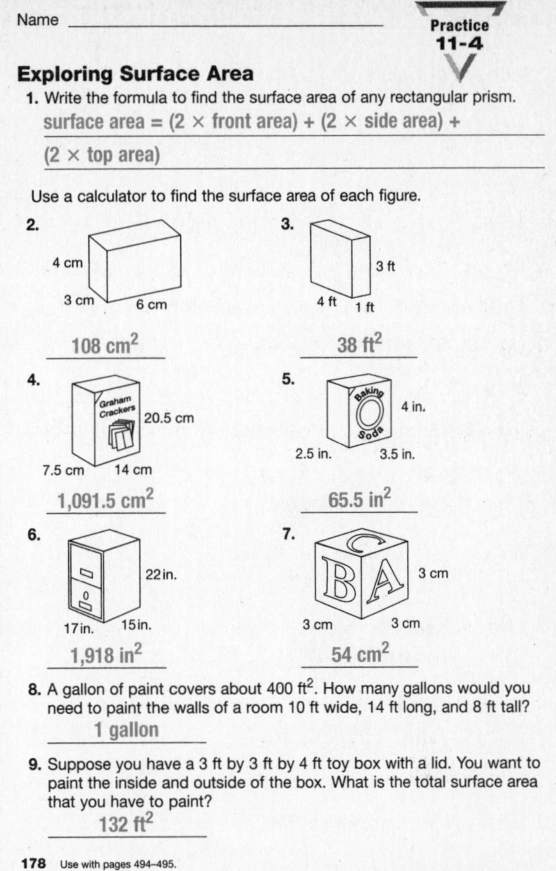

Name ____________________

Practice 11-4

Exploring Surface Area

1. Write the formula to find the surface area of any rectangular prism.

surface area = (2 × front area) + (2 × side area) + (2 × top area)

Use a calculator to find the surface area of each figure.

2.

108 cm^2

3.

38 ft^2

4.

$1{,}091.5 \text{ cm}^2$

5.

65.5 in^2

6.

$1{,}918 \text{ in}^2$

7.

54 cm^2

8. A gallon of paint covers about 400 ft^2. How many gallons would you need to paint the walls of a room 10 ft wide, 14 ft long, and 8 ft tall?

1 gallon

9. Suppose you have a 3 ft by 3 ft by 4 ft toy box with a lid. You want to paint the inside and outside of the box. What is the total surface area that you have to paint?

132 ft^2

178 Use with pages 494–495.

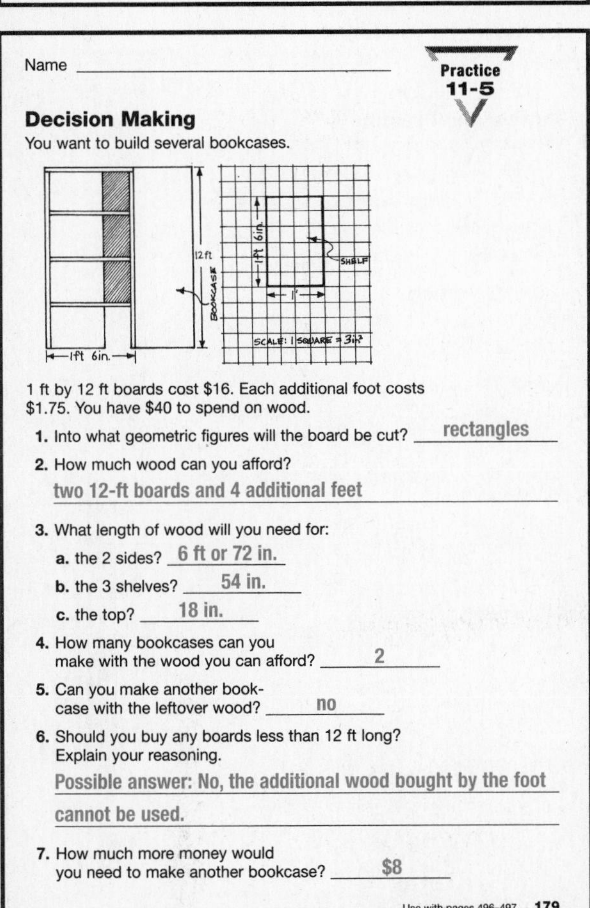

Name ____________________

Practice 11-5

Decision Making

You want to build several bookcases.

1 ft by 12 ft boards cost \$16. Each additional foot costs \$1.75. You have \$40 to spend on wood.

1. Into what geometric figures will the board be cut? rectangles

2. How much wood can you afford?

two 12-ft boards and 4 additional feet

3. What length of wood will you need for:

a. the 2 sides? 6 ft or 72 in.

b. the 3 shelves? 54 in.

c. the top? 18 in.

4. How many bookcases can you make with the wood you can afford? 2

5. Can you make another bookcase with the leftover wood? no

6. Should you buy any boards less than 12 ft long? Explain your reasoning.

Possible answer: No, the additional wood bought by the foot cannot be used.

7. How much more money would you need to make another bookcase? \$8

Use with pages 496–497. **179**

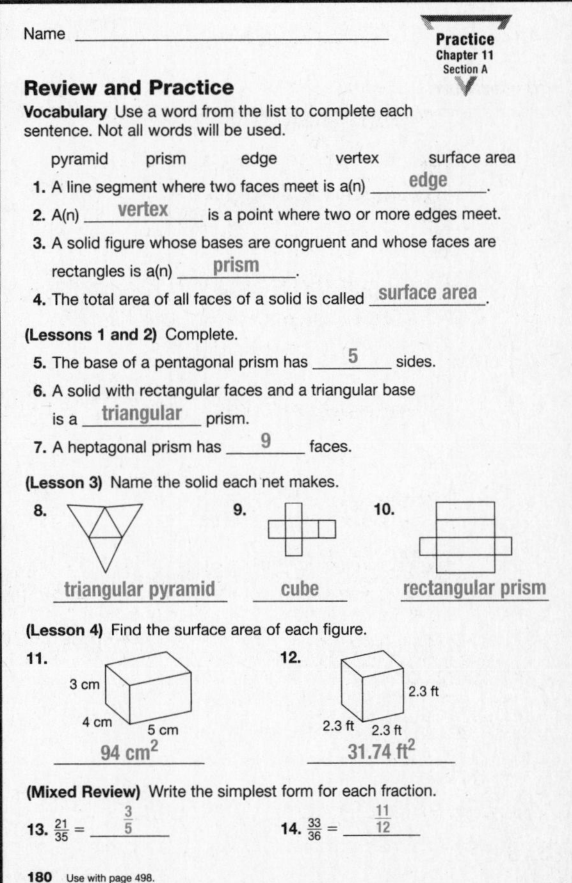

Name ____________________

Practice Chapter 11 Section A

Review and Practice

Vocabulary Use a word from the list to complete each sentence. Not all words will be used.

pyramid prism edge vertex surface area

1. A line segment where two faces meet is a(n) edge.

2. A(n) vertex is a point where two or more edges meet.

3. A solid figure whose bases are congruent and whose faces are rectangles is a(n) prism.

4. The total area of all faces of a solid is called surface area.

(Lessons 1 and 2) Complete.

5. The base of a pentagonal prism has 5 sides.

6. A solid with rectangular faces and a triangular base is a triangular prism.

7. A heptagonal prism has 9 faces.

(Lesson 3) Name the solid each net makes.

8. triangular pyramid

9. cube

10. rectangular prism

(Lesson 4) Find the surface area of each figure.

11.

94 cm^2

12.

31.74 ft^2

(Mixed Review) Write the simplest form for each fraction.

13. $\frac{21}{35} = \frac{3}{5}$

14. $\frac{33}{36} = \frac{11}{12}$

180 Use with page 498.

Name ______________________

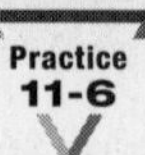
Practice 11-6

Ounces, Pounds, and Tons

Complete. Check the reasonableness of your answer.

1. 4 lb = 64 oz
2. 1 T = 2,000 lb
3. 6,000 lb = 3 T
4. 32 oz = 2 lb
5. 112 oz = 7 lb
6. 5 T = 10,000 lb
7. 5 lb 3 oz = 83 oz
8. 40 oz = 2 lb 8 oz
9. 3 T 21 lb = 6,021 lb
10. 100 oz = 6 lb 4 oz
11. 20,000 lb = 10 T
12. 4 T 100 lb = 8,100 lb
13. 9 lb 5 oz = 149 oz
14. 2,340 lb = 1 T 340 lb
15. 7 T 15 lb = 14,015 lb
16. 82 oz = 5 lb 2 oz

17. Which is less, 2 T or 2,600 lb? Explain.
2,600 lb; 2 × 2,000 lb = 4,000 lb

18. Which is less, 50 ounces or 4 lb? Explain.
50 oz; 4 × 16 oz = 64 oz

19. Which is greater, 3 T or 5,999 lb? Explain.
3 T; 3 × 2,000 lb = 6,000 lb

20. Which is greater, 5 lb 9 ounces or 90 ounces? Explain.
90 oz; 5 × 16 oz = 80, 80 + 9 = 89 oz

21. Estimate the number of pounds in 700 ounces. 35 to 45 lb

22. Estimate the number of tons in 19,680 pounds. 9.5 T or 10 T

Use with pages 500–501. 181

Name ______________________

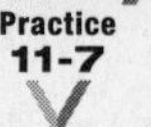
Practice 11-7

Grams and Kilograms

Use mental math to change to kilograms or grams.

1. 3 kg = 3,000 g
2. 2,500 g = 2.5 kg
3. 6.8 kg = 6,800 g
4. 4,301 g = 4.301 kg
5. 0.022 kg = 22 g
6. 1.542 kg = 1,542 g
7. 35,000 g = 35 kg
8. 89,901 g = 89.901 kg
9. 77 g = 0.077 kg
10. 100 kg = 100,000 g
11. 2.21 kg = 2,210 g
12. 2 g = 0.002 kg
13. 978 g = 0.978 kg
14. 6,082 g = 6.082 kg
15. 0.23 kg = 230 g
16. 20.4 kg = 20,400 g

17. How many kilograms?

227 g

0.227

18. How many grams?

15 kg

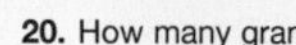
15,000

19. How many kilograms?

4.5 g

0.0045

20. How many grams?

12.35 kg

12,350

21. Apples cost $2.20 per kilogram. You need 500 g of apples to put in a fruit salad. How much money will you need to buy the apples?
$1.10

182 Use with pages 502–503.

Name ______________________

Practice 11-8

Temperature

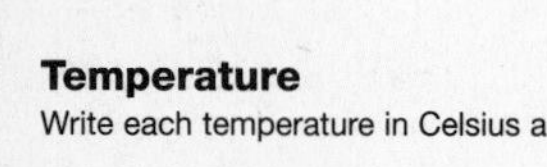

Write each temperature in Celsius and Fahrenheit.

1. 10°C and 50°F

2. 35°C and 95°F

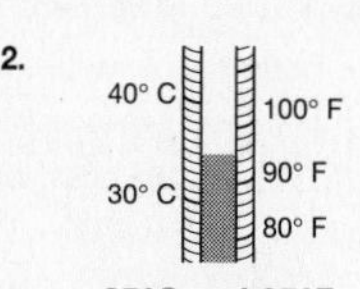

3. –20°C and –4°F

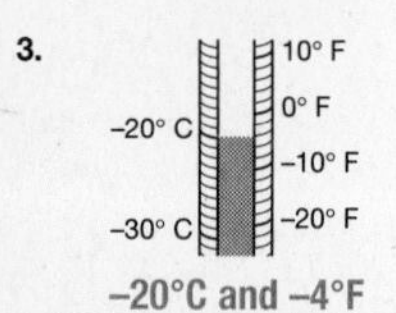

4. –10°C and 14°F

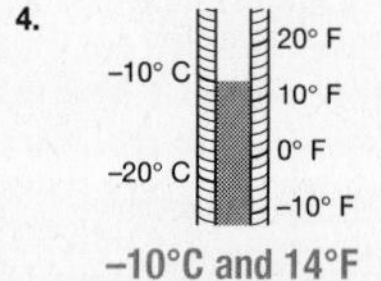

5. 5°C and 41°F

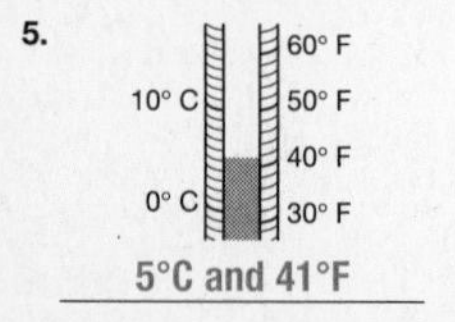

6. –5°C and 23°F

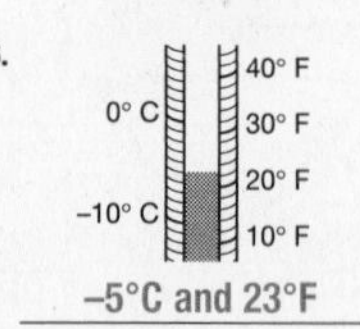

Find each change in temperature.

7. 22°C to 36°C 14°C
8. 18°F to 32°F 14°F
9. 40°F to 12°F 28°F
10. –2°C to –30°C 28°C
11. –5°C to 14°C 19°C
12. 86°F to 101°F 15°F

13. Which decrease in temperature would feel cooler: 35°C or 35°F? Explain.
35°C; because Celsius degrees are greater than Fahrenheit degrees

Use with pages 504–505. 183

Name ______________________

Practice Chapter 11 Section B

Review and Practice

Vocabulary Write true or false for each statement.

1. A ton is a unit of weight equal to 2,000 lb. true
2. A gram is a unit of mass equal to 1,000 kg. false
3. Water boils at 100° F and 212°C. false
4. There are 16 oz in one pound. true

(Lesson 6) Complete.

5. 80 oz = 5 lb
6. 8 T = 16,000 lb
7. 54 oz = 3 lb 6 oz
8. 31 lb = 496 oz

(Lesson 7) Complete.

9. 1.45 kg = 1,450 g
10. 34,980 g = 34.98 kg
11. 0.0008 kg = 0.8 g
12. 204 g = 0.204 kg

(Lesson 8) Use the thermometer to find each change in temperature.

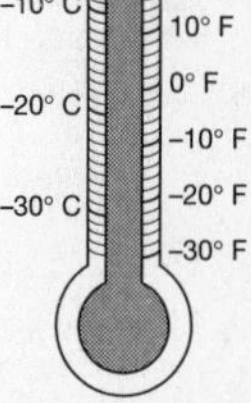

13. 35°C to 42°C 7°C
14. 32°F to –4°F 36°F
15. –7°C to 15°C 22°C
16. 50°F to 83°F 33°F
17. 18°F to 37°F 19°F
18. 28°C to –1°C 29°C

(Mixed Review) Find each product or quotient.

19. 819 × 26 = 21,294
20. 271 × 38 = 10,298
21. 358 × 46 = 16,468

22. 16)58 = 3 R10
23. 12)37 = 3 R1
24. 15)72 = 4 R12

184 Use with page 506.

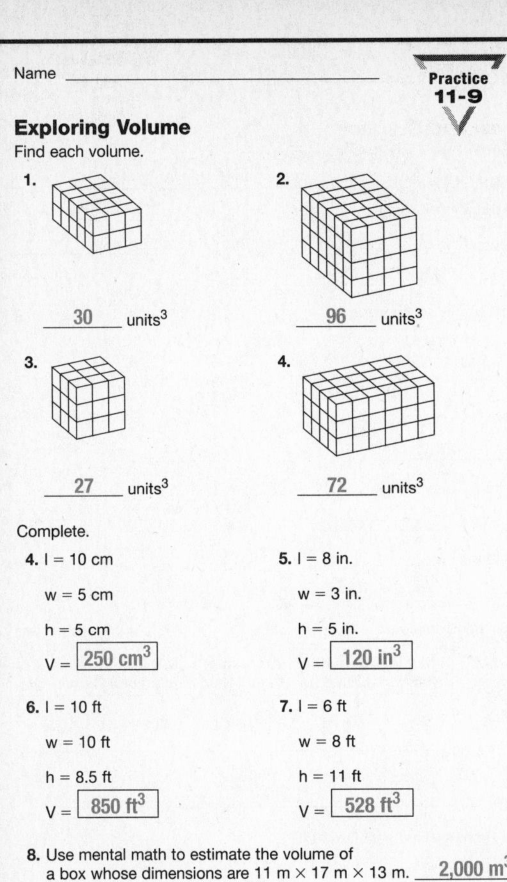

Name ____________________

Practice 11-9

Exploring Volume

Find each volume.

1. 30 units^3

2. 96 units^3

3. 27 units^3

4. 72 units^3

Complete.

4. l = 10 cm
w = 5 cm
h = 5 cm
V = 250 cm^3

5. l = 8 in.
w = 3 in.
h = 5 in.
V = 120 in^3

6. l = 10 ft
w = 10 ft
h = 8.5 ft
V = 850 ft^3

7. l = 6 ft
w = 8 ft
h = 11 ft
V = 528 ft^3

8. Use mental math to estimate the volume of a box whose dimensions are 11 m × 17 m × 13 m. 2,000 m^3

Use with pages 508–509. 185

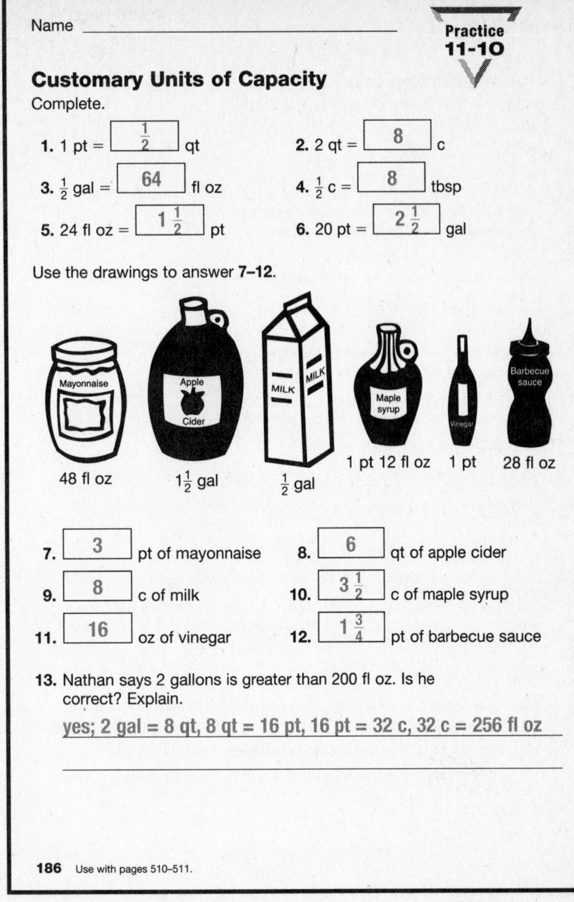

Name ____________________

Practice 11-10

Customary Units of Capacity

Complete.

1. 1 pt = $\frac{1}{2}$ qt
2. 2 qt = 8 c
3. $\frac{1}{2}$ gal = 64 fl oz
4. $\frac{1}{2}$ c = 8 tbsp
5. 24 fl oz = $1\frac{1}{2}$ pt
6. 20 pt = $2\frac{1}{2}$ gal

Use the drawings to answer **7–12**.

7. 3 pt of mayonnaise
8. 6 qt of apple cider
9. 8 c of milk
10. $3\frac{1}{2}$ c of maple syrup
11. 16 oz of vinegar
12. $1\frac{3}{4}$ pt of barbecue sauce

13. Nathan says 2 gallons is greater than 200 fl oz. Is he correct? Explain.
yes; 2 gal = 8 qt, 8 qt = 16 pt, 16 pt = 32 c, 32 c = 256 fl oz

186 Use with pages 510–511.

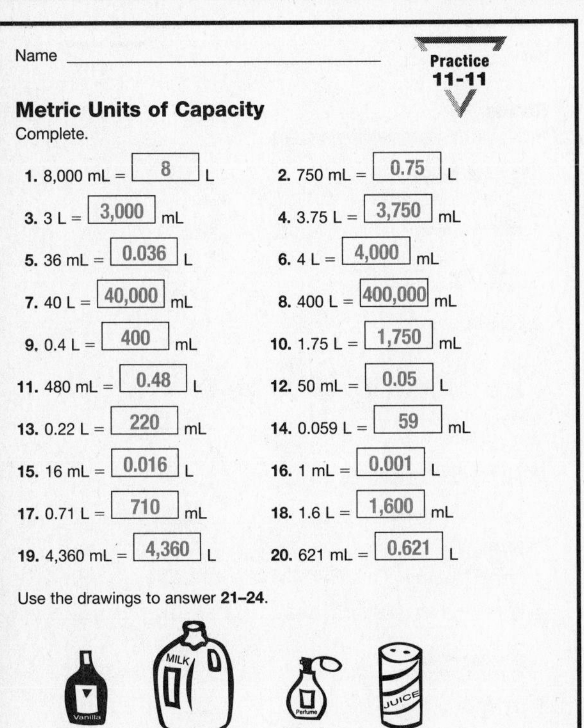

Name ____________________

Practice 11-11

Metric Units of Capacity

Complete.

1. 8,000 mL = 8 L
2. 750 mL = 0.75 L
3. 3 L = 3,000 mL
4. 3.75 L = 3,750 mL
5. 36 mL = 0.036 L
6. 4 L = 4,000 mL
7. 40 L = 40,000 mL
8. 400 L = 400,000 mL
9. 0.4 L = 400 mL
10. 1.75 L = 1,750 mL
11. 480 mL = 0.48 L
12. 50 mL = 0.05 L
13. 0.22 L = 220 mL
14. 0.059 L = 59 mL
15. 16 mL = 0.016 L
16. 1 mL = 0.001 L
17. 0.71 L = 710 mL
18. 1.6 L = 1,600 mL
19. 4,360 mL = 4,360 L
20. 621 mL = 0.621 L

Use the drawings to answer **21–24**.

21. 3,500 mL of milk
22. 250 mL of juice
23. 0.050 L of perfume
24. 0.075 L of vanilla

Use with pages 512–513. 187

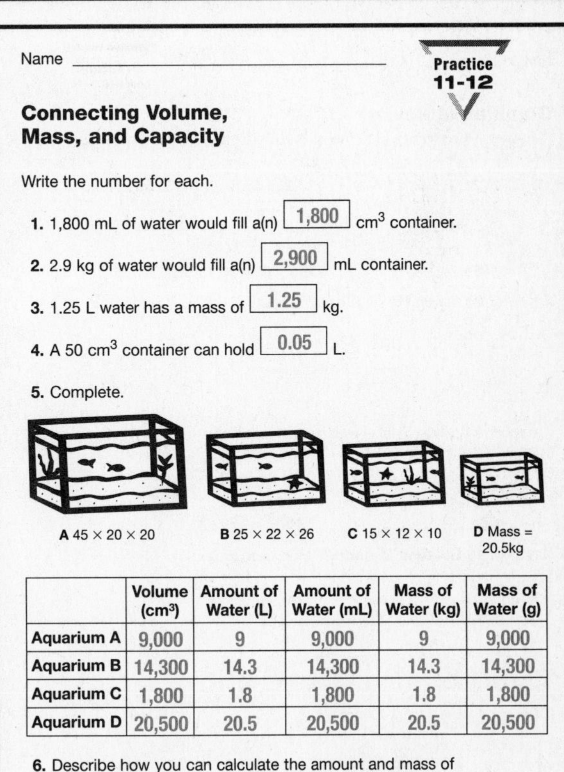

Name ____________________

Practice 11-12

Connecting Volume, Mass, and Capacity

Write the number for each.

1. 1,800 mL of water would fill a(n) 1,800 cm^3 container.
2. 2.9 kg of water would fill a(n) 2,900 mL container.
3. 1.25 L water has a mass of 1.25 kg.
4. A 50 cm^3 container can hold 0.05 L.
5. Complete.

	Volume (cm³)	Amount of Water (L)	Amount of Water (mL)	Mass of Water (kg)	Mass of Water (g)
Aquarium A	9,000	9	9,000	9	9,000
Aquarium B	14,300	14.3	14,300	14.3	14,300
Aquarium C	1,800	1.8	1,800	1.8	1,800
Aquarium D	20,500	20.5	20,500	20.5	20,500

6. Describe how you can calculate the amount and mass of water an aquarium can hold if you know its dimensions.
Find its volume in cm^3. Then convert cm^3 to grams.

188 Use with pages 514–515.

Name ______________________

Compare Strategies: Solve a Simpler Problem/Draw a Picture

Use Solve a Simpler Problem to solve the problem.

1. Mr. Mansfield likes to make pancakes for visitors. His basic recipe makes enough for 2 adults and 1 child. The recipe calls for 2 cups of flour and 2 eggs. Mr. Mansfield wants to know how much flour he needs to make pancakes for 10 adults and 5 children.
   a. How much flour will he need to make pancakes for 4 adults and 2 children? 4 cups flour
   b. How much flour will he need to make pancakes for 6 adults and 3 children? 6 cups flour
   c. How many people could he serve if he used 8 cups of flour? 8 adults and 4 children
   d. How much flour will he need to make pancakes for 10 adults and 5 children? 10 cups flour
   e. Describe the pattern you see.
   Possible answer: The number of cups of flour needed equals the number of adults served and twice as much as the number of children served.

Use Solve a Simpler Problem or any strategy to solve each problem.

2. Regina plants her tomato garden in rows of 6 and labels her plants with letters of the alphabet. For example, the plants in the first row were labeled A–F. In which row is plant W located?
   4th row
3. Mrs. Maynor has an interesting doll collection. Half of her dolls are baby dolls and $\frac{2}{3}$ of these are antique. The other half are fashion and rag dolls. All 15 of her fashion dolls are quite new but they only make up $\frac{1}{10}$ of the collection. How many antique baby dolls does she have?
   50

Name ______________________

Practice
Chapter 11
Section C

Review and Practice

Vocabulary Write a definition for each word.

1. mass Possible answer: the amount of matter that something contains
2. volume Possible answer: the number of cubic units needed to fill an object

(Lesson 9) Find each volume.

3. 7 in., 4 in., 3 in. — 84 in^3
4. 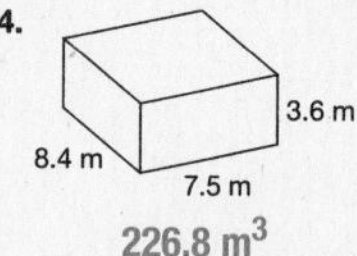

226.8 m^3

(Lessons 10 and 11) Complete.

5. 64 fl oz = 8 c
6. $6\frac{1}{2}$ gal = 52 pt
7. 10 tbsp = 5 fl oz
8. 48 fl oz = $1\frac{1}{2}$ qt
9. 0.5 L = 500 mL
10. 893 mL = 0.893 L

(Lesson 12) Complete.

11. (8 cm, 4 cm, 5 cm; Mass 4.6 kg)

Volume (cm^3)	Amount of Liquid (L)	Amount of Liquid (mL)	Mass of Liquid (kg)	Mass of Liquid (g)
160	0.16	160	0.16	160
4,600	4.6	4,600	4.6	4,600

(Mixed Review) Find each product.

12. $\frac{6}{9} \times \frac{5}{6} = \frac{5}{9}$
13. $\frac{8}{10} \times \frac{3}{4} = \frac{3}{5}$

Name ______________________

Cumulative Review

(Chapter 1 Lesson 4) Find the range, mode, and median for each set of data.

1. 6, 16, 21, 6, 17
   range 15
   mode 6
   median 16
2. 1.5, 10, 9.8, 6.2, 5.7, 3, 4.5
   range 8.5
   mode none
   median 5.7

(Chapter 2 Lesson 18) Find each difference.

3. $6.20 − 2.49 = $3.71
4. $34.00 − 5.75 = $28.25
5. $4.02 − 0.53 = $3.49
6. 3.41 − 1.88 = 1.53

(Chapter 9 Lesson 3) Use rounding, benchmarks, or compatible numbers to estimate each product.

7. $\frac{3}{4} \times 81$ 40–81
8. $3\frac{2}{7} \times 10$ 30–40
9. $1\frac{2}{3} \times 8$ 8–16
10. $\frac{5}{9} \times 22$ 11–22

(Chapter 10 Lessons 11 and 13) Find each area.

11. 8 cm, 24 cm — 192 cm^2
12. 1.4 mm, 2.3 mm — 3.22 mm^2
13. 18 ft, 5 ft — 45 ft^2

(Chapter 11 Lesson 7) Complete.

14. 385 kg = 385,000 g
15. 68 g = 0.068 kg
16. 19.3 kg = 19,300 g
17. 6,472 g = 6.472 kg

(Chapter 11 Lesson 8) Find each change in temperature.

18. 27°C to 8°C 19°C
19. 18°F to −7°F 25°F
20. −5°C to 19°C 24°C
21. 82°F to 45°F 37°F

Name ______________________

Practice
12-1

Ratios

Write each ratio in three ways. Simplify.

1. cats to kittens 2 to 3 2:3 $\frac{2}{3}$

2. puppies to dogs 2 to 1 2:1 $\frac{2}{1}$
3. rabbits to bunnies 3 to 5 3:5 $\frac{3}{5}$

4. chicks to chickens 3 to 1 3:1 $\frac{3}{1}$
5. large fish to small fish 1 to 5 1:5 $\frac{1}{5}$
6. ducklings to ducks 5 to 2 5:2 $\frac{5}{2}$
7. Which shows the ratio 1:2? A 1:3? C
   A. frogs to tadpoles B. tadpoles to frogs C. frogs to tadpoles

Name ______________________

Practice 12-2

Patterns in Ratio Tables

Complete.

1.

7	14	21	28	35
8	16	24	32	40

2.

3	6	9	12	15
5	10	15	20	25

3.

5	10	15	20	25
6	12	18	24	30

4.

4	8	12	16	20
10	20	30	40	50

5.

2	4	6	8	10
9	18	27	36	45

6.

7	14	21	28	35
11	22	33	44	55

7. In a game, each player gets 3 letter cubes. Complete the ratio table that shows how many letter cubes for 2, 3, 4, 5, or 6 players.

Number of Players	2	3	4	5	6
Number of Cubes	6	9	12	15	18

8. A table of equal ratios includes $\frac{10}{35}$.
   a. Name another ratio in the table. Possible answer: $\frac{2}{7}$
   b. Write a proportion for these ratios. Possible answer: $\frac{10}{35} = \frac{2}{7}$

9. A table of equal ratios includes $\frac{12}{18}$.
   a. Name another ratio in the table. Possible answer: $\frac{2}{3}$
   b. Write a proportion for these ratios. Possible answer: $\frac{12}{18} = \frac{2}{3}$

Name ______________________

Practice 12-3

Exploring Equal Ratios

Complete.

1. This graph shows two ordered pairs of equal ratios. Name the ratio it shows. $\frac{1}{2}$ and $\frac{2}{4}$

2. Plot another ratio on the graph that is equal to the others. Name the ratio. Possible answer: $\frac{4}{8}$

Use grid paper. Plot the ordered pairs from each ratio table on the graph.

3.

4	8	12	16	20
3	6	9	12	15

4.

1	2	3	4	5
3	6	9	12	15

Plot a set of equal ratios on each graph. Possible answers:

5.

6.

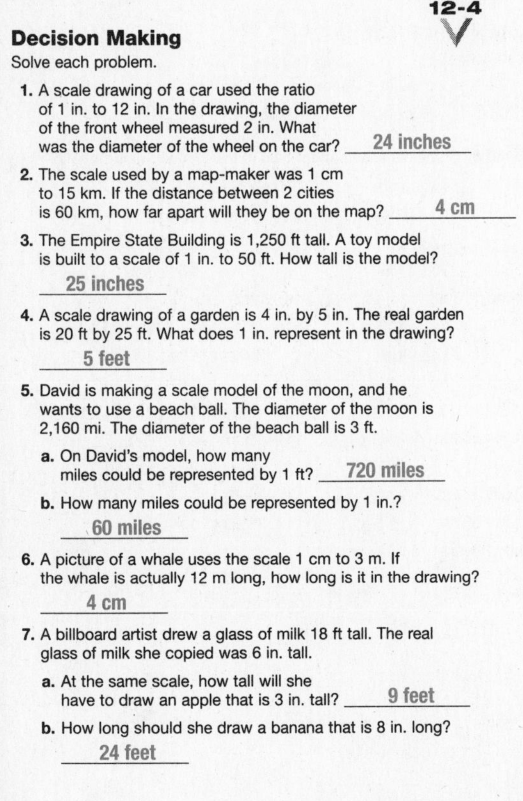

Name ______________________

Practice 12-4

Decision Making

Solve each problem.

1. A scale drawing of a car used the ratio of 1 in. to 12 in. In the drawing, the diameter of the front wheel measured 2 in. What was the diameter of the wheel on the car? 24 inches
2. The scale used by a map-maker was 1 cm to 15 km. If the distance between 2 cities is 60 km, how far apart will they be on the map? 4 cm
3. The Empire State Building is 1,250 ft tall. A toy model is built to a scale of 1 in. to 50 ft. How tall is the model? 25 inches
4. A scale drawing of a garden is 4 in. by 5 in. The real garden is 20 ft by 25 ft. What does 1 in. represent in the drawing? 5 feet
5. David is making a scale model of the moon, and he wants to use a beach ball. The diameter of the moon is 2,160 mi. The diameter of the beach ball is 3 ft.
   a. On David's model, how many miles could be represented by 1 ft? 720 miles
   b. How many miles could be represented by 1 in.? 60 miles
6. A picture of a whale uses the scale 1 cm to 3 m. If the whale is actually 12 m long, how long is it in the drawing? 4 cm
7. A billboard artist drew a glass of milk 18 ft tall. The real glass of milk she copied was 6 in. tall.
   a. At the same scale, how tall will she have to draw an apple that is 3 in. tall? 9 feet
   b. How long should she draw a banana that is 8 in. long? 24 feet

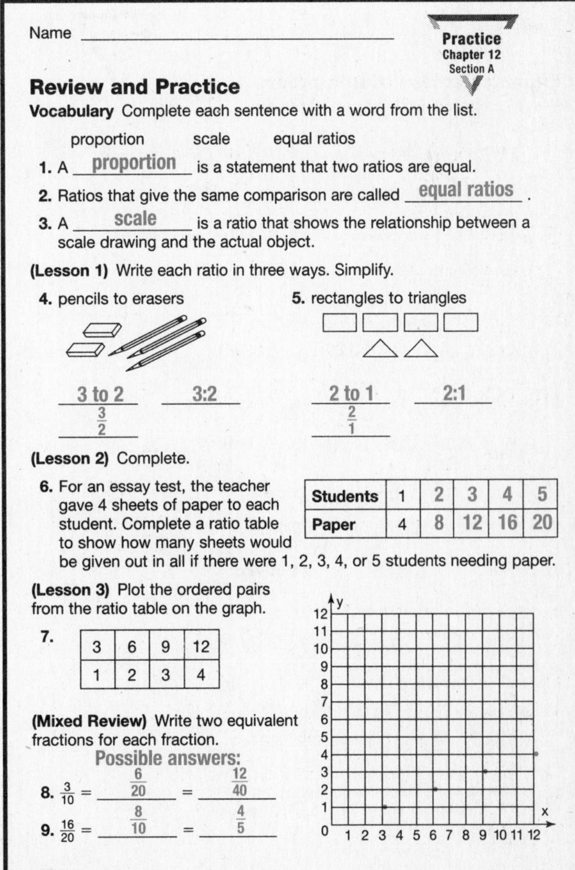

Name ______________________

Practice Chapter 12 Section A

Review and Practice

Vocabulary Complete each sentence with a word from the list.

proportion   scale   equal ratios

1. A proportion is a statement that two ratios are equal.
2. Ratios that give the same comparison are called equal ratios.
3. A scale is a ratio that shows the relationship between a scale drawing and the actual object.

(Lesson 1) Write each ratio in three ways. Simplify.

4. pencils to erasers: 3 to 2, 3:2, $\frac{3}{2}$
5. rectangles to triangles: 2 to 1, 2:1, $\frac{2}{1}$

(Lesson 2) Complete.

6. For an essay test, the teacher gave 4 sheets of paper to each student. Complete a ratio table to show how many sheets would be given out in all if there were 1, 2, 3, 4, or 5 students needing paper.

Students	1	2	3	4	5
Paper	4	8	12	16	20

(Lesson 3) Plot the ordered pairs from the ratio table on the graph.

7.

3	6	9	12
1	2	3	4

(Mixed Review) Write two equivalent fractions for each fraction. Possible answers:

8. $\frac{3}{10} = \frac{6}{20} = \frac{12}{40}$
9. $\frac{16}{20} = \frac{8}{10} = \frac{4}{5}$

Name ____________________

Practice 12-5

Exploring Percent Patterns

1. Use the table to help you complete these sentences.
   a. Equivalents of tenths are multiples of __10__ %.
   b. Equivalents of fifths are multiples of __20__ %.
   c. Equivalents of halves are multiples of __50__ %.

Halves	Fifths	Tenths	Percents
		$\frac{1}{10}$	10%
	$\frac{1}{5}$	$\frac{2}{10}$	20%
		$\frac{3}{10}$	30%
	$\frac{2}{5}$	$\frac{4}{10}$	40%
$\frac{1}{2}$		$\frac{5}{10}$	50%

Complete each pattern. You may use a calculator to help.

2. $\frac{1}{8}$ = __$12\frac{1}{2}$__ %
   $\frac{2}{8}$ = __25__ %
   $\frac{3}{8}$ = __$37\frac{1}{2}$__ %
   $\frac{4}{8}$ = __50__ %

3. $\frac{1}{4}$ = __25__ %
   $\frac{2}{4}$ = __50__ %
   $\frac{3}{4}$ = __75__ %
   $\frac{4}{4}$ = __100__ %

4. $\frac{1}{6}$ = __$16\frac{2}{3}$__ %
   $\frac{2}{6}$ = __$33\frac{1}{3}$__ %
   $\frac{3}{6}$ = __50__ %
   $\frac{4}{6}$ = __$66\frac{2}{3}$__ %

5. $\frac{1}{3}$ = __$33\frac{1}{3}$__ %
   $\frac{2}{3}$ = __$66\frac{2}{3}$__ %
   $\frac{3}{3}$ = __100__ %

6. Explain how knowing $\frac{1}{2}$ = 50% can help you to find the percent equivalent of $\frac{2}{4}$.
   $\frac{2}{4} = \frac{1}{2}$; so if $\frac{1}{2}$ = 50%, $\frac{2}{4}$ = 50%

Name ____________________

Practice 12-6

Estimating Percent of a Number

Estimate. Possible answers: Estimates may vary.

1. 76% of 80 __about 60__
2. 61% of 20 __about 12__
3. 30% of 32 __about 10 or 11__
4. $16\frac{2}{3}$% of 54 __about 9__
5. 22% of 40 __about 8__
6. 49% of 200 __about 100__
7. 64% of 60 __about 40__
8. 12.5% of 41 __about 4 or 5__
9. 27% of 99 __about 25__
10. 19% of 40 __about 8__
11. 75% of 82 __about 60__
12. 71% of 110 __about 75__
13. 42% of 105 __about 42 or 50__
14. 12.5% of 161 __about 20__
15. 67% of 20 __about 14__
16. 32% of 152 __about 50__

16. Explain how finding 25% of 160 can help you estimate 73% of 160.
    Possible answer: Find 25% and subtract it from 160 to find 75% (close to 73%) of 160.

17. Explain how finding $\frac{1}{6}$ of 18 can help you find $16\frac{2}{3}$% of 17.
    $16\frac{2}{3}$% equals $\frac{1}{6}$; 6 divides evenly into 18, so $16\frac{2}{3}$% of 17 is 3.

18. Amanda says she can use the benchmark $\frac{1}{4}$ to estimate the sale price of a hat that is 75% off. Explain how she can do this.
    25% of the original price is the sale price; 25% = $\frac{1}{4}$.

Name ____________________

Practice 12-7

Finding Percent of a Number

Choose a method. Find the percent of each.

1. 4% of 7.25 = __0.29__
2. 10% of 8 = __0.8__
3. 80% of \$8.20 = __\$6.56__
4. 45% of 800= __360__
5. 25% of 500 = __125__
6. 85% of 40 = __34__
7. 75% of 24 = __18__
8. 30% of \$89 = __\$26.70__
9. 8% of 64 = __5.12__
10. 12% of 450 = __54__
11. 65% of 720 = __468__
12. 50% of 126 = __63__
13. 5% of 800 = __40__
14. 15% of 200 = __30__
15. 23% of 400 = __92__
16. 6% of 10 = __0.6__
17. 95% of 575 = __546.25__
18. 53% of 120 = __63.6__
19. 48% of 82 = __39.36__
20. 25% of 280 = __70__
21. 80% of 650 = __520__
22. 30% of 400 = __120__

23. Since 30% of 60 = 18, 60% of 60 = __36__
    Explain. 60% is twice 30%; 36 is twice 18.

24. Since 80% of 45 = 36, 40% of 90 = __36__
    Explain. The percentage was halved, but the number was doubled, so the answer is the same.

25. If a percent of a number equals the number, what percent of the number was taken? __100%__

Name ____________________

Practice Chapter 12 Section B

Review and Practice

Vocabulary

1. Give 5 examples of common percent benchmarks.
   Possible answers: 1%, 10%, 25%, $33\frac{1}{3}$%, and 50%

(Lesson 5) Complete each pattern. You may use a calculator to help.

2. $\frac{6}{25}$ = __24__ %
   $\frac{7}{25}$ = __28__ %
   $\frac{8}{25}$ = __32__ %
   $\frac{9}{25}$ = __36__ %

3. $\frac{9}{20}$ = __45__ %
   $\frac{10}{20}$ = __50__ %
   $\frac{11}{20}$ = __55__ %
   $\frac{12}{20}$ = __60__ %

(Lesson 6) Estimate. Estimates may vary.

4. $33\frac{1}{3}$% of 70 __about 20__
5. 18% of 51 __about 10__
6. 11% of 99 __about 10__
7. 25% of 844 __about 211__

(Lesson 7) Find the percent of each.

8. 3% of 4.5 = __0.135__
9. 12% of 14 = __1.68__
10. 48% of \$50,000 = __\$24,000__
11. 1% of \$3.45= __\$0.03__
12. 90% of 83 = __74.7__
13. 7% of 24.8 = __1.736__
14. 15% of \$25.15 = __\$3.77__
15. 100% of 21 = __21__
16. 42% of 103 = __43.26__
17. 99% of 23 = __22.77__

(Mixed Review) Multiply or divide.

18. 256 × 3.41 = __872.96__
19. 509 × 4.87 = __2,478.83__
20. 360 × 13.9 = __5,004__
21. 35)469 __13 R14__
22. 83)8,597 __103 R48__
23. 21)\$2.31 __\$0.11__

Name ______________________

Practice 12-8

Exploring Fairness

Complete the table. Tell if the probability of the outcomes is equally likely or not. If the outcomes are not equal, tell which outcome is more likely. Then decide if the situation is fair or unfair.

	Situation	Probability of Outcome	Fairness
1.	Spin the spinner. Outcomes: 1, 3, 5, or 7	equally likely	fair
2.	Choose a coin. Outcomes: dime, quarter, or nickel	not equally likely Quarter is more likely.	unfair
3.	Draw a card. Outcomes: A or B	not equally likely B is more likely.	unfair
4.	Draw a card. Outcomes: odd or even	equally likely	fair

5. What are the possible outcomes of two spins of the spinner in **1**?
(1,1), (1,3), (1,5), (1,7), (3,1), (3,3), (3,5), (3,7), (5,1), (5,3), (5,5), (5,7), (7,1), (7,3), (7,5), (7,7)

6. Two cubes are painted red on 3 sides and blue on 3 sides. Tina and Charlene toss the cubes. Tina earns one point when both cubes land with one color up. Charlene earns one point if the cubes land with both colors up. Is this a fair game? Explain.
Yes; probability of (blue,blue) and (red,red) is the same as probability of (blue,red) and (red,blue).

7. Sam and Randy have a bag of marbles. There are 20 red marbles and 25 blue marbles. In turn, they reach into the bag without looking and take out 2 marbles. Sam earns one point if both marbles are the same color. Randy earns one point if the marbles are different colors. Is this a fair game? Explain.
No; there are more possible outcomes for Randy.

Name ______________________

Practice 12-9

Exploring Predicting from Samples

A bowl contains black beans, red beans, and white beans. The list shows the results of three samples.

Sample 1	11	black
	10	red
	4	white
Sample 2	8	black
	12	red
	5	white
Sample 3	15	black
	10	red

1. a. How many beans are there all together in the 3 samples? 75
   b. How many black beans were in the samples? 34
   c. How many red beans were in the samples? 32
   d. How many white beans were in the samples? 9
2. Predict the most common color bean. black
3. Predict the least common color bean. white
4. If sample 2 were the only sample, what color bean would you predict to be the most common? red

Three more samples (4, 5, 6) were taken.

Sample 4	5	black
	16	red
	4	white
Sample 5	16	black
	8	red
	1	white
Sample 6	7	black
	13	red
	5	white

5. In samples 4–6:
   a. What was the most common color bean? red
   b. What was the least common color bean? white
6. In samples 1–6 how many beans were:
   a. black 62 b. white 19 c. red 69
7. Describe the number of each color bean you think is in the bowl.
Possible answer: About the same number of black and red, and very few white

Name ______________________

Practice 12-10

Exploring Predicting from Experiments

Write the numbers 1, 3, 5, 7, and 9 twice, each on separate slips of paper. Put the slips of paper in a bag and use them to answer **1–7**.

1. Experiment to find how many different sums will occur by selecting 2 slips of paper. Actual answer: 9
2. Which do you think is more likely to occur; a sum of 10 or a sum of 4? Explain.
10; there are 5 outcomes with a sum of 10, but only 2 outcomes with a sum of 4.
3. Is the chance of getting an odd number sum certain, likely, equally likely as unlikely, or impossible? Explain.
impossible; the sum of 2 odd numbers is an even number.
4. Which 4 sums are least likely to occur? 2, 4, 16, 18
5. Name one sum that will never occur.
Possible answers: 0, 3, 17, 100
6. What do you think is more likely to occur when you take 2 slips of paper: getting 2 different numbers or 2 matching numbers? Explain.
2 different numbers; there are more different number outcomes than matching number outcomes.
7. Which do you think is more likely to occur; getting a sum less than 10 or a sum greater than or equal to 10? Explain.
sum greater than or equal to 10; there are 15 outcomes of 10 or greater and 10 outcomes less than 10.

Name ______________________

Practice 12-11

Analyzing Strategies: Make an Organized List

1. James won 4 trophies for sports. He won 1 each for soccer, football, basketball, and tennis. How many different ways can he arrange his trophies in a straight line on his bedroom shelf?
   a. Call the sports S, F, B, and T. List all the combinations if S is the first trophy on the shelf.
   SFBT, SBFT, STBF, STFB, SFTB, SBTF
   b. If F is first: FSBT, FSTB, FTSB, FTBS, FBTS, FBST
   c. If B is first: BSFT, BSTF, BTSF, BTFS, BFST, BFTS
   d. If T is first: TFSB, TFBS, TBFS, TBSF, TSBF, TSFB
   e. How many different ways can the trophies be arranged? 24
2. The next year, James wins another trophy for hockey. How many different ways can he arrange the 5 trophies?
120
3. The football team will choose 2 colors for their uniforms. They can choose white, red, blue, or gold. A red and white uniform is the same as a white and red uniform. How many color combinations can they choose?
6
4. The basketball team travels 26 miles from school to their game. They have been traveling for 20 minutes. When they travel 5 miles farther, they will be halfway there. How far have they traveled?
8 miles

Name ______________________

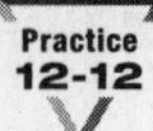

Expressing Probabilities as Fractions

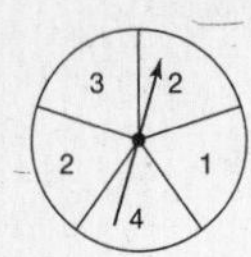

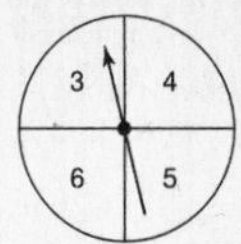

A quiz show contestant spins each spinner once and adds the numbers together. If the sum is 6 or 8, the contestant wins $100. If the sum is 4 or 10, the contestant wins $1,000.

Make tree diagrams to show the possible sums. Give the probability of each sum as a fraction. Simplify.

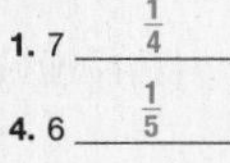

1. 7 $\frac{1}{4}$ 2. 4 $\frac{1}{20}$ 3. 5 $\frac{3}{20}$

4. 6 $\frac{1}{5}$ 5. 8 $\frac{1}{5}$ 6. 9 $\frac{1}{10}$

7. 10 $\frac{1}{20}$ 8. 6 or 8 $\frac{2}{5}$ 9. 4 or 10 $\frac{1}{10}$

10. What is the probability of getting a sum of 2? 0

11. What is the probability of gettting a sum of 4, 5, 6, 7, 8, 9, or 10? 1

12. Does the contestant have a greater chance of winning $100 or $1,000? $100

13. There are 3 red, 5 green, and 4 yellow marbles in a bag. Without looking, you choose one. Give the probability of choosing a marble of each color. Express as a fraction. Simplify.

a. red $\frac{1}{4}$ b. green $\frac{5}{12}$ c. yellow $\frac{1}{3}$

Name ______________________

Practice
12-13

Exploring Expected and Experimental Results

A bag contains 5 red markers, 3 blue markers, and 2 green markers.

1. If you select one marker without looking, what is the expected probability of getting:

a. a red marker? $\frac{1}{2}$ b. a blue marker? $\frac{3}{10}$

c. a green marker? $\frac{1}{5}$ d. a purple marker? 0

2. Suppose you select a marker, record its color, and put it back in the bag. If you repeat this 50 times, how many times would you expect to select:

a. a red marker? 25 times b. a blue marker? 15 times

c. a green marker? 10 times d. a pink marker? 0 times

Use the spinner to answer **3–6**. Decide whether each result is likely or unlikely.

3. Outcome: R
Trial: 36 spins
Result: Get R, 14 times
likely

4. Outcome: B
Trial: 300 spins
Result: Get B, 98 times
unlikely

5. Outcome: G
Trial: 120 spins
Result: Get G, 95 times
unlikely

6. Outcome: R or G
Trial: 200 spins
Result: Get R or G 95 times
likely

7. A 1–6 number cube is tossed 200 times. About how many times would a number greater than 3 be expected?
about 100 times

Name ______________________

Practice
Chapter 12
Section C

Review and Practice

Vocabulary Write a definition for each.

1. outcome a possible result in a probability experiment

2. probability the ratio of the number of ways an event can occur to the number of outcomes

(Lesson 8) Use the spinner to answer **3** and **4**. Write if each game is fair or unfair.

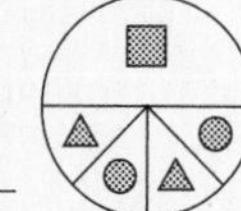

3. Player 1 gets 1 point if the spinner lands on a square. Player 2 gets 1 point if the spinner lands on a circle or a triangle. fair

4. Player 1 gets 1 point if the spinner lands on a square. Player 2 gets 1 point if the spinner lands on a triangle. unfair

(Lesson 9) A bag contains different numbers of the letters A, B, C, and D. Use the sample results to answer **5** and **6**.

Sample 1 Sample 2 Sample 3

5. Predict the most common letter in the bag. B

6. If Sample 1 were the only sample, what would you predict for the most common letter? A

(Lessons 10, 11, and 13) Give all the outcomes for the experiment. Write whether they are equally likely or not.

7. Choose one number from the bag.
4, 6, 9, 11, 15, 17, 21; equally likely

(Lesson 12) The numbers 1, 2, 7, 9, 12, and 13 are in a bag. Give the probability of each outcome as a fraction.

8. of pulling out an even number $\frac{1}{3}$

9. of pulling out an odd number $\frac{2}{3}$

(Mixed Review) Find each sum or difference.

10. 4.7 + 13.19 = 17.89 11. 51.8 − 27.36 = 24.44

Name ______________________

Cumulative Review

(Chapter 8 Lesson 13) Solve. Use any strategy.

1. Aaron gave half of his change to a friend. He then lost 5 cents. He had 50 cents left. How much money did he begin with? 110 cents or $1.10

2. Tamara has a total of 12 sheets of construction paper. She has only red and green. She has 4 fewer green sheets than red. How many red sheets does she have? 8

(Chapter 9 Lesson 5) Find each product. Simplify.

3. $\frac{3}{4} \times \frac{4}{5} =$ $\frac{3}{5}$ 4. $\frac{5}{7} \times \frac{7}{9} =$ $\frac{5}{9}$

5. $\frac{5}{6} \times \frac{6}{10} =$ $\frac{1}{2}$ 6. $\frac{5}{8} \times \frac{3}{5} =$ $\frac{3}{8}$

(Chapter 11 Lesson 4) Find the surface area of each figure.

7. 5 ft, 6 ft, 3 ft 8. 3.6 cm

$126\ ft^2$ $77.76\ cm^2$

(Chapter 11 Lesson 11) Complete.

9. 0.9 L = 900 mL 10. 560 mL = 0.56 L

(Chapter 12 Lesson 1) Write each ratio in three ways. Simplify.

11. 12.

5 to 1 5:1 $\frac{5}{1}$ 3 to 6 or 1 to 2 3:6 or 1:2 $\frac{3}{6}$ or $\frac{1}{2}$

(Chapter 12 Lesson 7) Find the percent of each number.

13. 15% of $28 = $4.20 14. 50% of 213 = 106.5